ANALOG COMPUTER TECHNIQUES

Analog Computer Techniques

CLARENCE L. JOHNSON

Captain, U.S. Air Force
Assistant Professor, Department of Mathematics
U.S. Air Force Institute of Technology

McGRAW-HILL BOOK COMPANY, INC.

New York   Toronto   London

1956

ANALOG COMPUTER TECHNIQUES

Library of Congress Catalog Card Number 56-7560

THE MAPLE PRESS COMPANY, YORK, PA.

To My Wife, Lillian
and My Daughter, Tonya Sue

PREFACE

The electronic differential analyzer, frequently referred to as the electronic analog computer, has become an extremely important tool to the engineer, physicist, and applied mathematician in the past decade. Many of the rapid advances in the field of automation would have been impossible without this tool.

The treatment of the electronic differential analyzer contained in this book was written as an aid to the computer operator. The presentation of the material is such that the average person with a knowledge of Ohm's law, Kirchhoff's laws, and a basic knowledge of differential equations can read and understand the majority of the material presented. In a few isolated instances Laplace-transform notation is used to prove a statement. The results obtained, however, are stated in such a manner that they can be applied to the setup of computer problems without a knowledge of Laplace-transform theory.

In the various stages of development, the material contained in this book has been used for the past two years in the computer courses taught to advanced undergraduate and graduate students at the U.S. Air Force Institute of Technology at Wright-Patterson Air Force Base, Ohio.

The analog-computer course was included in the curricula because of the relatively large number of students undertaking independent study investigations in the fields of guidance systems and automatic control. The use of computing devices in the level of work attempted was virtually mandatory.

Prior to the inauguration of the computer courses, too much of the student's effort in his thesis work was directed toward learning to use the computer and too little toward the actual investigation of his problem. It is the author's belief that this situation has been improved by the inclusion in the curricula of the material in this book.

The author further believes that the engineer, whether his specialty be electronics, mechanics, chemistry, or aerodynamics, has an increasing need to be familiar with both analog and digital computers. Although he may never be called upon to operate a computer, he should recognize the capability of a particular class of computers to solve a problem with which he may be confronted.

The arrangement of the material in this book was chosen in such a manner as to permit laboratory work to accompany the classroom work.   For this reason the material proceeds rapidly in the early chapters into the discussion of amplitude- and time-scale factor adjustment and the setup of linear systems of differential equations.   Nonlinear components and function-generating techniques are also considered in the early chapters.   The later chapters consider such topics as the application of analog computers to the solution of problems other than ordinary differential equations, a more detailed description of computer components, checking computer results, and repetitive analog computers.   The book is concluded with a brief introduction to the logic operation of the digital integrating differential analyzer.

A brief review of the terminology of differential equations and a brief introduction to operator notation is included in the Appendix as an aid to the less advanced reader.

The author is indebted to Professor C. E. Warren of The Ohio State University for his valuable suggestions during the preparation of an earlier form of the manuscript, and to Professor R. T. Harling of the U.S. Air Force Institute of Technology and other faculty members of The Ohio State University and the U.S. Air Force Institute of Technology who have influenced the writing of this book.

The author wishes to acknowledge the able assistance of Mrs. Ada Williams for the typing of the earlier manuscript and of Mrs. Frances Borum for typing the manuscript in its present form.

CLARENCE L. JOHNSON

CONTENTS

CHAPTER 1

INTRODUCTION

1-1. Historical Development. In the period of years immediately following World War II, there has been developed a tool which has had much influence upon the methods of analysis employed by engineers. This tool is the electronic analog computer. The credit for its early development, both in this country and in England, is not easily placed because of wartime security measures.

If any two men can be credited with the first published use of operational amplifiers as computer components, they are C. A. Lovell and D. B. Parkinson of Bell Telephone Laboratories. Their use of operational amplifiers was in the computer of the M9 antiaircraft-gun director built by Western Electric Company.* J. B. Russell of Columbia University noted the circuits utilized in the M9 computer and brought them to the attention of Ragazzini, Randall, and Russell,[1]† who proceeded to build the first general-purpose electronic analog computer under contract with the National Defense Research Committee. This work led to the publication of the first article, in May, 1947, describing the operational amplifier as a computer component. G. A. Philbrick is credited by some with having independently pioneered the use of high-gain d-c amplifiers as computer components in unpublished work conducted prior to World War II.

In 1947, the Reeves Instrument Corporation, under a Navy contract, developed a computer which was the forerunner of the present-day REAC. At about the same time, many others began the independent development of analog computers. No attempt will be made here to assign credit for the very rapid developments made since the publication of Ragazzini's first paper. The list of individual contributors would be quite large and would require a major research effort to ensure proper recognition for all concerned. Due credit should also be given to those men responsible for the earlier development of the

---

* Instruction booklet prepared by the Bell Telephone Laboratories for the Western Electric M9 antiaircraft-gun director.

† References denoted by superscripts appear at the end of each chapter.

d-c amplifier.   Without their efforts, d-c analog computers would not be possible today.

The main purpose of this brief historical review has been to impress upon the reader the relatively short time between the construction of the first d-c analog computer and its general acceptance as a tool by engineers throughout the country.   Ragazzini's paper was published in 1947, and by 1949 several computing facilities had sprung into existence using equipment similar to that described in the paper.

It is the rapid development of the field of analog computation that has inspired the preparation of this book.   The development of new equipments and techniques has left a gap in the literature such that each individual when learning to use electronic analog computers must, to a certain extent, travel the path of learning the hard way.   There is considerable literature available, in the form of papers, that will guide the computer operator in the application of special techniques to particular problems, but nowhere does there exist a treatment of the use of the analog computer sufficiently simple to serve as introductory material yet sufficiently complete to be useful to the more advanced machine operator.   It is the purpose of the author to attempt to shorten the period of transition from neophyte to accomplished analog-computer operator for the engineer learning to use this new tool.

1-2. Classification of Computing Equipment.   For many years the engineer has had available computing devices of various types to aid him in his work.   The classification of the various instruments available should help to clarify exactly the type of equipment to be discussed extensively in the following pages.

Computing equipment may be divided into two main classifications: analog and digital.   The *analog computer operates by representing the variables of a problem by physical quantities easily generated or controlled such as shaft rotations or electrical voltages*.   The representation is such as to give continuous correspondence to the variables of the problem being studied.   *A digital computer counts and obeys logic rules exactly*. A major difference between analog and digital computers is the accuracy attainable.   Accuracy of a digital computer can be extended by simply carrying more significant figures, whereas the accuracy of an analog device is limited primarily by the accuracy of individual components and of the measuring device.

There are many types of analog computers in use today.   These may be subdivided into two broad categories: *general-purpose* and *special-purpose*.   Figure 1-1 shows a few of the analog computers and the class to which each belongs.   The special-purpose computers will not be considered further in this work.   The general-purpose computers can be further subdivided into two classes: the *direct-* or *physical-analog* computers, and the *indirect-* or *mathematical-analog* computers.

The *network analyzer*, which belongs in the direct-analog class, is the oldest of the general-purpose analog computers. Its operation is based upon the analogy of the mechanical behavior of dashpots, springs, and masses to the corresponding electrical behavior of resistors, condensers, and inductors.

There are several reasons for the network analyzer's not having achieved the widespread use that the electronic analog computer has

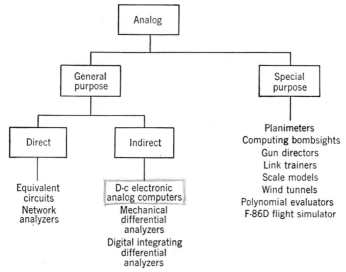

FIG. 1-1. Classification of analog-computing equipment.

realized. First, the cost of a large analyzer installation is in the same order of magnitude as that of the large-scale digital computer and the mechanical differential analyzer ($100,000 to $500,000). Second, although the equivalent electrical networks for mechanical systems may be easily derived, the actual simulation is much more difficult because of the absence of perfect components. The resistance associated with inductors, the leakage of capacitors, and the inductance of resistors all introduce errors into the system. It is the consideration of such factors that makes the simulation of many systems more difficult than on the electronic analog computer.

Despite its disadvantages, there are computational tasks for which the physical-analog computer remains unexcelled. An example is the analysis of electrical power-distribution systems. Several of the major network analyzers in the country are kept busy a large portion of the time on this one type of problem.   Other problems such as the dynamic analysis of structural problems, e.g., an aircraft wing, can be handled well on this type of computer.   New network analyzers will probably continue to be built by power companies, aircraft manufacturers, and universities to supplement the capacity of existing facilities.

The mathematical-analog computers include the *mechanical differential analyzers*, the *digital integrating differential analyzers*,[*] and the *electronic differential analyzers*.   The mechanical differential analyzers are capable of accuracies up to five significant figures and usually consist of ball-and-disk integrators having mechanical or electromechanical couplings.   They are at present in a very unenviable position of being squeezed by the accuracy of the digital computer on one hand and the speed and ease of operation of the electronic differential analyzer on the other hand.   Since the cost of a mechanical differential analyzer is of the same order of magnitude as that of the large-scale digital computer, it is very doubtful whether another large computer of this type will ever be constructed.

The digital integrating differential analyzer is a newcomer in the computation field.   The existence of such devices is widely known, but few people, other than those actively engaged in their operation, understand their basic principles of operation.   An attempt will be made in Chap. 13 to familiarize the reader with this type of equipment in order that he may be more aware of its capabilities and limitations.

The electronic differential analyzer is the device that will be treated most extensively in the subsequent pages.   Other than in Chap. 13, the major effort will be to present the limitations and capabilities of this class of equipment.   *Any future reference to analog computers will mean specifically the electronic differential analyzer*.

1-3. Problems Solvable on the Electronic Analog Computer.   There is a considerable overlap of fields of usefulness of analog and digital computers.   In general, a large-scale digital computer can do any job which can be accomplished on an analog computer, but many problems can be handled adequately on an analog computer far more rapidly and easily than by any other means.   The correct choice of

---

[*] The *digital integrating differential analyzer* is, by the strictest definition, a digital computer.   The technique of problem preparation is, however, very similar to that used for the other mathematical analog computers.   For that reason the author has arbitrarily listed the computer as an analog device.   Some authorities prefer to list the digital integrating differential analyzer in a category separate from other computers, i.e., as a *digital analog computer*.

computer is important to the economical solution of problems. Factors to consider in making the choice are the accuracy required and the nature of the problem. In general, if more than four-significant-figure accuracy is required, the electronic analog computer cannot satisfy the requirements. Few analog computer laboratories can do that well.

The type of problems best adapted to solution on an electronic analog computer are those involving systems of simultaneous differential equations, linear or nonlinear, with constant or nonconstant coefficients. Fortunately, the complexity of problem setup is increased only slightly for nonlinear problems and problems involving nonconstant coefficients. Some problems, other than those which belong in the category of ordinary differential equations, can be satisfactorily handled on an analog computer. These will be discussed in later chapters.

Analog-computer results are normally presented graphically as a continuous plot of the variable quantities. In many instances this method of presentation is most convenient for engineering use. The graphical representation of results has another important aspect. It is relatively easy for the engineer, as he operates the analog computer, to visualize the results as the actual dynamic response of the physical system under investigation. Thinking of the analog computer as just a mathematical device is to be discouraged as much as possible. The usefulness of the computer will be greatly enhanced if the operator views it as a tool to help him think in terms of the physical system.

1-4. Major Components. The major types of components of an electronic analog computer are relatively few in number. First, and the most important components, are d-c amplifiers or *operational amplifiers*. It is these amplifiers that become *summers* and *integrators* upon the addition of proper feedback and input impedances. Second, it is necessary to be able to set coefficients in a problem. As will be shown later, this may be accomplished either by the use of potentiometers or by adjusting the ratio of feedback and input impedances applied to the operational amplifiers. Third, it is necessary to have a set of controls capable of starting and stopping the computation. In addition, it is desirable to have a control position to perform the function of *holding* the problem solution at any point in the solution. These control operations are performed by a system of relays. Usually provision is made in the control system for the automatic application of the initial conditions of the problem while the computer controls are in the RESET position. A knowledge of the actual operation of the operate-reset relays is unimportant for the solution of simple routine problems but is very important to the operator as the problem complexity increases.

If problems other than those involving linear differential equations with constant coefficients are to be solved, units capable of multiplying variable quantities must be provided. As problem complexity increases, there arises more and more frequently the need for arbitrary-function-generating equipment capable of generating functions not easily represented mathematically. Similarly, more complex problems often require the representation of nonlinear phenomena. This is accomplished by the introduction of diodes or relays into the computing circuits.

The basic components mentioned in the preceding paragraphs, together with suitable recording equipment, make up the major portion of the equipment used in the solution of problems on analog computers. Each of these components will be treated extensively in succeeding chapters.

1-5. Summary. It is desirable to emphasize to the beginner that the understanding of the manner in which an analog computer performs its operations is extremely important. This is true, perhaps even to a greater extent than for any other computational aid. Without an understanding of the actual operation and limitations of the equipment the operator can never rise above the level of knob twister. An effort will be made throughout the remainder of this book to present the fundamental principles of analog computation in a manner that will allow the reader to attain that understanding easily.

REFERENCE

1. Ragazzini, J. R., R. H. Randall, and F. A. Russell: Analysis of Problems in Dynamics by Electronic Circuits, *Proc. IRE*, May, 1947, pp. 444–452.

CHAPTER 2

THE LINEAR COMPUTER COMPONENTS

2-1. Introduction. Theoretically, there are two logical philosophies along which an analog computer for use in solving differential equations may be developed. The first of these might be based upon repeated differentiation, and the second upon a process of repeated integration. From mathematical considerations, both systems are

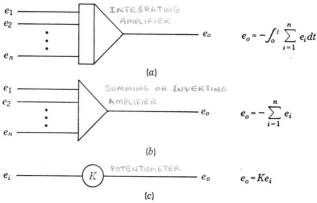

$$e_o = -\int_o^t \sum_{i=1}^n e_i\, dt$$

(a)

$$e_o = -\sum_{i=1}^n e_i$$

(b)

$$e_o = Ke_i$$

(c)

Fig. 2-1. Symbolism frequently used to represent the computer components necessary to solve linear differential equations with constant coefficients. All voltages e_i and e_o referred to in the diagram are varying d-c voltages measured with respect to a common ground. The components shown are (a) an integrating amplifier, (b) a summing or inverting amplifier, and (c) a potentiometer.

adequate. From an engineering approach, however, the process of differentiation has a serious drawback. Differentiation is a "noise"-amplifying process, and all electronic gear, to a greater or lesser extent, produces random noise. This noise, however slight, results in a much higher noise level if differentiation is used. The second possibility, that of repeated integration, offers no such difficulty; the noise is smoothed, since integration is an averaging process. *Repeated integration is the basis of the electronic differential analyzers as we know them today.*

7

In order to solve a system of linear differential equations with constant coefficients, the following types of equipment must be available:

1. Devices capable of performing the process of integration
2. Devices capable of summing several quantities
3. Devices capable of multiplying a quantity by a constant
4. Devices capable of multiplying by the constant -1

The symbolism of Fig. 2-1 may be adopted to represent the above devices. Note that the ability to perform sign inversions and to sum two or more quantities has been given to the integrating amplifier and to the summing or inverting amplifier. Assuming that the above devices are available, they may be interconnected in such a manner as to produce the solution of any linear differential equation with constant coefficients. The method of connection is illustrated by the following example.

Example 2-1

$$\frac{d^2x}{dt^2} + a_1 \frac{dx}{dt} + a_2x = f(t) \tag{2-1}$$

Equation (2-1) may be rewritten in the form

$$\frac{d^2x}{dt^2} = -a_1 \frac{dx}{dt} - a_2x + f(t) \tag{2-2}$$

Then, assuming that d^2x/dt^2 is a known quantity, it may be integrated to give dx/dt and this in turn may be integrated to produce x. From Eq. (2-2) above, it

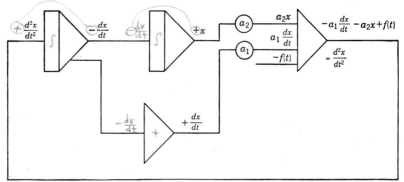

Fig. 2-2. Computer circuit showing the component interconnections necessary to solve Eq. (2-1).

can be seen that, having x and dx/dt, it is only necessary to multiply each by an appropriate constant and sum them together with $f(t)$ in order to get d^2x/dt^2, the quantity that was assumed to have been known. The block diagram of Fig. 2-2 illustrates the method.

First examination of the block diagram may lead one to believe that he is reaching down and lifting himself by the bootstraps. This is not the case, however, as the system operates much as any closed-loop servo system. The rate of change of a quantity depends on the magnitude of the quantity and the time history of itself and its derivatives. It is very important that one reason out the flow of information in the above closed-loop system.

2-2. The Operational Amplifiers. In the above illustrative example, the magnitude of the constants a_1 and a_2 must be less than unity,

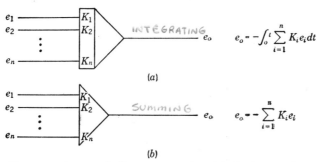

(a)

(b)

FIG. 2-3. More complete symbolism representing (a) the integrating amplifiers, (b) summing amplifiers. The symbols show the gain associated with each input of the amplifiers.

since a potentiometer is only able to multiply by a constant less than unity. This need not be the case in general, however, as the integrators and summing amplifiers have the ability to multiply by constants other than unity. The transfer functions of an integrating amplifier and of a summing amplifier are, therefore, more completely represented as in Fig. 2-3.

Until now, it has been assumed that the processes of integration and summation can be performed. It might be well at this point to show one means by which this may be done. A more detailed block diagram of the above *operational amplifiers* is given in Fig. 2-4.

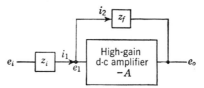

FIG. 2-4. Block diagram of an operational amplifier showing the high-gain d-c amplifier and the feedback and input impedances z_f and z_i.

In the figure $-A$ represents the gain of the amplifier, and z_f and z_i are the feedback and input impedances, respectively. If the amplifier is assumed to draw no current at its input grid, then from Fig. 2-4, Eqs. (2-3) to (2-6) can be written

$$i_1 = i_2 \tag{2-3}$$

$$i_1 = \frac{e_i - e_1}{z_i} \tag{2-4}$$

$$i_2 = \frac{e_1 - e_o}{z_f} \tag{2-5}$$

$$e_o = -A e_1 \tag{2-6}$$

From Eqs. (2-3) to (2-5),

$$\frac{e_i - e_1}{z_i} = \frac{e_1 - e_o}{z_f} \qquad (2\text{-}7)$$

Substituting Eq. (2-6) in Eq. (2-7) gives

$$\frac{e_i + e_o/A}{z_i} = -\frac{e_o/A + e_o}{z_f} \qquad (2\text{-}8)$$

Simplifying Eq. (2-8) gives

$$\frac{e_o}{e_i} = -\frac{A z_f}{z_f + z_i + A z_i} \qquad (2\text{-}9)$$

Multiplying numerator and denominator by $1/A$ and factoring z_i from the denominator gives the final form of the transfer function

$$\frac{e_o}{e_i} = -\frac{z_f}{z_i} \frac{1}{1 + 1/A(z_f/z_i + 1)} \qquad (2\text{-}10)$$

If A is sufficiently high, a good approximation for Eq. (2-10) is

$$\frac{e_o}{e_i} = -\frac{z_f}{z_i} \qquad (2\text{-}11)$$

An alternate and simpler derivation of Eq. (2-11) can be made by assuming that the voltage e_1 is equal to zero in Fig. 2-4. This assumption is valid to a good approximation providing the gain A of the amplifier is sufficiently high. Suppose the amplifier output e_o is restricted to remain within some finite region of voltage, usually ± 100 volts. Since $e_o = -A e_1$, it is apparent that e_1 is approximately equal to zero for $A \gg 1$. Further, since the amplifier can be assumed to draw no current,

$$i_1 = i_2$$

and
$$i_1 = \frac{e_i}{z_i} = i_2 = -\frac{e_o}{z_f}$$

Rearranging and solving for e_o/e_i again gives

$$\frac{e_o}{e_i} = -\frac{z_f}{z_i} \qquad (2\text{-}11)$$

The derivation of this important result by the latter method has the disadvantage of not emphasizing the nature of the approximations made in the derivation. For the present, however, it is not necessary to discuss the second-order effects of the operational amplifier. These effects are, of course, important in the design of the amplifiers and in attempting to understand the limitations of the equipment. They are, however, less important to the beginner learning to use the analog computer.

In later derivations of transfer functions of computer circuits, the derivations will frequently depend upon the approximation

$$e_1 = -\frac{e_o}{A} \cong 0$$

For most analog-computing equipment the approximation is very good. The value of amplifier gain ranges from 2×10^3 for some repetitive equipment to over 10^8 for at least one of the better commercially available computers.

In Eq. (2-11), if z_f and z_i are both 1-megohm resistors,

$$\frac{e_o}{e_i} = -\frac{z_f}{z_i} = -1 \tag{2-12}$$

Similarly, if z_i is 0.1 megohm and z_f is 1.0 megohm, the transfer function is

$$\frac{e_o}{e_i} = -\frac{z_f}{z_i} = -\frac{1 \times 10^6}{0.1 \times 10^6} = -10 \tag{2-13}$$

Equations (2-12) and (2-13) show that, to change the gain of a summing amplifier, it is only necessary to vary the size of the input resistor. (Normally, the feedback resistor is held constant at 1 megohm.)

If z_f is a condenser, then*

$$z_f = \frac{1}{j\omega C} = \frac{1}{pC} \tag{2-14}$$

and

$$\frac{e_o}{e_i} = -\frac{z_f}{z_i} = -\frac{1/pC}{R} = -\frac{1}{pRC} \tag{2-15}$$

If $C = 1 \times 10^{-6}$ farad and $R = 1 \times 10^6$ ohms,

$$\frac{e_o}{e_i} = -\frac{1}{10^6 \times 10^{-6}p} = -\frac{1}{p} \tag{2-16}$$

or

$$e_o = -\int e_i \, dt \tag{2-17}$$

Similarly, it may be noted that the gain of an integrator can be varied by changing the size of the input resistor, just as in the case of the summing amplifier.

A differentiator could be as easily formed by letting z_i be a condenser and z_f be a resistor; then

$$\frac{e_o}{e_i} = -\frac{z_f}{z_i} = -\frac{R}{1/pC} = -pRC \tag{2-18}$$

* The equivalence of $j\omega$ and the operator p is demonstrated in Sec. A-5. A brief introduction to operator notation is included in Sec. A-3.

Differentiation is seldom used in the solution of problems on analog computers, as the noise amplification produced by differentiation is very undesirable. At times it is preferable to rewrite a set of differential equations completely rather than to differentiate. If differentiation cannot be avoided (a very rare situation), then an approximate differentiation may be used to keep the noise at a usably low level. A circuit for producing approximate derivatives will be discussed in a later section.

So far, the transfer function of the integrator and of the summing amplifier have been developed without showing that each has the

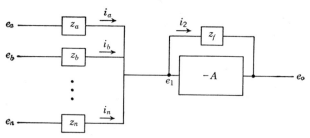

FIG. 2-5. Block diagram of an amplifier having a feedback impedance z_f and several input impedances z_a, z_b, . . . , z_n connected in parallel to the grid input of the amplifier.

ability to sum several functions at its input. This may be most easily demonstrated by considering the block diagram of Fig. 2-5.

In Fig. 2-5 the single input has been replaced by several inputs e_a, e_b, . . . , e_n. Since the gain of the amplifier is very large, e_1 may be set equal to zero, since

$$e_1 = -\frac{e_o}{A} \cong 0 \qquad (2\text{-}19)$$

The current drawn by the amplifier may be neglected as before; therefore

$$i_a + i_b + \cdots + i_n = i_2 \qquad (2\text{-}20)$$

Replacing i_a, i_b, . . . , i_n by equivalent expressions, Eq. (2-20) becomes

$$\frac{e_a}{z_a} + \frac{e_b}{z_b} + \cdots + \frac{e_n}{z_n} = -\frac{e_o}{z_f} \qquad (2\text{-}21)$$

or $\qquad e_o = -\frac{z_f}{z_a} e_a - \frac{z_f}{z_b} e_b - \cdots - \frac{z_f}{z_n} e_n = -z_f \sum_{i=a}^{n} \frac{e_i}{z_i} \qquad (2\text{-}22)$

2-3. Potentiometers. Potentiometers are frequently used in analog-computer setups to perform multiplication by a constant less than 1.

Very often these potentiometers are 10-turn helical wire-wound types of high resolution and excellent linearity (usually from 1 to 0.05 per cent of full scale). By means of a vernier dial, parameters of the problems may be accurately and conveniently set. A loading correction will have to be applied, in most cases, to compensate for the loading on the potentiometer.

The potentiometers most commonly used in analog computation vary in total resistance from 10,000 to 100,000 ohms. The lower limit

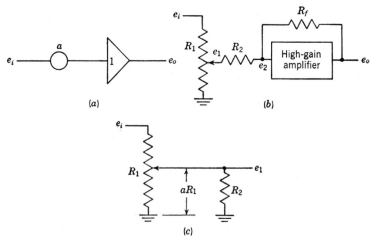

FIG. 2-6. Block diagram of a potentiometer when used as the input to an amplifier: (a) schematic representation; (b) detailed circuit connections; (c) equivalent circuit representation from which the potentiometer loading effect can be calculated.

of the potentiometer resistance is determined by the power available from the amplifier feeding the potentiometer. The upper limit is determined by the loading effect and the mechanical ability to manufacture sufficiently rugged wire-wound potentiometers with total resistances greater than 100,000 ohms.

Potentiometers are used most frequently as the inputs to operational amplifiers. Figure 2-6a shows the schematic representation, and Fig. 2-6b gives a more detailed schematic drawing for this application. Since A, the amplifier gain, is very large, the approximation $e_2 = -e_o/A \cong 0$ can be made. The equivalent circuit of Fig. 2-6c is based on this approximation. From the equivalent circuit the effect of potentiometer loading can be easily evaluated.

In Fig. 2-6c, if $R_2 = \infty$,

$$\frac{e_1}{e_i} = \frac{aR_1}{R_1} = a \qquad (2\text{-}23)$$

If, however, R_2 is a finite value such as is used as the input impedance of an amplifier, $e_1 \neq ae_i$. The loading effect for finite values of R_2 can be shown by deriving the transfer function of the potentiometer with load

$$\frac{e_1}{e_i} = \frac{aR_1R_2/(aR_1 + R_2)}{(1 - a)R_1 + aR_1R_2/(aR_1 + R_2)} \qquad (2\text{-}24)$$

POTENTIOMETER
TRANSFER FUNCTION
$$\frac{e_1}{e_i} = \frac{aR_2}{aR_1 + R_2 - a^2R_1} \qquad (2\text{-}25)$$

Subtracting both sides of Eq. (2-25) from the decimal potentiometer setting a gives an expression for the loading error ϵ:

$$\epsilon = a - \frac{e_1}{e_i} = a - \frac{aR_2}{aR_1 + R_2 - a^2R_1} \qquad (2\text{-}26)$$

The importance of the potentiometer loading error can be seen by inserting typical values into Eq. (2-26). For a potentiometer of 30,000 ohms total resistance, loaded with a 100,000-ohm load and set at 0.6 of its maximum setting, in Eq. (2-26) $a = 0.6$, $R_1 = 30,000$, and $R_2 = 100,000$. The error is therefore

$$\epsilon = 0.600 - 0.559 = +0.041 \qquad (2\text{-}27)$$

or approximately 6 per cent. It is obvious that either a correction must be added to the setting to compensate for loading or the potentiometer must be set with the load applied by comparing it to a known standard. Both these methods of error correction are commonly employed. Failure to correct for potentiometer loading can introduce errors into problems greater than the problem tolerances will permit.

2-4. Computer Design Differences. At present there are quite a large number of analog computers commercially available. Each of these differs in some respects from all the others. The basic principles involved in the use of all the computers is the same, however. A few hours spent with the instruction manual for a particular make of computer will allow an operator to adapt himself to the peculiarities of the equipment and utilize it to the full extent of his capabilities.

The symbols representing the computer components vary somewhat for different computers because of the design differences. The symbolism used thus far has been that commonly used for computers such as the REAC* and Electronic Associates computers. For example, each amplifier on the REAC is permanently wired with input and feedback impedances of fixed value. There is, therefore, no necessity

* REAC—Reeves Electronic Analog Computer, trade-mark of Reeves Instrument Corporation, New York.

to draw each resistive and capacitive element in the patch diagram. Some computer designs require that the input resistors, feedback resistors, and condensers be patched externally on the computer. Circuit diagrams for these computers must, therefore, show all input and feedback elements.

The manufacturers of computers utilizing external plug-in components have developed small decade resistance elements with trimming potentiometers for use as the input impedances of amplifiers. These decade resistors may be adjusted to 1 part in 1,000 by means of a bridge circuit. They reduce considerably the requirement for potentiometers as coefficient setting devices, as arbitrary gains can be formed when they are used.

On computers having fixed gains, potentiometers must be used to set coefficients at values other than those available. This is not true when decade resistors are used, since an arbitrary amplifier gain can be formed by applying the basic relationship $e_o/e_i = -z_f/z_i$. If the feedback impedance is either a 1-megohm resistor or a 1-μf capacitor, the magnitude of the resistive input required to produce the desired input gain can be calculated by the relationship

$$R = \frac{1}{\text{desired gain}} \quad \text{megohms} \quad (2\text{-}28)$$

In one respect the decade resistors in use at present are inferior to precision potentiometers. The decade resistors are usually adjustable to 1 per cent and rely upon a trimmer potentiometer attached to them for more precise adjustment. The trimmer potentiometer has a finite end resistance associated with it, so that there remains a small but finite region of resistance values at which the decade resistors cannot be set. In most applications, however, this effect is negligible.

Two computers that show a good contrast in the use of internally wired fixed resistors and external plug-in resistors are the REAC, manufactured by the Reeves Instrument Corporation, and the GEDA,* manufactured by the Goodyear Aircraft Corporation. The REAC uses fixed resistors throughout; however, provision has been made to allow the use of external computing impedances on some of the amplifiers. The GEDA (L-3 model) provides a few permanently wired resistors but depends to a great extent upon the use of external plug-in resistors.

Two notations for drawing computer diagrams have evolved from the basic design differences of the various computers. When using

* GEDA—Goodyear Electronic Differential Analyzer, trade-mark of Goodyear Aircraft Corporation, Akron, Ohio.

computers with fixed internal resistors and, therefore, fixed input gains, the symbolism given in the middle column of Fig. 2-7, under the heading of REAC, is most convenient. The symbolism under the

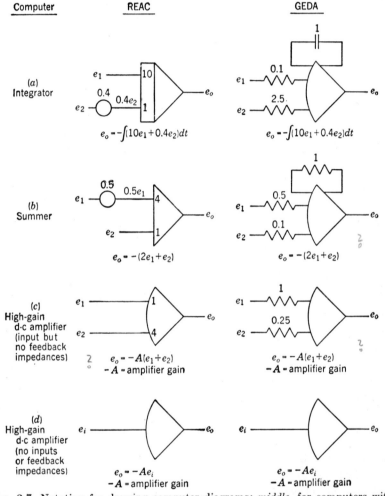

FIG. 2-7. Notation for drawing computer diagrams: *middle*, for computers with fixed internal resistors; *right*, for computers with plug-in resistors. Values of resistors and capacitors are given in megohms and microfarads.

heading GEDA is more convenient for those computers using predominantly plug-in resistors. In all cases the notations for both REAC and GEDA shown in the same row of Fig. 2-7 imply identical circuit configuration.

Some explanation of the notation used in rows c and d in the figure is necessary. In *c* is represented a high-gain d-c amplifier with input resistors but with no feedback impedances shown. When this circuit is considered alone, the magnitudes of the input resistors are unimportant, as the amplifier is assumed to draw no current. The high-gain amplifier is never used in the simple form shown, however, but is always a part of a more complex circuit such as a division circuit. When it is used in that manner, a feedback path is present through a multiplier unit and the input gains (or resistances) have significance. It is important to note that the gain inserted in the REAC symbol at each input of the high-gain amplifier corresponds to the reciprocal of the input impedance in megohms.

In some applications it is desirable to use computer amplifiers in a completely general manner; i.e., with arbitrary combinations of resistors and capacitors as feedback and input elements. In these cases it is necessary to show all the impedances that are connected to the amplifier. In Fig. 2-7 the high-gain amplifier is shown (row *d*) as a segment of a circle for both REAC and GEDA computers. It should be emphasized here that for computers such as the GEDA the simple triangle is usually used as the symbol for a high-gain d-c amplifier. The circular segment is used here, however, to prevent any possible confusion between the REAC symbol for a summing amplifier and the similar symbol frequently used to signify a high-gain d-c amplifier.

Other than for some repetitive computers, which will be discussed separately in a later chapter, one or the other of the two notations appearing in Fig. 2-7 can be used in preparing computer diagrams for any existing analog computers. It is true that the more detailed notation in the right-hand column can be used for all computers, but the brevity of the REAC notation is one big advantage favoring its use where it is applicable.

Both notations have been widely used in the literature, and therefore the reader should become completely familiar with both. Throughout this book both notations will be used, to aid the reader in gaining familiarity with both. In later chapters the notation commonly used with fixed resistor computers will be adopted almost exclusively because of its brevity.

2-5. Concluding Remarks. The derivation of the transfer function of the operational amplifier is treated in detail in a large number of papers discussing the elementary phases of analog-computer application. Several papers and books treating this phase of analog-computer operation are listed at the end of this chapter.[1-4]

Information concerning the characteristics of the various analog computers can best be obtained direct from the manufacturer.

Instruction books for the computers are a very good source of introductory material for analog computation.

PROBLEMS

2-1. Give the equation expressing the output as a function of the inputs for
each of the circuits shown in Fig. P 2-1.   Values of resistors and capacitors are
listed in megohms and microfarads.

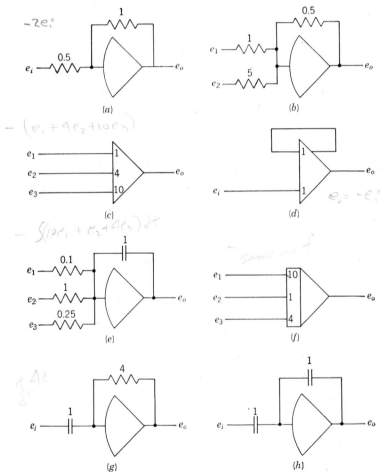

Fig. P 2-1

2-2. Plot a loading correction curve for a 30,000-ohm potentiometer, loaded by
a 0.1-megohm resistor.

2-3. Plot a loading correction curve for a 0.1-megohm potentiometer loaded by
a 0.1-megohm resistor.

REFERENCES

1. Korn, G. A., and T. M. Korn: "Electronic Analog Computers," McGraw-Hill Book Company, Inc., New York, 1952.
2. Ragazzini, J. R., R. H. Randall, and F. A. Russell: Analysis of Problems in Dynamics by Electronic Circuits, *Proc. IRE*, May, 1947, pp. 444–452.
3. Pickens, D. H.: Electronic Analog Computer Fundamentals, *Proc. IRE*, vol. 25, no. 3, pp. 144–147, August, 1952.
4. Soroka, W. W.: "Analog Methods in Computation and Simulation," McGraw-Hill Book Company, Inc., New York, 1954.

CHAPTER 3

TIME- AND AMPLITUDE-SCALE FACTORS

3-1. Factors Influencing the Choice of Time Scale. The two most important factors to consider in preparing a system of equations for analog-computer solution are:

1. Time-scale factor
2. Amplitude-scale factor

If either of these factors is not properly handled, an analog computer cannot give satisfactory results.

One of the attributes of an electronic analog computer that contributes greatly to the versatility of the equipment is the ease with which the time scale of a problem can be changed. When the time scale of a problem is changed, the machine-problem variables remain proportional to the corresponding variables in the physical system. The rates at which the changes occur are changed, however, so that the solution of the problem will be either slowed or speeded. Fortunately, there is usually a considerable range of speeds at which a particular problem may operate satisfactorily, but often many factors must be carefully considered to achieve any results at all.

In choosing a time scale at which to operate a particular problem, many factors must be considered. Usually these conflict and a compromise must be made. Some of the factors to be considered are:

1. Errors in integrations are accentuated by long computer runs.
2. Slowly varying outputs of integrators are invariably associated with low-input voltages and often with very low potentiometer settings in the problem.
3. Higher frequencies contribute to phase shift in the operational amplifiers and have the same influence as "negative damping."
4. Servo devices used for multiplication operate satisfactorily only at quite low frequencies.
5. The dynamics of recording devices must be considered so that transients in the recorder response do not affect the recording.

In the succeeding paragraphs, each of the above factors will be discussed in more detail.

Even if perfect integrating amplifiers were available for analog computers, errors in integrations would still result. In fact, the greatest error is usually due to the uncertainty present in setting a voltage that is to be integrated. Suppose it is desired to integrate a constant A. The voltage representing the constant can be set with an accuracy limited by the precision of the device used as a measuring instrument. Invariably, some error ϵ will exist in the setting. The output of the integrator will therefore be

$$f(t) = \int (A + \epsilon) \, dt = At + \epsilon t \tag{3-1}$$

The error signal is multiplied by the time of the integration.

The actual integrators used in analog computers are not perfect. Errors occur because of the finite gain of the amplifier, the mismatch of feedback and input elements, and the very small but finite grid current flowing at the input of the amplifier. All these error terms are similar in effect to ϵ above. The effect of these errors is decreased by keeping computing times small.

The error associated with the setting of a potentiometer is approximately a constant; therefore, the percentage error is much less for a large setting than for a small setting. Slowly varying integrator outputs imply small input voltages. As will be seen later, the time-scale factor determines the relative magnitude of input and output voltages of integrators for any particular problem.

A factor which indicates that problems should be run at slow speeds is the phase shift that occurs in the d-c amplifiers at higher computing speeds. This phase shift can be attributed to the distributed capacitance throughout the amplifier circuitry. A relatively important factor in the design of d-c amplifiers is keeping phase shift small over as wide a frequency range as is possible.

Most analog computers will show no effects of amplifier phase shift in the computer results until a certain frequency is reached. The frequency at which phase shift becomes troublesome is a function of the number of amplifiers in the computing circuit and is thus different for different problems. It may be helpful to state that a model C-101 REAC will usually start to show the effects of phase shift at angular frequencies of about 20 radians/sec in a sinusoid generator formed of three amplifiers. The effect will appear as a slight divergence in the computer results. The frequency at which divergence first occurs varies with different makes of computers. It is helpful to the operator to check this critical frequency for the particular computer he is using. This will give him a basis for choosing the proper operating speeds for problems to be run on that computer.

Servomultipliers frequently impose a frequency limitation on the operating speeds of problems. These devices operate by continuously positioning potentiometers to positions proportional to their input voltages. Needless to say, the rate of change of the input voltage must remain sufficiently small that the servo can accurately follow it.

High-accuracy servomultipliers usually have poorer response rates than have less precise servomultipliers. As a rule of thumb, however, it may be stated that the *maximum* frequency giving a flat response for various servomultipliers ranges from 1 or 2 cps for the slower multipliers to 10 cps for the fastest available ones. For any particular application, other design characteristics of servomultipliers may become the limiting factor in their operation. These factors are the maximum acceleration rate and the maximum angular rate of the servomultiplier unit.

3-2. Determination of Approximate Problem Frequencies. In selecting the time scale at which to operate a problem, some information regarding the form of solution of the problem is necessary. It is desirable to know the frequencies and the exponential time constants which exist in the solution. In many instances, familiarity with the system to be represented on the computer will supply the necessary estimates of frequencies and time constants. Even though nothing is known about the physical problem, sufficient information can usually be obtained from the mathematical representation with little expenditure of effort. This is true particularly in the case of systems of linear differential equations.

If the roots of the characteristic equation of a system of equations are known, the necessary information is immediately available. In most cases, however, the roots of the characteristic equation are unknown, and the labor involved in their determination is prohibitive when considered simply as an aid in the setup of the equations for analog computer solution. To be useful, any method of estimating frequencies must be easy to apply and must give consistently usable results. Fortunately, such a scheme of approximating the frequencies involved in a problem solution does exist.

Consider the system of equations

$$a_1 \frac{dx}{dt} + a_2 x = a_3 y \tag{3-2}$$

$$b_1 \frac{d^2 y}{dt^2} + b_2 \frac{dy}{dt} + b_3 y = b_4 x + b_5 z + b_6 \tag{3-3}$$

$$c_1 \frac{d^2 z}{dt^2} + c_2 \frac{dz}{dt} + c_3 z = c_4 y \tag{3-4}$$

From the above system of equations, the characteristic equation can be obtained by the expansion of a three-by-three determinant. The roots are then obtainable by the solution of a fifth-degree polynomial. Obviously, the method is not attractive. A simple approximation of the solution frequencies can be obtained by finding the time constant or the undamped natural frequency of each equation when removed completely from the system and treated as a homogeneous equation. For the above system of equations the homogeneous equation corresponding to Eq. (3-2) is

$$a_1 \frac{dx}{dt} + a_2 x = 0 \tag{3-5}$$

The solution of Eq. (3-5) is

$$x = A e^{-(a_2/a_1)t} \tag{3-6}$$

The time constant is therefore

$$\tau = \frac{a_1}{a_2} \tag{3-7}$$

Correspondingly, the undamped natural frequencies of Eqs. (3-3) and (3-4) can be immediately written down if it is recalled that a second-order differential equation is expressable in the form[*1]

$$\frac{d^2\theta}{dt^2} + 2\zeta\omega_n \frac{d\theta}{dt} + \omega_n{}^2\theta = 0 \tag{3-8}$$

where ω_n is the undamped natural frequency and ζ is the damping ratio. The undamped natural frequency of Eq. (3-3) is

$$\omega_{n_y} = \sqrt{\frac{b_3}{b_1}} \tag{3-9}$$

Similarly, the undamped natural frequency of Eq. (3-4) is

$$\omega_{n_z} = \sqrt{\frac{c_3}{c_1}} \tag{3-10}$$

The frequencies obtained in this manner are not the system frequencies, but experience has shown that the results are usually adequate for use in determining a need for a time-scale change. After obtaining the undamped natural frequencies of the uncoupled equations, it is then possible to arrive at a compromise time scale for the problem. The factors mentioned in Sec. 3-1 must be considered in making this choice.

* The general form of the differential Eq. (3-8) is discussed in Sec. A-2.

3-3. Approximate Frequencies of Higher-order Systems. The large majority of systems of ordinary differential equations that arise from the consideration of physical systems are composed of first- and second-order equations. Occasionally, however, an engineer is confronted with differential equations of higher order than the second. In order to determine the desirability of a time-scale change, a knowledge of the undamped natural frequency is necessary. The rules for obtaining the undamped natural frequency of higher-order systems are much less widely known than those for a second-order system. Routh's stability criterion[*2] can give the formula for the undamped natural frequency of a third-order differential equation. It is strongly recommended that the engineer working with analog-computer equipment become familiar with Routh's criterion for determining system stability. Reference will again be made to this simple means of determining system stability in the section dealing with the checking of computer results.

Applying Routh's criterion to the characteristic equation of a third-order system represented by

$$p^3 + a_2 p^2 + a_1 p + a_0 = 0 \qquad (3\text{-}11)$$

gives the coefficient table

$$
\begin{array}{c|cc}
p^3 & 1 & a_1 \\
p^2 & a_2 & a_0 \\
p^1 & \dfrac{a_1 a_2 - a_0}{a_2} & \\
p^0 & a_0 &
\end{array}
$$

In order for an undamped oscillation to exist, the third row of the table must be zero or $a_0 = a_1 a_2$. For this condition, the auxiliary equation is

$$a_2 p^2 + a_0 = 0 \qquad (3\text{-}12)$$

The roots of Eq. (3-12) are

$$p = \pm j \sqrt{\frac{a_0}{a_2}} \qquad (3\text{-}13)$$

The results may be restated. For a third-order system expressed in the form of Eq. (3-11), the undamped natural frequency is equal to $\sqrt{a_0/a_2}$, and the condition under which undamped oscillation can exist is that $a_0 = a_1 a_2$. If all the coefficients in Eq. (3-11) are positive, then the condition for stability is that $a_0 < a_1 a_2$.

---

* Routh's stability criterion is stated without proof in Sec. A-4.

It is very interesting to note at this point that the undamped natural frequency of a third-order system is obtained by the application of the same formula as for a second-order system, namely, the square root of the zero-order coefficient over the second-order coefficient.

For equations of higher order than the third, the most practical means of determining the desirability of a time-scale change is by considering the effect the change would have in making the magnitude of the coefficients of the higher-order terms more nearly equal the magnitude of the lower-order coefficients. Having the magnitude of the higher-order coefficients near the magnitude of the lower-order coefficients ensures having problem frequencies of the order of magnitude of 1 radian/sec.

3-4. The Influence of Recorder Characteristics on the Choice of Time Scale. Many beginners have a tendency to neglect recorder characteristics completely when choosing a time scale for a particular problem. Recorder characteristics must be considered if the computer results are to be useful. It is ridiculous to spend the time and effort necessary to set up a problem on a computer and then find it necessary to rescale the problem because satisfactory recordings cannot be made.

The types of recording equipment available for analog computers are extremely varied. In general most of the devices can be divided into three categories: servo-driven recorders, galvanometer-type instruments, and cathode-ray oscilloscopes. Servo-driven plotting devices are relatively precise but slow in operation. A plotting speed of 8 in./sec is considered quite good for this type of equipment. Very few servo-driven recorders can adequately record frequencies as high as 2 or 3 cps at relatively large plotting amplitudes. For different inputs, the servo-driven recorder will be limited in usefulness by one of three factors: its acceleration rate, its maximum writing speed, or its frequency response. In designing recorders of this type, it is extremely important that the inertia of moving parts be kept as low as possible to improve these three factors.

Galvanometer-type recording instruments usually have much higher frequency-response characteristics than do servo-driven recorders. They consist of two types: direct-inking recorders, and hot-wire recorders. In either type, the writing arm is driven by a galvanometer movement and the paper is moved at a constant rate past the writing instrument. The direct-inking type has the disadvantage of plotting on a curved coordinate system to coincide with the arc of the pens. The hot-wire recorder uses a heat-sensitive paper. The paper is drawn across a raised straight edge, allowing the plot to be made in a rectangular coordinate system. The chief disadvantage of the hot-wire recorder is the relatively higher cost of the paper.

Galvanometer-driven recorders have linear frequency-response characteristics up to about 300 cps when adequate frequency-compensation networks are provided in the amplifiers. They are limited, however, to plotting a variable function against the independent variable of the problem. Usually, these recorders have provision for the plotting of one to six variables simultaneously on adjacent channels.

The greatest disadvantage common to most galvanometer-type recorders is the relatively low-accuracy plots that they produce. The graphs produced by most galvanometer-type recorders can be read accurately to only about 5 per cent of full scale.

The high-frequency response of galvanometer recorders does not give the computer operator a free choice of computing speeds. The speed at which the paper is drawn past the recorder pen can be the critical factor in choosing a proper operating speed for a problem. Some recorders have only one paper speed, while others have as many as eight or nine different speeds, ranging from 1 mm/sec to 10 cm/sec.

Cathode-ray oscilloscopes are usually used to view the solution of problems solved on repetitive computers. Permanent recordings of the oscilloscope display can be made with an oscilloscope camera.

In summary, it can be stated that some of the factors mentioned above indicate that problem operating speeds should be high; others, that they should be low. A compromise must therefore be made. Problem frequencies of approximately 1 radian/sec in machine time are often considered as optimum. Linear problems using galvanometer-type recording instruments can usually be run appreciably faster than this. Problems using servomultipliers and servo-driven recorders frequently must be slowed down to provide lower problem frequencies than 1 radian/sec. No fixed rules apply, but a frequency range in problem solutions of 0.02 to 3.0 cps will usually be suitable.

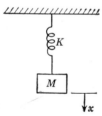

FIG. 3-1. Spring pendulum with the physical constants $M = 0.02$ slug and $K = 20$ lb/ft.

Example 3-1. As an illustration of the proper choice of time-scale factor, consider the simple mechanical system illustrated in Fig. 3-1. The mass M of the spring pendulum is 0.02 slug, and the spring constant K is 20 lb/ft. The equation of motion of the system is therefore

$$0.02 \frac{d^2x}{dt^2} + 20x = 0 \tag{3-14}$$

By referring to the form of the second-order differential equation as expressed in Eq. (3-8), it can be immediately determined that the undamped natural frequency of oscillation of the system is

$$\omega_n = \sqrt{\frac{20}{0.02}} = 31.6 \text{ radians/sec}$$

This frequency is too fast for best operation of most analog computers (with the exception of the repetitive computers), and thus the time-scale factor of the problem should be changed in order to slow down the computer solution of the problem.

As previously stated, problem frequencies of 1 radian/sec are considered optimum for the computer, but other factors influence the final choice of time-scale factor for a particular problem. If the results of the problem are to be recorded on a servo-driven plotting board, then frequencies somewhat less than 1 radian/sec are best. If the results are to be plotted on a galvanometer-type recorder, then frequencies somewhat greater than 1 radian/sec are adequate and will reduce the solution time of the problem.

Assuming that the problem results are to be recorded on a servo-driven recorder, slowing the problem solution by a factor of 50 would be a good choice of time-scale factor. This would give a new undamped natural frequency for the machine solution of $\omega_n = 0.63$ radian/sec. This choice is completely compatible with the capabilities of the computer and the recorder to be used.

If a galvanometer-type recorder were used in recording the results of the problem instead of a servo-driven recorder, then a better choice of time-scale factor would have been to slow the problem by a factor of 10 rather than 50. This would have resulted in a solution frequency on the computer of 3.16 radians/sec or approximately 0.5 cps. Again this frequency is compatible with the computer and recorder capabilities, but only one-fifth the time would be required to solve the problem that was required in the previous case. This time saving can be very important when it is desired to solve a problem for a large number of different parameters.

Example 3-2. As a second illustration of the proper choice of time scale, consider a mechanical system representing a single wheel of an automobile. In this problem it is desired to determine the system response to a periodic disturbance. A complete representation of the automobile suspension system is much too complex to be considered at this point and would only serve to confuse the beginner with needless details. The system to be considered is as illustrated in Fig. 3-2. M_1 represents one-quarter of the mass of the automobile; K_1 is the spring constant of the main spring; C_1 is the shock-absorber damping constant; M_2 is the mass of the wheel and axle; and K_2 is the spring constant of the tire (assumed to be linear for simplicity). The differential equations of motion of the system are

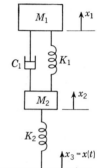

FIG. 3-2. Simplified representation of a single wheel of an automobile suspension system. M_1 equals one-quarter of the mass of the automobile, M_2 is the mass of the wheel and axle combined, K_1 and C_1 are the constants associated with the main spring and shock absorber, respectively, and K_2 is the linearized spring constant of the pneumatic tire.

$$M_1 \frac{d^2x_1}{dt^2} + C_1\left(\frac{dx_1}{dt} - \frac{dx_2}{dt}\right) + K_1(x_1 - x_2) = 0$$

$$M_2 \frac{d^2x_2}{dt^2} + C_1\left(\frac{dx_2}{dt} - \frac{dx_1}{dt}\right) + K_1(x_2 - x_1) + K_2(x_2 - x_3) = 0 \qquad (3\text{-}15)$$

$$x_3 = x(t)$$

The magnitudes of the physical constants are

$$M_1 = 25 \text{ slugs} \quad K_1 = 1,000 \text{ lb/ft}$$
$$M_2 = 2 \text{ slugs} \quad K_2 = 4,500 \text{ lb/ft} \qquad (3\text{-}16)$$

It is desired to determine the magnitude of the damping coefficient of the shock absorber necessary to produce a minimum translational motion of the mass M_1 for a periodical displacement x_3 of magnitude 0.2 ft and duration 0.01 sec. The frequency of the recurring step displacement shall be approximately the undamped natural frequency of the main mass M_1.

The first step involved in the computer setup of any problem is the determination of the approximate frequencies to be encountered in its solution. From these the best choice of time-scale factor can be established. The undamped natural frequency of the main mass in this problem is

$$\omega_{n,x1} = \sqrt{\frac{K_1}{M_1}} = 6.33 \text{ radians/sec}$$

The undamped natural frequency of the mass M_2, when all coupling terms in the system are neglected, is

$$\omega_{n,x2} = \sqrt{\frac{K_1 + K_2}{M_2}} = 52.4 \text{ radians/sec}$$

Since the problem is linear and a galvanometer-type recording device is adequate, the problem can be operated at a speed such that frequencies appreciably higher than 1 radian/sec are present. The frequency of the mass M_2 (52.4 radians/sec) is too great, however, for best computer operation. Furthermore, the problem setup is complicated by the high gains that would be necessary if the problem were run at natural time. On the other hand, to slow the problem down considerably would reduce the frequency of the x_1 equation below the optimum. The low frequencies encountered would require low potentiometer settings to be used, and there would be some loss of accuracy because of this. A compromise must be made, and the logical choice seems to be to slow the problem by a factor of 10, giving new undamped natural frequencies of $\omega_{n,x1} = 0.63$ radian/per machine sec and $\omega_{n,x2} = 5.24$ radians per machine sec.

At this time it is necessary to leave this problem. Its setup will be completed in a later section after the necessary techniques are made available.

3-5. Performing the Time-scale Change. The actual mechanism of making a time change is very simple. To accomplish a time-scale change it is only necessary to make a substitution of variable for the independent variable in the problem. If it is desired to change the time scale of a problem by a factor a, where a is a positive constant and t is the independent variable of the problem, the substitution $t = \tau/a$ is made. If a is greater than unity, the solution is slowed by the factor a. If a is less than unity, the problem is speeded up by the factor $1/a$. It is essential that the same variable substitution be made throughout the entire problem or all physical significance of the problem will be lost.

Upon making the substitution $t = \tau/a$ in a system of differential equations, the derivatives become

$$\frac{d}{dt} = \frac{d}{d\tau/a} = a\frac{d}{d\tau} \tag{3-17}$$

since $d(\tau/a) = (1/a)\,d\tau$, for $a = $ constant.

Similarly,
$$\frac{d^2}{dt^2} = \frac{d}{dt}\left(a\frac{d}{d\tau}\right) = a^2\frac{d^2}{d\tau^2} \tag{3-18}$$

and
$$\frac{d^n}{dt^n} = a^n\frac{d^n}{d\tau^n} \tag{3-19}$$

Example 3-3. As an example of performing a time-scale change, consider the second-order differential equation

$$\frac{d^2x}{dt^2} + 2\frac{dx}{dt} + 16x = f(t) \tag{3-20}$$

with the initial conditions

$$x(0) = 0 \qquad \frac{dx}{dt}(0) = 1 \tag{3-21}$$

The undamped natural frequency of the system can be obtained by considering the homogeneous equation. The undamped natural frequency is found to be

$$\omega_n = \sqrt{16} = 4 \text{ radians/sec} \tag{3-22}$$

To slow the problem down by a factor of 2, the variable substitution required is $t = \tau/2$. Performing this substitution gives

$$4\frac{d^2x}{d\tau^2} + 4\frac{dx}{d\tau} + 16x = f\left(\frac{\tau}{2}\right) \tag{3-23}$$

with the new initial conditions

$$x(0) = 0 \qquad \frac{dx}{d\tau}(0) = \frac{1}{2} \tag{3-24}$$

The undamped natural frequency of the new equation is found to be

$$\omega_n = \sqrt{16/4} = 2 \text{ radians/machine sec} \tag{3-25}$$

The desired time-scale change was accomplished.

It should be emphasized at this point that, if a time-scale-factor change is performed upon a problem, it should be taken into consideration when interpreting the results of a problem. A very common error made by the beginner is to forget that the recorded derivatives are derivatives with respect to τ rather than t. It is always necessary to perform the time-scale-factor change in reverse upon the time scale and the magnitude of the derivatives before labeling the graphical results of a problem solution.

Example 3-4. As a second illustration of the process of transforming the time-scale factor of an equation to one more suited to solution on an analog computer, consider Legendre's equation

$$(1 - t^2)\frac{d^2y}{dt^2} - 2t\frac{dy}{dt} + n(n + 1)y = 0 \tag{3-26}$$

It is desired to find the solution of the equation over a range of independent variable $0 \leq t \leq 0.99$ for $n = 1$; then at $t = 0$, the undamped natural frequency is

$$\omega_n = \sqrt{\frac{n(n + 1)}{1 - t^2}} = \sqrt{2} \text{ radians/sec} \tag{3-27}$$

At $t = 0.99$, the undamped natural frequency is

$$\omega_n = \sqrt{\frac{n(n + 1)}{1 - t^2}} = \sqrt{\frac{2}{0.0199}} \cong 10 \text{ radians/sec} \tag{3-28}$$

Since only a period of $0 \leq t \leq 0.99$ sec is of interest, it seems desirable to slow the solution down by a factor of 10. Making the substitution $t = \tau/10$ in Eq. (3-26) gives

$$\left(1 - \frac{\tau^2}{100}\right)100\frac{d^2y}{d\tau^2} - 2\tau\frac{dy}{d\tau} + n(n + 1)y = 0 \tag{3-29}$$

The solution of the problem for the range of $0 \leq \tau/10 \leq 0.99$ will now take 9.9 sec on the computer.

3-6. Choice of Amplitude-scale Factor. The choice of proper amplitude-scale factor for a problem is as important as the choice of time scale. It should be made following the time-scale change, if any, but before any attempt is made to prepare a block diagram of the problem.

The choice of proper amplitude-scale factor should be made with the following points in mind:

1. Voltage levels throughout the machine should be kept at an optimum value; for instance, the normal operating range of a REAC is ± 100 volts. Maximum voltages near zero should be avoided, and maximum voltages in excess of 100 volts should be avoided to prevent overloading of the amplifiers. This is not an absolute limit but is subject to the load placed on the amplifier. In determining scale factor, if an attempt is made to keep all peak voltages in the neighborhood of ± 50 volts, satisfactory operation will usually be achieved even if considerable error is made in estimating the maximum magnitude of the problem variables.

2. The choice of amplitude-scale factor should be made in a manner that will preserve, as much as possible, the relation between the physical system and the system wired into the computer. This permits a ready interpretation of voltages read from the computer directly in

terms of the units of the problem, i.e., feet, pounds, seconds.   This
ready cross-reference from voltages to the units of the problem should
be simple enough that little or no hand computation is necessary.

3. The system used in adjusting scale factor should be sufficiently
simple that no confusion will arise in its use.

In arriving at a workable scheme for adjusting scale factor, the
above three considerations should be taken into account.   The first
consideration must be satisfied or the scale factor or time-scale change
has not been properly chosen.   All the commonly used schemes for
adjusting scale factor are equally able to fulfill this requirement;
therefore, it will offer no influence in our choice of scheme.   The
second and third considerations, relation of machine voltages to problem units, and simplicity, must then be the deciding factors.

One scheme that is sometimes used is the association of a scale
factor, say a_x, with each problem variable such that

$$a_x \leq \frac{1}{\text{maximum expected value of } |x|} \frac{\text{machine units}}{\text{physical units}} \qquad (3\text{-}30)$$

where a machine unit is assigned a value of 100 volts.[3]   This system
has a natural disadvantage, since, for a system expressed in terms of
x, y, and θ, the following relationship between machine units and
problem units might exist:

$$a_x = \frac{1}{4} \frac{\text{machine units}}{\text{feet}}$$

$$a_\theta = 20 \frac{\text{machine units}}{\text{radians}} \qquad (3\text{-}31)$$

$$a_y = 4 \frac{\text{machine units}}{\text{feet}}$$

Indeed, even the scale factor associated with the same variable in
different parts of the same problem may vary.   With this system, the
machine operator is forced to think mainly in terms of machine units
rather than in units of the problem itself, and the problem loses some
of its physical identity.

A scheme that permits a much more natural approach to scale-factor
adjustment is to assign a machine unit to be equal to 1 volt; therefore

$$a_x = \frac{\text{machine units}}{\text{physical units}} = \frac{\text{volts}}{\text{physical units}} = 1 \qquad (3\text{-}32)$$

Multiplication of each of the problem variables, x, y, θ, . . . , by the
appropriate constant a_x, a_y, a_θ, . . . , changes the units of the problem from the physical units to units of volts.   The form of the equa-

tions remains exactly the same, however, and no labor is involved since all the dimensional constants are equal to unity.

The great advantage of this system lies in the exact equivalence of the machine equation to the physical equation. Upon reading a voltage from the computer, the operator can immediately visualize the voltage as representing a certain number of units in the physical system. To translate volts into problem units, the operator needs to know only the number of units (volts) of the machine variable represented at the point where the voltage is read. For example, suppose 20 volts is measured as the output of an amplifier which supplies 40θ in a problem. If the dimensions of θ in physical units are radians, then

$$40\theta = 20 \text{ volts} = 20 \text{ radians} \qquad (3\text{-}33)$$
$$\theta = 0.5 \text{ radian} \qquad (3\text{-}34)$$

Up until now, nothing has been done that in any way adjusts the voltage level of a problem on the computer to the proper operating range. The actual voltage-amplitude adjustment is made by multiplying each equation through by an appropriate constant. In order to determine the proper constants by which to multiply the equations, it is necessary to know the maximum values each variable and its derivatives can take on during the solution of the problem. Means of approximating the size of problem variables and choosing the proper equation scale factors are considered in subsequent sections of this chapter.

3-7. Approximating the Magnitude of the Variables of a Problem. The guess one makes as to the maximum size of the variables of a problem need not be "picked from a hat." Intelligent guesses can be made from a knowledge of the physical system and from the mathematics of the problem statement. For example, the equation representing the aileron motion δ_a of an aircraft in flight is of the form

$$a_1 \frac{d^2\delta_a}{dt^2} + a_2 \frac{d\delta_a}{dt} + a_3\delta_a = f(t) \qquad (3\text{-}35)$$

where $f(t)$ represents the control forces acting upon the aileron. The limited statement of the problem made here implies the following:

1. δ_a will probably not exceed approximately 20 to 30° or the problem could not represent the physical system.

2. The undamped natural frequency of the above equation is

$$\omega_n = \sqrt{\frac{a_3}{a_1}} \qquad (3\text{-}36)$$

If ω_n is greater than unity, the maximum value of $d\delta_a/dt$ is approximately proportionately greater than the maximum value of δ_a. Correspondingly, if ω_n is less than unity, $d\delta_a/dt$ (max) is proportionately less than δ_a.

The validity of the above assumption regarding the magnitude of the derivative of δ_a can be seen by considering the sinusoidal function

$$f(t) = \sin \omega_1 t \qquad (3\text{-}37)$$

Differentiating Eq. (3-37) successively gives

$$\frac{df(t)}{dt} = \omega_1 \cos \omega_1 t \qquad (3\text{-}38)$$

$$\frac{d^2f(t)}{dt^2} = -\omega_1{}^2 \sin \omega_1 t \qquad (3\text{-}39)$$

$$\left|\frac{d^n f(t)}{dt^n}\right| = |\omega_1{}^n \cos \omega_1 t| \qquad (3\text{-}40)$$

It may be immediately observed that the maximum magnitude of the first derivative is ω_1 times greater than the maximum magnitude of the variable $f(t)$. Correspondingly, the second derivative has a maximum magnitude $\omega_1{}^2$ times as great as the maximum value of $f(t)$, and the nth derivative has a maximum $\omega_1{}^n$ times as great as the maximum value of $f(t)$. Generalizing the above results, it is apparent that, if the form of a problem solution is sinusoidal in nature and if the damping is not great, the maximum value of the derivatives of a variable may be predicted from a knowledge of the maximum magnitude of the variable and the frequency of oscillation.

The accuracy of the estimation of the maximum magnitude of derivatives obtained in this manner is dependent upon how closely the frequency is known and how much damping is present in the system. The presence of damping makes the values found for the derivatives conservatively large, so that the estimates obtained are the upper limits of the magnitudes of the derivatives.

After assigning a maximum value to each of the variables in the problem, it is necessary to multiply each of the equations by an appropriate constant. The constants are chosen so that the voltage appearing on the output of the amplifiers used in the problem will not cause them to overload and yet will be as high as possible in order to keep the signal-to-noise ratio large. The procedure is illustrated in detail by the following examples.

Example 3-5. The equations of motion representing a "tuned" pendulum free to translate in the vertical direction and to rotate about its axis are

$$\frac{d^2x}{dt^2} + 1,000x - 100\theta = 0 \qquad (3\text{-}41)$$

$$\frac{d^2\theta}{dt^2} + 1,000\theta - 100x = 0 \qquad (3\text{-}42)$$

The units of x and θ are inches and radians respectively, and the assigned initial conditions are

$$x(0) = 2 \text{ in.} \quad \frac{dx}{dt}(0) = \frac{d\theta}{dt}(0) = \theta(0) = 0 \tag{3-43}$$

The physical system represented is shown in Fig. 3-3.

The first step in the setup procedure is to decide how fast the problem should operate. For a problem of this type, a Brush recording is adequate; furthermore, it is desirable to record the results for a relatively long period of time in order to observe the influence of the coupling in the system. Problem frequencies of approximately one cycle per second seem to be a good choice for this problem. Sufficient detail will be obtainable from the graphical results, and yet excessive plotting time will not be required. Upon checking the undamped natural frequencies of the system, ω_n is found to be

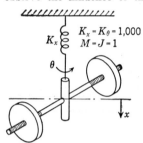

$K_x = K_\theta = 1{,}000$
$M = J = 1$

$$\omega_n = \sqrt{1{,}000} = 31.6 \text{ radians/sec} \tag{3-44}$$

for both the x and θ modes, and the frequency is

$$\frac{\omega_n}{2\pi} = f = \frac{31.6}{2\pi} \cong 5 \text{ cps} \tag{3-45}$$

Fig. 3-3. Tuned torsional pendulum capable of illustrating the transfer of energy from one mode of oscillation to a second mode of oscillation. For complete energy transfer the ratio of the moment of inertia and torsional spring constant must equal the ratio of the mass and translational spring constant.

Slowing the problem down by making the substitution $t = \tau/5$ gives the new equations

$$25\frac{d^2x}{d\tau^2} + 1{,}000x - 100\theta = 0 \tag{3-46}$$

$$25\frac{d^2\theta}{d\tau^2} + 1{,}000\theta - 100x = 0 \tag{3-47}$$

The new undamped natural frequencies of the system are

$$\omega_n = \sqrt{\frac{1{,}000}{25}} = 6.33 \text{ radians/sec} \tag{3-48}$$

This information may now be used to aid in choosing the proper amplitude-scale factor for the problem. Since ω_n is approximately 6 radians/sec, $dx/d\tau$ (max) is approximately six times greater than x (max), and $d\theta/d\tau$ (max) is approximately six times larger than θ (max). From the initial conditions of the problem it is found that, at $t = 0$, all the system energy is in the form of potential energy in the spring, which is stretched to a length of 2 in. Therefore, $-2 \le x \le 2$ in., and an approximate range of $dx/d\tau$ can be established as -12 in./sec $\le dx/d\tau \le 12$ in./sec. From a knowledge of the behavior of the system (and the symmetry of the equations) it can be predicted that the ranges of θ and of $d\theta/d\tau$ are

$$-2 \text{ radians} \le \theta \le 2 \text{ radians} \tag{3-49}$$
$$-12 \text{ radians/sec} \le d\theta/d\tau \le +12 \text{ radians/sec} \tag{3-50}$$

After multiplying the problem variables by the appropriate dimensional constants, the following relationships between the dimensions of the machine variables and problem variables are obtained:

$$
\begin{aligned}
1 \text{ volt} &= 1 \text{ in.} & 1 \text{ volt} &= 1 \text{ in./sec} \\
1 \text{ volt} &= 1 \text{ radian} & 1 \text{ volt} &= 1 \text{ radian/sec}
\end{aligned} \tag{3-51}
$$

Since it is desirable that all amplifiers shall have a maximum output of approximately 50 volts, it can be immediately determined that $25x$, 25θ, $4\,dx/d\tau$, and $4\,d\theta/d\tau$ are satisfactory as outputs of amplifiers. In order to avoid using a potentiometer between the amplifiers, since only gains of 1, 4, and 10 are available on a REAC, these quantities may be changed for greater convenience, giving $20x$, 20θ, $5\,dx/d\tau$, and $5\,d\theta/d\tau$ as the desired outputs of their respective amplifiers. For ease in setting up the equations in the form of a block diagram, Eq. (3-46) can be multiplied by 0.2 and Eq. (3-47) can be multiplied by 0.2, giving

$$5\frac{d^2x}{d\tau^2} + 200x - 20\theta = 0 \qquad (3\text{-}52)$$

$$5\frac{d^2\theta}{d\tau^2} + 200\theta - 20x = 0 \qquad (3\text{-}53)$$

The block diagram of the computer setup using the abbreviated notation normally used for a REAC computer is shown in Fig. 3-4a. Figure 3-4b shows the identical circuit when drawn in the more detailed form required for the GEDA. In Fig. 3-4a, potentiometers 1 and 2 are set to unity for the stated values of the parameters. They were included in the diagram so that the system response could be investigated for several values of the coefficients of the x and θ terms in Eqs. (3-41) and (3-42).

The choice of constant by which to multiply Eqs. (3-46) and (3-47) was made by considering the highest-order derivative that occurs explicitly in the problem setup of each equation. In the circuit diagram of Figs. 3-4a and 3-4b, it was assumed that the second derivatives were not needed as recorded quantities. Therefore, it was not necessary to consider their maximum values, as they do not appear explicitly at any point in the diagram.

If it is necessary to record $d^2x/d\tau^2$ and $d^2\theta/d\tau^2$, each must be formed explicitly in the computer setup and the magnitude of each must be considered when choosing the appropriate equation multiplier constants. From a knowledge of the problem frequencies and the maximum magnitude of x and θ it can easily be determined that

$$-72 \leq \frac{d^2x}{d\tau^2} \leq 72 \text{ in./sec} \qquad (3\text{-}54)$$

$$-72 \leq \frac{d^2\theta}{d\tau^2} \leq 72 \text{ radians/sec} \qquad (3\text{-}55)$$

A satisfactory constant by which to multiply both Eqs. (3-46) and (3-47) is thus 0.04. Performing this multiplication gives the new equations

$$\frac{d^2x}{d\tau^2} + 40x - 4\theta = 0 \qquad (3\text{-}56)$$

$$\frac{d^2\theta}{d\tau^2} + 40\theta - 4x = 0 \qquad (3\text{-}57)$$

The setup of Eqs. (3-56) and (3-57) is shown in the circuit diagram of Fig. 3-5.

A comparison of Figs. 3-4a and 3-5 reveals that two more amplifiers are necessary in the latter circuit. These two amplifiers are used to generate the highest-order derivatives of the problem. This adequately demonstrates the undesirability of generating explicitly the highest-order derivatives of a problem unless it is necessary from the statement of the problem. To do so without good reason is wasteful of equipment and effort.

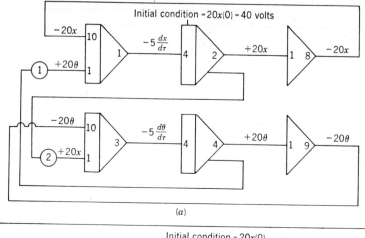

(a)

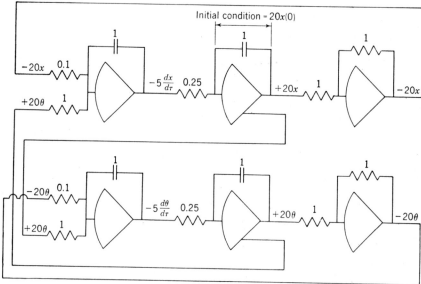

(b)

FIG. 3-4. Circuit diagrams of the computer setup of the tuned torsional pendulum. (a) The notation found most convenient for computers having fixed input and feedback impedances; (b) the detailed representation required when using computers having external plug-in impedances. Impedance values are in megohms and microfarads.

In Fig. 3-4a each line on the circuit diagram represents a patch cord on the computer showing the proper component interconnections. As the problem complexity increases, the interconnections become more and more difficult to trace out using this notation. To reduce this difficulty, a more convenient notation has been adopted.

The new notation consists of indicating each potentiometer twice, at both the input and the output of the amplifiers to which it is connected.   Long interconnecting leads between amplifiers are indicated

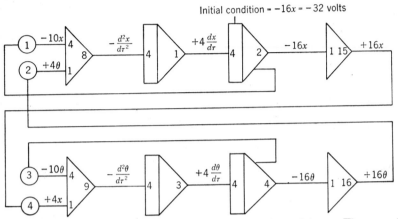

Fig. 3-5. The computer setup of the tuned torsional pendulum.   The second derivatives of the problem variables have been formed, requiring the use of two extra amplifiers in the circuit.

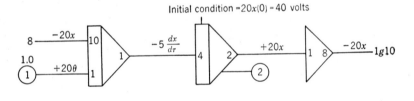

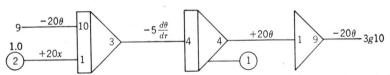

Fig. 3-6. An equivalent notation for the tuned-torsional-pendulum problem circuit diagram given in Fig. 3-4a.   Long interconnecting lines are eliminated from the circuit diagram to allow easier preparation and interpretation of the diagram.

at inputs by the number of the amplifier to which the output is connected and at outputs by both the amplifier number and the gain to which the input is connected.   Using this notation, the circuit diagram of Fig. 3-4a may be redrawn as in Fig. 3-6.   The new diagram is simpler to draw and much easier to use.   The advantage is small for small problems but is very great for large setups.   A similar simplification can be made when drawing circuit diagrams for computers such as the GEDA. In this case long interconnecting wires are not shown on the diagram, and each end is terminated by identically numbered circles or triangles to identify the proper connections.

After discussing the process of performing a time-scale change on a system of equations, it is now possible to complete the automobile-suspension-system problem begun in Example 3-2, Sec. 3-4.

Example 3-6. Rewriting the equations of motion of the system (see Example 3-2) and inserting the known parameters, the equations become

$$25\frac{d^2x_1}{dt^2} + C_1\frac{dx_1}{dt} + 1,000x_1 = C_1\frac{dx_2}{dt} + 1,000x_2 \tag{3-58}$$

$$2\frac{d^2x_2}{dt^2} + C_1\frac{dx_2}{dt} + 5,500x_2 = 1,000x_1 + 4,500x_3 + C_1\frac{dx_1}{dt} \tag{3-59}$$

$$
\begin{aligned}
x_3 = x(t) &= 0.2 & 0.00 < t < 0.01 \\
&= 0.0 & 0.01 < t < 1.01 \\
&= 0.2 & 1.01 < t < 1.02 \\
&= 0.0 & 1.02 < t < 2.02
\end{aligned}
\tag{3-60}
$$

$$\begin{matrix} \cdot & \cdot & \cdot & \cdot \\ \cdot & \cdot & \cdot & \\ \cdot & \cdot & \cdot & \end{matrix}$$

In Example 3-2 it was indicated that a time-scale-factor change should be made. It was also indicated there that a logical change would be to slow the problem solution by a factor of 10. This can be accomplished by making the substitution $t = \tau/10$ in Eqs. (3-58) to (3-60). The equations obtained after making this substitution are

$$2,500\frac{d^2x_1}{d\tau^2} + 10C_1\frac{dx_1}{d\tau} + 1,000x_1 = 10C_1\frac{dx_2}{d\tau} + 1,000x_2 \tag{3-61}$$

$$200\frac{d^2x_2}{d\tau^2} + 10C_1\frac{dx_2}{d\tau} + 5,500x_2 = 1,000x_1 + 4,500x_3 + 10C_1\frac{dx_1}{d\tau} \tag{3-62}$$

$$
\begin{aligned}
x_3 = x\left(\frac{\tau}{10}\right) &= 0.2 & 0.0 < \tau < 0.1 \\
&= 0.0 & 0.1 < \tau < 10.1 \\
&= 0.2 & 10.1 < \tau < 10.2 \\
&= 0.0 & 10.2 < \tau < 20.2
\end{aligned}
\tag{3-63}
$$

$$\begin{matrix} \cdot & \cdot & \cdot \\ \cdot & \cdot & \cdot \\ \cdot & \cdot & \cdot \end{matrix}$$

In any problem, a tabulation of the estimated range of variation of the variables is an essential step in the satisfactory setup of the problem. Such estimates for this problem are

$$x_1 = 0.16 \text{ ft} \tag{3-64}$$

$$x_2 = 0.16 \text{ ft} \tag{3-65}$$

$$\frac{dx_1}{d\tau} \cong 0.16\omega_{n,x_1} = (0.16)(0.63) = 0.1 \text{ ft/machine sec} \tag{3-66}$$

$$\frac{dx_2}{d\tau} \cong 0.16\omega_{n,x_2} = (0.16)(5.24) = 0.84 \text{ ft/machine sec} \tag{3-67}$$

$$x_3 = 0.2 \text{ ft} \tag{3-68}$$

These estimates were made by setting all derivatives equal to zero in Eqs. (3-61) and (3-62) and considering only the simplified equations

$$5{,}500x_2 = 4{,}500x_3 \qquad (3\text{-}69)$$
$$1{,}000x_1 = 1{,}000x_2 \qquad (3\text{-}70)$$

Approximations obtained in this manner are admittedly very crude. They often prove to be extremely useful, but it must be kept in mind that they may be off considerably. For that reason, it is usually desirable to choose scale factors giving maximum estimated voltages approximately one-half the allowable voltages. By this choice, errors as large as a factor of 2 may be tolerated in the initial approximation with little effect on the quality of the problem setup.

From the above approximations, it is seen that Eq. (3-61) can be multiplied by a factor of 0.2 and Eq. (3-62) can be multiplied by 0.4, giving the final equations from which the circuit diagram can easily be prepared:

$$500 \frac{d^2x_1}{d\tau^2} + 2C_1 \frac{dx_1}{d\tau} + 200x_1 = 2C_1 \frac{dx_2}{d\tau} + 200x_2 \qquad (3\text{-}71)$$

$$80 \frac{d^2x_2}{d\tau^2} + 4C_1 \frac{dx_2}{d\tau} + 2{,}200x_2 = 400x_1 + 1{,}800x_3 + 4C_1 \frac{dx_1}{d\tau} \qquad (3\text{-}72)$$

$$
\begin{aligned}
450x_3 &= 90 & 0.0 &< \tau < 0.1 \\
&= 0 & 0.1 &< \tau < 10.1 \\
&= 90 & 10.1 &< \tau < 10.2 \qquad (3\text{-}73)\\
&= 0 & 10.2 &< \tau < 20.2 \\
& \quad . \quad . & & \quad . \\
& \quad . \quad . & & \quad . \\
& \quad . \quad . & & \quad .
\end{aligned}
$$

The method of generating the forcing function $450x_3$, as shown in the lower portion of Fig. 3-7, utilizes techniques that have not been discussed as yet. The circuit is included here only for the sake of completeness, and it is not intended that the reader attempt to fully understand its operation at this time. For the present, let it suffice to say the circuit will operate satisfactorily by periodically switching 90 volts into integrator 3 as the voltage applied to differential relay 2 (DR 2) reaches $-a$ volts. Differential relay 1 (DR 1) then switches the 90 volts off again as $10 \cos 0.317\tau$ becomes greater than $+a$. The voltage a is adjusted as required so that the relays both remain closed for 0.1 sec. The necessary periodicity is achieved by feeding $10 \cos 0.317\tau$ to the differential relays so that they produce a pulse once each 10.1 sec. A more complete discussion of the differential relays and their operation is given in a later chapter.

The graphical results of the runs made for values of $C_1 = 0$ and $C_1 = 100$ are included in Fig. 3-8a and b respectively. Examination of these results reveals that the predicted values of $x_1(t)$ and $x_3(t)$ obtained from Eqs. (3-69) and (3-70) are very conservative. This is true because the applied forcing function is of very short duration in comparison to the time constants of the system. Had this fact been considered, considerably better approximations could have been made. The important thing to note here is that, even with the very rough approximations used, the computer setup obtained on the first trial was usable.

In the setup of linear problems, the choice of scale factor is perhaps not so important as in the setup of nonlinear systems. It is possible

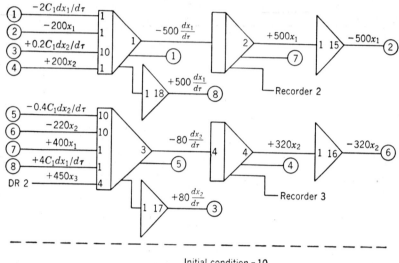

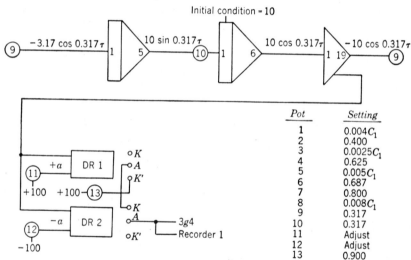

FIG. 3-7. Circuit diagram for the computer solution of the automobile-suspension-system problem described in Example 3-2. The portion of the circuit diagram given below the dashed line is used to generate the forcing function needed in the problem. It is not intended that the reader fully understand that portion of the circuit at this time.

to change the magnitude of the initial conditions and the forcing functions applied to linear system of equations, and the output of all amplifiers in the system will be changed proportionately. The situation is not the same in the case of nonlinear problems. The scale factor *cannot* be varied at will by simply changing the initial conditions

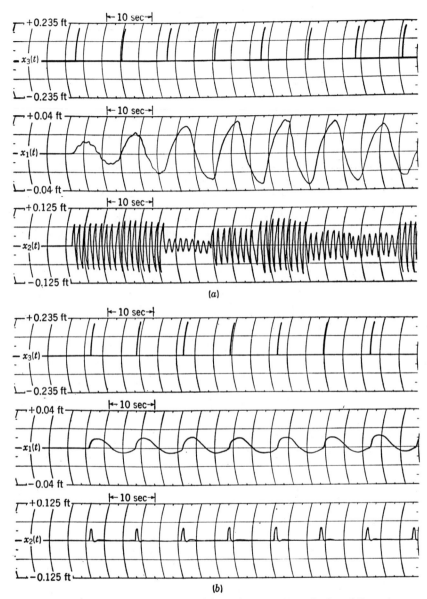

Fig. 3-8. The graphical results obtained from the computer solution of the automobile-suspension-system problem (a) for $C_1 = 0$, (b) for $C_1 = 100$ lb-sec/ft.

or forcing function of the problem! It is, therefore, highly recommended that the newcomer to the field of analog computation assign a fixed scale factor of 1 volt = 1 unit, or any other scheme which is consistent with the scale factor used in multiplication, and retain the same scale factor throughout all problems, linear or nonlinear. Any changes in scale factor can then be made by multiplying the equations individually by appropriate constants. Adherence to this procedure will save the neophyte from many embarrassing moments upon first attempting to perform the solution of nonlinear equations on analog computers.

3-8. Summary. The choice of time base and scale factor in a problem is truly the key to satisfactory computer operation. Any expenditure of time in analysis of a problem prior to attempting the setup will usually pay large dividends in total time saved.

The methods of analysis used in the preliminary study of problems may be very inexact but may still reveal considerable information as to the nature of the solution. In the case of highly nonlinear systems, simple analysis is not always possible. In those cases, the problem preparation should proceed on a trial basis. If the computer setup is not satisfactory, it can then be modified to allow satisfactory computer operation.

As an aid toward the successful solution of problems, all work should be carried out systematically. All steps in the problem preparation should be tabulated for later use in checking. The tabulation of the steps taken in the problem preparation should include the following items:

1. Problem title.
2. Brief description of the problem, including any diagrams necessary to the understanding of it.
3. The system equations.
4. A check solution, if known.
5. The range of the problem variables, if known; if unknown, estimated values with an indication of how they were obtained.
6. The range over which the parameters of the problem are to be varied.
7. The time-scale change to be made.
8. The new equations after performing the time-scale change.
9. The final equations adjusted for scale to prevent overloading of amplifiers.
10. The problem circuit diagram.
11. A tabulation of potentiometer settings.
12. A tabulation of the runs made in the course of the investigation.

PROBLEMS

3-1. Determine the time constant of the solution of the equation

$$10 \frac{dx}{dt} + 15x = 10$$

How many seconds are required for the results to approach to within 2 per cent of the steady-state value?

For each of the Probs. 3-2 to 3-4, determine (a) the undamped natural frequency, (b) the damping ratio, (c) the actual frequency of oscillation.

3-2.
$$5 \frac{d^2x}{dt^2} + 5 \frac{dx}{dt} + 20x = 10$$

3-3.
$$2 \frac{d^2y}{dt^2} + 0.05 \frac{dy}{dt} + 0.1y = 0$$

where $dy/dt(0) = 0$ and $y(0) = 1$.

3-4.
$$\frac{d^2y}{dt^2} + 4 \frac{dy}{dt} + 0.5y = 1$$

3-5. Determine the undamped natural frequency of the equation

$$3 \frac{d^3y}{dt^3} + 15 \frac{d^2y}{dt^2} + 50 \frac{dy}{dt} + 200y = 10$$

3-6. Apply Routh's criterion (see Sec. A-4) to the equation of Prob. 3-5 to determine whether its solution is stable or unstable.

3-7. Make the necessary substitution of variables in the following equations to slow the solutions by a factor of 10:

a.
$$0.01 \frac{d^2y}{dt^2} + 0.02 \frac{dy}{dt} + y = 10$$

b.
$$5 \frac{dy}{dx} + 100y = 100 \sin x$$

c.
$$\frac{d^2y}{dx^2} + (a - b \cos 2x)y = 0$$

d.
$$\frac{d^2y}{dt^2} + \mu(1 - y) \frac{dy}{dt} + y = 0$$

3-8. Determine the approximate frequency and time constant present in the system of equations

$$\frac{d^2x_1}{dt^2} + 4 \frac{dx_1}{dt} + 10x_1 = 5x_2 + 10$$

$$20 \frac{dx_2}{dt} + 5x_2 = 5x_1$$

Determine the exact exponential time constant and frequency components present in the system solution. HINT: Determine the characteristic equation and factor it into real and quadratic factors. A quadratic factor can be expressed in the form

$$p^2 + 2\zeta\omega_n p + \omega_n^2$$

Ans. Approximate values: $\tau = 4$ sec, $\omega_n = 3.17$ radians/sec. Exact values: $\tau = 8.4$ sec, $\omega_n = 3.24$ radians/sec, $\omega = 2.42$ radians/sec.

3-9. Determine the approximate maximum magnitudes of the dependent variable and its derivatives in each of the following equations:

a.
$$\frac{d^2y}{dt^2} + 25y = 0 \qquad y(0) = 10 \qquad \frac{dy}{dt}(0) = 0$$

b.
$$100\frac{d^2y}{dt^2} + 5\frac{dy}{dt} + 0.5y = 10$$

c.
$$10\frac{d^2y}{dt^2} + 7\frac{dy}{dt} + 5y = 5\sin 2t$$

3-10. The determination of the exact maximum amplitudes of the variables of a problem can frequently be quite laborious, but rough approximations are often easily made. Determine the approximate range of the variables in the system of equations

$$10\frac{d^2y_1}{dt^2} + 5\frac{dy_1}{dt} + 2y_1 = 0.2y_2$$

$$2\frac{d^2y_2}{dt^2} + \frac{dy_2}{dt} + 5y_2 = 10y_3$$

$$y_3 = 10(1 - e^{-3t})$$

3-11. Prepare a circuit diagram for the computer solution of the system of equations stated in Prob. 3-10. In the computer diagram adjust the amplitude scale so that the maximum expected magnitude of the variable or derivative appearing at the output of any amplifier will lie in the range 15 to 100 volts.

3-12. A time-scale change $t = \tau/4$ has been made in the solution of a problem. A recorder is used to record the output of an amplifier having 25 $dy/d\tau$ as its output. The recorder is calibrated so that full-scale deflection is obtained when 30 volts is applied to the input of the recorder. What is the proper full-scale labeling of the recorded quantity? (Assume 1 volt = 1 problem unit in the computer solution.)

REFERENCES

1. Brown, G. S., and D. P. Campbell: "Principles of Servomechanisms," p. 49, John Wiley & Sons, Inc., New York, 1948.
2. Gardener, M. F., and J. L. Barnes: "Transients in Linear Systems," p. 197, John Wiley & Sons, Inc., New York, 1952.
3. Korn, G. A., and T. M. Korn: "Electronic Analog Computers," p. 23, McGraw-Hill Book Company, Inc., New York, 1952.

CHAPTER 4

THE SYNTHESIS OF SERVOMECHANISM SYSTEMS

4-1. Introduction. One of the most fruitful applications of analog computers has been the analysis of servomechanism systems. Experience has shown that the computing elements lend themselves very naturally to simulation of closed- or open-loop control systems. The proper application of a computer can save many hours of calculation in determining the proper range of coefficients to produce stability or an optimum response to a disturbing influence in a servomechanism system.

When applying the classical methods of synthesis of servomechanism systems, one determines the frequency response of the system. To determine the actual time response of the system is possible, but it entails a very considerable amount of calculation in translating the results from the frequency domain to the time domain. In engineering applications, the end result desired in evaluating any servomechanism system is the time response of the system. Fortunately, this is the result obtained from the analog computer. Furthermore, the graphical nature of the display of analog computer results is an advantage rather than a disadvantage to the engineer.

It is not the author's intention to imply herein that an analog computer can in any way reduce the requirements of knowledge of servomechanism-synthesis techniques for the designer. Truly, the computer can save endless hours of calculation, but it can tell nothing as to the nature of a network that must be added to a particular system in order to permit a stable configuration. At present, only the classical approach to servomechanism synthesis and design can give this information.

It is beyond the scope of this book to enter into an exhaustive treatment of servomechanisms. Only the peculiarities of systems that will aid the reader successfully to set up similar systems on an analog computer will be mentioned.

4-2. The Block-diagram Notation. A very convenient method of representing complex physical systems is by means of block diagrams.

Using this notation, very complex systems can be represented as groups of properly interconnected blocks where each block represents a small portion of the system. If the complex system is broken down into a sufficiently large number of components, the behavior of each component can be represented mathematically by a simple equation.

Each block of a block diagram has three characteristics: an input, an output, and a *transfer function* $Y(p)$ where $Y(p)$ is an operator that relates the behavior of the output and input. In Fig. 4-1a the characteristics of a block are illustrated. The equation relating the input and output is

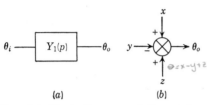

$$\frac{\theta_o}{\theta_i} = Y_1(p)$$

(a)   (b)

FIG. 4-1. Block-diagram notation: (a) a block having a transfer function $Y_1(p)$; (b) a differential symbol indicating the algebraic addition of several quantities.

Although a block can have several additive inputs, a standard symbol has been adopted in the study of servomechanisms to represent the sum (or difference) of several quantities. This symbol is called a *differential* and is illustrated in Fig. 4-1b. The signs associated with each input of the differential indicate whether the quantity is to be summed in the positive or negative sense. Thus

$$\theta_o = x - y + z$$

The block diagrams used to represent servomechanism systems normally have only a single input to each block. When several quantities are to be combined, a differential symbol is used.

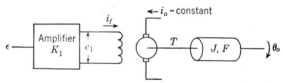

FIG. 4-2. A simple controller consisting of an amplifier, a d-c shunt-controlled motor, and a load. The combined inertia and damping coefficients of the motor and load are J and F, respectively.

To illustrate the usefulness of block diagrams, consider the simple system illustrated in Fig. 4-2. The system consists of a d-c shunt-controlled motor, a load, and an amplifier that supplies a voltage proportional to an input signal ϵ to the field winding of the motor. For simplicity, the inertia and viscous damping of the load member and motor have been combined into the single constants J and F respectively. The torque output of the motor is T.

To facilitate writing the equations of the system it can be subdivided into smaller parts as illustrated in Fig. 4-3a.   The equivalent block diagram of the system is shown in Fig. 4-3b.

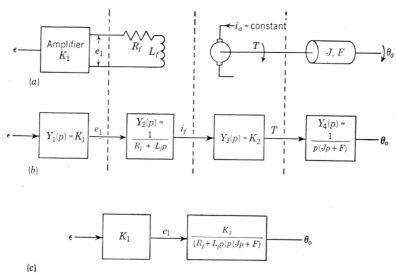

Fig. 4-3. Block diagram representation of the simple controller shown in Fig. 4-2. The dotted lines in (a) indicate that portion of the circuit represented in the corresponding block of (b).   In (c) the latter three blocks of (b) have been lumped into a single transfer function.

The relation between the voltage produced by the amplifier e_1 and the input signal of the amplifier ϵ is

$$\frac{e_1}{\epsilon} = K_1 \qquad (4\text{-}1a)$$

The ratio of the field current i_f and the amplifier voltage is

$$\frac{i_f}{e_1} = \frac{1}{R_f + L_f p} \qquad (4\text{-}1b)$$

where R_f and L_f are the resistance and inductance, respectively, of the motor field winding.   The torque T produced by the motor is

$$\frac{T}{i_f} = K_2 \qquad (4\text{-}1c)$$

where K_2 is a constant determined by the characteristics of the motor. The equation giving shaft position θ_o can be written directly by the application of Newton's laws

$$(Jp^2 + Fp)\theta_o = T$$

or
$$\frac{\theta_o}{T} = \frac{1}{p(Jp + F)} \qquad (4\text{-}1d)$$

Equations (4-1b) to (4-1d) can be combined by successive substitution to form a single transfer function relating the shaft position and amplifier voltage. Performing this substitution gives

$$\frac{\theta_o}{e_1} = \frac{K_2}{(R_f + L_fp)p(Jp + F)} \qquad (4\text{-}2)$$

It should be noted by the reader that the new transfer function, Eq. (4-2), could have been more simply obtained by multiplying the transfer functions of the component parts that were combined:

$$\frac{e_o}{e_i} = Y_1(p)Y_2(p)Y_3(p) \qquad (4\text{-}3)$$

The block diagram of the system as expressed in Eq. (4-2) is shown in Fig. 4-3c. The representation of the system can, of course, be reduced

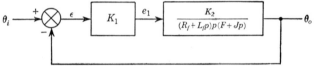

$$\theta_i \xrightarrow{+} \bigotimes \xrightarrow{\epsilon} \boxed{K_1} \xrightarrow{e_1} \boxed{\frac{K_2}{(R_f + L_fp)p(F + Jp)}} \longrightarrow \theta_o$$

FIG. 4-4. Simple positional servomechanism formed by the addition of a feedback loop to the controller of Fig. 4-2.

to a single block by multiplying the transfer function of the two remaining blocks to obtain the expression

$$\frac{\theta_o}{\epsilon} = \frac{K_1K_2}{(R_f + L_fp)p(Jp + F)}$$

The system of Fig. 4-2 can be converted into a simple closed-loop positional servomechanism by the addition of an error-detecting device to determine the error between a desired shaft position θ_i and the actual position θ_o. If this error is denoted by ϵ, then the servomechanism can be represented as shown in Fig. 4-4.

It is beyond the scope of this book to treat the writing of equations of physical system extensively. The purpose of this section has been merely to indicate the useful purpose that block diagrams can serve. The reader who desires more detailed information regarding the block-diagram representation of physical systems (mechanical, electrical, and hydraulic) should refer to texts discussing servomechanisms and allied topics.[1-3]

4-3. Setup of a Simple Servomechanism System. The most common method of representation of a servomechanism system is by block diagrams. A typical example of this notation is shown in Fig. 4-5. In the figure,

$$\epsilon = \theta_i - \theta_o \qquad (4\text{-}4a)$$

$$e_1 = K_1\epsilon \qquad (4\text{-}4b)$$

$$e_2 = e_1 - K_3p\theta_o \qquad (4\text{-}4c)$$

$$\theta_o = \frac{K_2}{p^2 + ap} e_2 \qquad (4\text{-}4d)$$

When starting the setup of a servomechanism system for an analog computer, the natural tendency for the beginner is to expand the system into a single transfer function. This in general is improper and usually further complicates the system setup. Close examination of

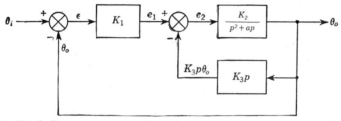

FIG. 4-5. Block-diagram representation of a simple servomechanism having position feedback and also rate feedback from a tachometer.

the system block diagram reveals a considerable similarity to an actual computer setup diagram. Advantage can be taken of this similarity by considering each block separately.

The transfer function of each block can be expanded into differential-equation form, with the input serving only as the forcing function of the equation. After completing the setup of the individual transfer functions distributed throughout the system, the complete setup of the system can be obtained by the interconnection of the individual setups in the manner indicated by the block diagram of the servo system.

The procedure is illustrated by the setup of the servo system of Fig. 4-5. Figure 4-6a illustrates the formation of the error signal $-\epsilon$ by the addition of θ_i and $-\theta_o$; Fig. 4-6b shows the generation of $-e_2$. θ_o is formed by expanding Eq. (4-4d), giving

$$p^2\theta_o + ap\theta_o = K_2e_2 \qquad (4\text{-}5)$$

The setup of this equation is shown in Fig. 4-6c.

The term $K_3p\theta_o$ (Fig. 4-6b) can be obtained by differentiating θ_o and multiplying by a constant K_3. As has been mentioned previously,

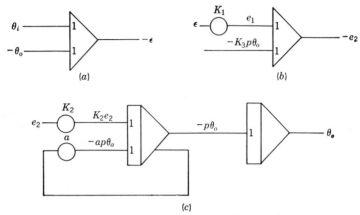

(a)   (b)

(c)

Fig. 4-6. The steps in the preparation of the circuit diagram for the computer solution of the servomechanism shown in Fig. 4-5. The circuit representing each portion of the system can be prepared separately, and later the circuit can be combined into a single setup. The steps are the formation of (a) $-\epsilon$, (b) $-e_2$, (c) θ_o.

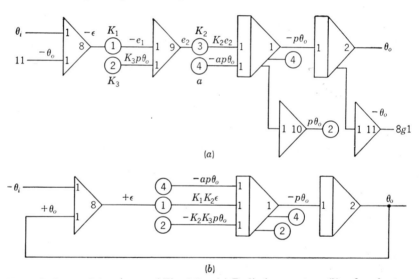

(a)

(b)

Fig. 4-7. Setup of the system of Fig. 4-5. (a) Preliminary setup; (b) reduced setup after the unnecessary circuit components have been eliminated.

this is undesirable, as differentiation is a noise-amplifying process. Instead, if it is observed that $-p\theta_o$ is already available, it is necessary only to multiply this quantity by the constant K_3 to obtain $K_3 p\theta_o$, the quantity needed in the formation of e_2. Finally, by interconnecting the various portions of the system and adjusting signs, the complete computer diagram of Fig. 4-7a is obtained.

At this point it is usually desirable to reexamine the circuit diagram to determine whether an excessive amount of equipment has been used. In the diagram of Fig. 4-7a, the amplifier forming $-\theta_o$ and the amplifier forming $-\epsilon$ can be eliminated by summing $+K_1\theta_o$ and $-K_1\theta_i$ on the input of the amplifier forming e_2. In this particular case, however, this will not be done, as the error ϵ is a quantity which is usually desirable to record. If the simplification were to be made, ϵ would no longer be generated explicitly at any point in the diagram. One simplification can be made, however, as e_2 is not a quantity that is of particular interest. Amplifier 9 can, therefore, be completely eliminated from the circuit, and this eliminates the need for amplifiers 10 and 11 providing that $-\theta_i$ is available rather than θ_i. The final diagram of the circuit is shown in Fig. 4-7b.

If it is necessary to examine the behavior of the system for many different values of K_1, K_2, and K_3, then it may be more convenient to use the diagram shown in Fig. 4-7a. In this diagram each potentiometer setting is a function of only one of the arbitrary constants. In the reduced setup, the settings of potentiometers 1 and 2 are each a function of two of the constants of the system. Similarly, to change K_2 in Fig. 4-7b it is necessary to set two potentiometers rather than one.

As a second illustration of the setup of a servomechanism system, consider the simple positional servomechanism system shown in Fig. 4-4. Two alternatives present themselves in the preparation of the circuit diagram: the denominator of the second block can be expanded to form a polynomial in p, or the function can be formed by parts. Here, for illustrative purposes, the circuit will be formed by parts. The transfer function of the second block

$$\frac{\theta_o}{e_1} = \frac{K_2}{(R_f + L_f p)p(Jp + F)}$$

can be rewritten as

$$\frac{\theta_o}{e_1} = Y_1(p)Y_2(p) = \frac{K_2}{R_f + L_f p} \frac{1}{p(Jp + F)}$$

or, inserting a dummy variable e_2,

$$\frac{\theta_o}{e_2} = \frac{1}{p(Jp + F)}$$

$$\frac{e_2}{e_1} = \frac{K_2}{R_f + L_f p}$$

The circuit diagram of the system is shown in Fig. 4-8. The notation used is that most suited to the Goodyear GEDA or other computers utilizing external plug-in resistors. In the circuit diagram, the values of the resistors and capacitors are given in literal form in megohms and microfarads, respectively.

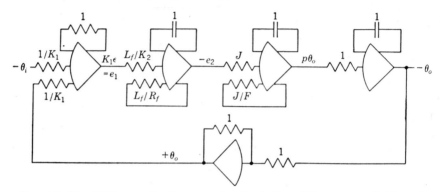

FIG. 4-8. Circuit diagram for the computer simulation of the servomechanism of Fig. 4-4. The values of resistors and capacitors needed in the circuit are given in megohms and microfarads.

4-4. Setup of a Transfer Function. Occasionally the engineer will be confronted by a transfer function representing a system, or portion of a system, which does not give a desirable computer setup when the setup is made in the conventional manner. Such a class of transfer functions are those expressions involving a polynomial in p, divided by a polynomial in p, such as

$$\frac{\theta_o}{\theta_i} = \frac{ap^2 + bp + c}{p^3 + dp^2 + ep + f} \tag{4-6}$$

A conventional approach to the setup of this problem will first be used. Only in this manner can the difficulties involved be pointed out. As a first step, expand the equation into differential equation form, giving

$$p^3\theta_o + dp^2\theta_o + ep\theta_o + f\theta_o = ap^2\theta_i + bp\theta_i + c\theta_i \tag{4-7}$$

Since the first and second derivatives of θ_i are needed in setting up this equation, the equation can be divided by p^2 to eliminate the necessity of differentiating θ_i twice on the computer. (This may be done only if all initial conditions are zero.) The result of this operation gives

$$p\theta_o + d\theta_o + e\frac{\theta_o}{p} + f\frac{\theta_o}{p^2} = a\theta_i + b\frac{\theta_i}{p} + c\frac{\theta_i}{p^2} \tag{4-8}$$

Now, only integrations are necessary, and Eq. (4-8) can be used to derive the circuit diagram of Fig. 4-9. At this point it seems that no difficulties have been encountered. It is not until a particular forcing function has been chosen and the problem is placed upon the computer that difficulties arise. If θ_i is a sinusoidal forcing function, all will be well. If, however, it is decided to excite the system with a step input (a ramp-type input would be worse), the troubles begin. Assume

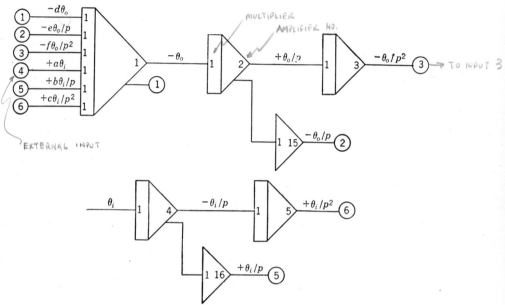

FIG. 4-9. Circuit diagram for the computer solution of Eq. (4-6). In the diagram the forcing function θ_i is integrated twice. This is a common source of trouble.

$\theta_i = 1$ for $0 < t$; then

$$\int_0^t \theta_i \, dt = t \tag{4-9}$$

and

$$\int_0^t \int_0^t \theta_i \, dt^2 = \frac{t^2}{2} \tag{4-10}$$

This simply means that sooner or later amplifiers 4 and 5 in the diagram of Fig. 4-9 must overload. Reducing the input voltage and attenuating the output of integrator 4 before integrating the second time will only prolong the time before overloading of the amplifiers occurs.

A far better approach to this problem, and incidentally one which uses less computing equipment, is given below. Again, using the same equation as an example,

$$\frac{\theta_o}{\theta_i} = \frac{ap^2 + bp + c}{p^3 + dp^2 + ep + f} \tag{4-11}$$

One can proceed by dividing both the numerator and the denominator by the highest power of p in the numerator, namely, p^2, giving

$$\frac{\theta_o}{\theta_i} = \frac{a + b/p + c/p^2}{p + d + e/p + f/p^2} \tag{4-12}$$

Solving this equation for the highest derivative and grouping the terms

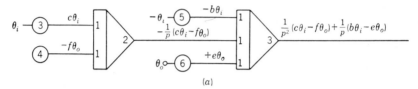

(a)

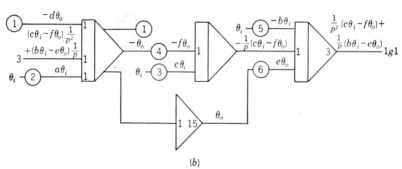

(b)

FIG. 4-10. An improved circuit diagram for the computer solution of Eq. (4-6). (a) Partial system setup; (b) complete setup.

according to powers of p gives

$$p\theta_o = a\theta_i - d\theta_o + (b\theta_i - e\theta_o)\frac{1}{p} + (c\theta_i - f\theta_o)\frac{1}{p^2} \tag{4-13}$$

It is important to note that

$$(b\theta_i - e\theta_o)\frac{1}{p} + (c\theta_i - f\theta_o)\frac{1}{p^2} = f(p) \tag{4-14}$$

can be formed as in Fig. 4-10a. Figure 4-10b gives the complete circuit diagram of Eq. (4-13).

Careful examination of this circuit diagram reveals that θ_i and θ_o always appear at the input of integrators in pairs, and with opposite sign. With a step input, providing the system is stable, there will be no amplifier whose output will increase without bound. It is also apparent that fewer amplifiers are needed in the setup than in the setup of Fig. 4-9.

In the foregoing discussion, the assumption was made that the initial conditions in the system were all zero. When initial conditions are present, they must be accounted for by methods of the Laplace transform. The above technique of computer setup may still be used, as is shown by the following example.

Consider the system

$$\frac{x_o}{x_i} = \frac{ap + b}{p^2 + cp + d} \tag{4-15}$$

If initial conditions are present, the system equation can be expressed in Laplace-transform notation as

$$(s^2 + cs + d)X_o(s) - sx_o(0) - \frac{dx_o}{dt}(0) - cx_o(0) = (as + b)X_i(s) \tag{4-16}$$

or $\quad X_o(s) = \dfrac{as + b}{s^2 + cs + d} X_i(s) + \dfrac{sx_o(0) + dx_o/dt(0) + cx_o(0)}{s^2 + cs + d} \tag{4-17}$

The setup of the first term on the right side of Eq. (4-17) proceeds identically with the procedure outlined previously. The second term is considered separately and the results of the two circuits summed to form x_o.

With some forcing functions, the setup may be reduced to a single setup[4] as illustrated below for a unit-step input. If the numerator and denominator of the second term on the right side of Eq. (4-17) are multiplied by s, the expression becomes

$$X_o(s) = \frac{as + b}{s^2 + cs + d} X_i(s) + \frac{s^2 x_o(0) + [dx_o/dt(0) + cX_o(0)]s}{s^2 + cs + d} \frac{1}{s} \tag{4-18}$$

Recalling that the Laplace transform of a unit step is $1/s$, then since

$$X_i(s) = \frac{1}{s} \tag{4-19}$$

Eq. (4-19) can be rewritten as

$$X_o(s) = \frac{s^2 x_o(0) + [a + dx_o/dt(0) + cx_o(0)]s + b}{s^2 + cs + d} \frac{1}{s} \tag{4-20}$$

Following the procedure outlined for Eqs. (4-11) to (4-13) above, Eq. (4-20) can be rewritten as

$$sX_o(s) = x_o(0) - cX_o(s) + \left[a + \frac{dx_o}{dt}(0) + cx_o(0) - dX_o(s) \right] \frac{1}{s} + \frac{b}{s^2} \tag{4-20a}$$

The circuit diagram for Eq. (4-20a) is shown in Fig. 4-11.

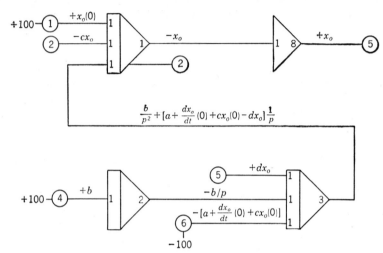

FIG. 4-11. The computer setup demonstrating the method of including initial conditions in the setup of a transfer function.

4-5. Setup of the Factored Form of a Transfer Function. Still another form of presentation of transfer functions is the factored form such as

$$\frac{x_o}{x_i} = \frac{K(p + a)(p + b)}{p(p + c)(p + d)} \tag{4-21}$$

It is sometimes useful to set up this type of equation by using more complex input and feedback networks than are used to make up simple adders or integrators. This specific example will not be set up here, but a few forms of transfer functions which are sometimes useful will be developed.

Recalling that the ratio of the output voltage to the input voltage of a high-gain d-c amplifier is the negative of the ratio of the feedback impedance to the input impedance, one may proceed to develop the transfer function for any combination of input and feedback impedances desired.

One of the simplest and most frequently used complex feedbacks is shown in Fig. 4-12. The feedback and input impedances are

$$z_f = \frac{R_2/pC_1}{R_2 + 1/pC_1} \tag{4-22}$$

$$z_i = R_1 \tag{4-23}$$

Therefore
$$\frac{e_o}{e_i} = -\frac{R_2}{R_1}\frac{1}{\tau p + 1} \qquad GEDA \qquad (4\text{-}24)$$

where
$$\tau = C_1 R_2 \qquad (4\text{-}25)$$

The above transfer function is in a form readily used on machines such as the GEDA where all impedances are patched externally. It is not, however, ideally suited to use on machines of the REAC type, where decade resistance elements are usually not available. A parallel form of the above transfer function can be developed using potentiometers, fixed resistors, and capacitors that will, in general, be more

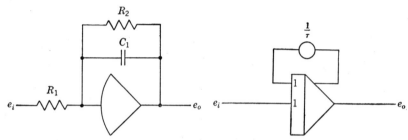

FIG. 4-12. A high-gain d-c amplifier having a resistive input and a parallel resistor and capacitor in the feedback path.

FIG. 4-13. REAC circuit having a transfer function of the same form as the circuit of Fig. 4-12.

useful for machines provided with fixed internal resistors and condensers (Fig. 4-13). A comparison of the circuit of Fig. 4-13 with the circuit of Fig. 4-12 shows that the former differs from the latter only in that the condenser and resistors have been given fixed values of 1 μf and 1 megohm, respectively, and a potentiometer has been inserted in series with the fixed resistor in the feedback. To derive the transfer function in this form, it is necessary to write the equation represented by the circuit. In operator form this is

$$e_o = -\frac{e_i}{p} - \frac{1}{\tau}\frac{e_o}{p} \qquad (4\text{-}26)$$

After simplification this becomes

$$\frac{e_o}{e_i} = -\frac{\tau}{\tau p + 1} \qquad REAC \qquad (4\text{-}27)$$

It is apparent that the results obtained by either the circuit of Fig. 4-12 or that of Fig. 4-13 are similar, since the equations representing the circuits differ only by a constant.

A second example using a complex feedback and input impedance is the circuit of Fig. 4-14. In this circuit the transfer function is

$$\text{GEDA} \quad \frac{e_o}{e_i} = - \frac{R_2}{R_1} \frac{R_1 C_1 p + 1}{R_2 C_2 p + 1} = - \frac{R_2}{R_1} \frac{\tau_1 p + 1}{\tau_2 p + 1} \tag{4-28}$$

where $\tau_1 = R_1 C_1 \tag{4-29}$

and $\tau_2 = R_2 C_2 \tag{4-30}$

The analogous circuit in a form more readily usable for a REAC is shown in Fig. 4-15. Writing the equation from the diagram gives

$$\text{REAC} \quad e_o = -e_i - \frac{1}{\tau_1} \frac{e_i}{p} - \frac{1}{\tau_2} \frac{e_o}{p} \tag{4-31}$$

Therefore $\dfrac{e_o}{e_i} = - \dfrac{\tau_2}{\tau_1} \dfrac{\tau_1 p + 1}{\tau_2 p + 1} \tag{4-32}$

There are a very large number of transfer functions that can be generated by using complex input and feedback impedance networks. A

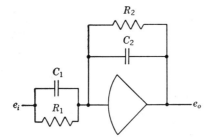

FIG. 4-14. One-amplifier circuit having a transfer function of the form $-R_2/R_1[(\tau_1 p + 1)/(\tau_2 p + 1)]$.

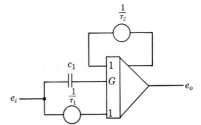

FIG. 4-15. REAC circuit having a transfer function $-\tau_2/\tau_1[(\tau_1 p + 1)/(\tau_2 p + 1)]$.

few of the possible combinations are shown in Table 4-1. A similar list was first published by The RAND Corporation[5] in 1950. The circuits shown in the table are all represented by RC networks, and it is left to the reader to translate these circuits into other forms if it is made necessary by the characteristics of the computer on which they are to be used.

Previously it has been emphasized that differentiation is a very undesirable operation to perform on an analog computer. The circuits shown in Table 4-1 frequently combine the operations of differentiation and integration together in the same transfer function. In general, the differentiation performed in these circuits will cause no difficulty, as there is usually a condenser feedback path that will offer

TABLE 4-1. ONE-AMPLIFIER CIRCUITS FOR THE GENERATION OF COMPLEX TRANSFER FUNCTIONS

1   $e_o = - \dfrac{1 + R_2 C_1 p}{R_1 C_1 p} \, e_i$

2   $e_o = - \dfrac{R_2 C_1 p}{1 + R_1 C_1 p} \, e_i$

3   $e_o = - \dfrac{R_2}{R_1(1 + R_2 C_1 p)} \, e_i$

4   $e_o = - \dfrac{R_2}{R_1} (1 + R_1 C_1 p) e_i$

5   $e_o = - \dfrac{C_1}{C_2} (1 + R_1 C_2 p) e_i$

6   $e_o = - \dfrac{R_1 C_1 p}{1 + R_1 C_2 p} \, e_i$

TABLE 4-1. ONE-AMPLIFIER CIRCUITS FOR THE GENERATION OF COMPLEX
TRANSFER FUNCTIONS (*Continued*)

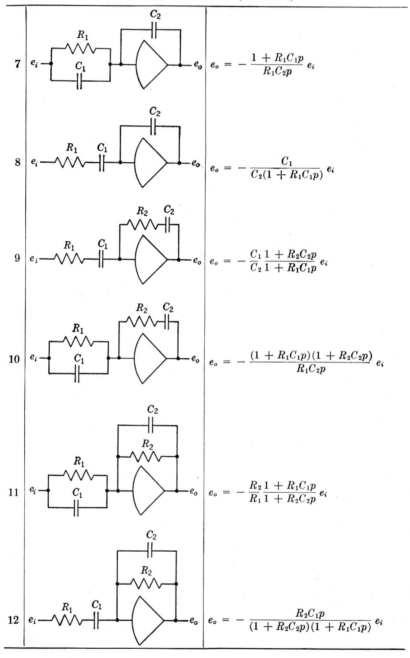

7    $e_o = -\dfrac{1 + R_1 C_1 p}{R_1 C_2 p}\, e_i$

8    $e_o = -\dfrac{C_1}{C_2(1 + R_1 C_1 p)}\, e_i$

9    $e_o = -\dfrac{C_1}{C_2}\dfrac{1 + R_2 C_2 p}{1 + R_1 C_1 p}\, e_i$

10    $e_o = -\dfrac{(1 + R_1 C_1 p)(1 + R_2 C_2 p)}{R_1 C_2 p}\, e_i$

11    $e_o = -\dfrac{R_2}{R_1}\dfrac{1 + R_1 C_1 p}{1 + R_2 C_2 p}\, e_i$

12    $e_o = -\dfrac{R_2 C_1 p}{(1 + R_2 C_2 p)(1 + R_1 C_1 p)}\, e_i$

TABLE 4-1. ONE-AMPLIFIER CIRCUITS FOR THE GENERATION OF COMPLEX
TRANSFER FUNCTIONS (*Continued*)

13    $e_o = -\dfrac{1 + R_2 C_2 p}{R_1[(C_1 + C_2)p + R_2 C_1 C_2 p^2]}\, e_i$

14    $e_o = -\dfrac{R_1 C_1 p(1 + R_2 C_2 p)}{1 + (R_2 + R_1)C_2 p}\, e_i$

15    $e_o = -\dfrac{R_2(C_1 + C_2)p\left(1 + \dfrac{R_1 C_1 C_2 p}{C_1 + C_2}\right)}{1 + R_1 C_1 p}\, e_i$

16    $e_o = -\dfrac{1 + (R_1 + R_2)C_1 p}{R_2 C_2 p(1 + R_1 C_1 p)}\, e_i$

a low impedance to the high-frequency components of the noise arising from the differentiation. In particular, this is true of all those circuits generating transfer functions with the power of p in the denominator equal to or greater than the power of p in the numerator. For those circuits of the table representing transfer function having a larger power of p in the numerator—circuits 4, 5, 10, 14, and 15—there is some possibility of noise trouble. The operation of these circuits should normally be checked carefully in the particular application where they are to be used before relying too heavily upon their satisfactory operation.

In this section circuits have been demonstrated that provide for the generation of several simple transfer functions using passive networks in conjunction with a high-gain d-c amplifier. No effort was made here to describe techniques by which any arbitrary transfer function can be synthesized using a single amplifier.

Mathews and Seifert* of the Dynamic Analysis and Control Laboratory, Massachusetts Institute of Technology, have described systematic procedures by which this can be done. They have presented a one-amplifier design and a three-amplifier design by which theoretically any linear transfer function can be synthesized. Both methods require of the reader a knowledge of network synthesis techniques.

The three-amplifier design has the advantage of simpler synthesis calculations, and in general the network configuration is more easily satisfied by practical sizes of physical components. Both the one-amplifier and three-amplifier methods can entail considerable labor in realizing satisfactory network designs. For that reason the author considers the method previously described in this chapter to be the most useful for normal applications.

Occasionally situations can arise in which the methods of Mathews and Seifert are invaluable. Such occasions might be ones in which (1) the size and complexity of the computer setup require that all possible simplifications be made to permit the problem to be solved on the existing computer facility; or (2) the transfer function is a portion of a simulation problem in which portions of the system are represented mathematically and portions are represented by the actual hardware comprising the physical system. In the latter case it is possible that the frequency response of the mathematical transfer function is such that the simulation on the computer is difficult. Since physical hardware is involved, a time-scale change cannot be made and the one- or three-amplifier setup may provide improved computer operation.

Since the method is slightly restricted in usefulness, it will not be described here. The interested reader is referred to the paper presented by Mathews and Seifert for further details.

4-6. Summary. In this chapter the author has attempted to introduce the reader to the methods of setup of various forms of representation of servomechanism systems. No effort has been made here to

---

* M. V. Mathews and W. W. Seifert, Transfer-function Synthesis with Computer Amplifiers and Passive Networks, a paper presented at the Western Computer Conference and Exhibit, sponsored jointly by the American Institute of Electrical Engineers, the Institute of Radio Engineers, and the Association for Computing Machinery, Los Angeles, Calif., Mar. 1, 2, 3, 1955.

show the representation of servomechanism systems containing non-linearities. The reader will find Chap. 7 very useful in preparing the computer setup of servomechanism systems containing nonlinear phenomena.

In 1951 Beck,[4] of the Naval Air Experiment Station, presented a paper at Cyclone Symposium I discussing the computer setup of transfer functions. In this paper Beck demonstrated the possibility of combining the setup of a transfer function, with initial conditions, into a single computer setup. This technique has been used here in Sec. 4-4. The general method of representation of transfer functions used by Beck is somewhat similar to the method used here; however, Beck reduced the setup of transfer functions to a mechanical rather than a logic process. It is the author's opinion that mechanical procedures of problem setup are not fully satisfactory, as they are soon forgotten unless they are used often.

PROBLEMS

4-1. Figure P 4-1 represents a servomechanism having a split-field servomotor, a load with viscous damping, and tachometric feedback. (a) Write the equations representing the servomechanism; (b) reduce the system of equations to a single transfer function.

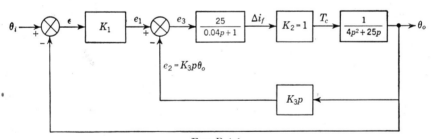

Fig. P 4-1

4-2. Prepare a circuit diagram for the computer solution of the servomechanism system shown in Fig. P 4-1. In your circuit diagram make provisions to allow the parameters K_1 and K_3 to be varied over the range 0 to 10. Assume the input to the servomechanism is a unit step ($\theta_i = 1$ for $t > 0$). Make any time-scale change and amplitude-scale changes that are necessary in order to keep the maximum output voltages of all amplifiers in the diagram in the range of 10 to 100 volts.

4-3. Prepare the circuit diagram for the computer solution of the transfer function obtained in Prob. 4-1b. Use the technique of problem preparation described in Sec. 4-4.

4-4. Redraw the circuit diagram of Fig. 4-8 using REAC notation. Prepare a table of potentiometer settings for your computer diagram.

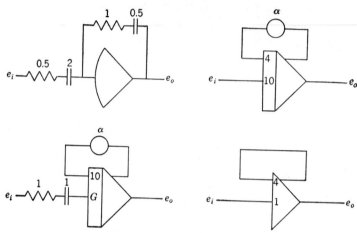

FIG. P 4-5

4-5. Derive the transfer function of each of the circuits given in **Fig. P** 4-5. Impedance values are in megohms and microfarads.

REFERENCES

1. Truxal, J. G.: "Automatic Feedback Control System Synthesis," McGraw-Hill Book Company, Inc., New York, 1955.
2. Brown, G. S., and D. P. Campbell: "Principles of Servomechanisms," John Wiley & Sons, Inc., New York, 1948.
3. Gardner, M. F., and J. L. Barnes: "Transients in Linear Systems," John Wiley & Sons, Inc., New York, 1942.
4. Beck, C.: A Method of Solving Problems on the REAC by the Use of Transfer Functions without Passive Networks, "Project Cyclone, Symposium I on REAC Techniques," pp. 131–136, Reeves Instrument Corporation (under contract with the U.S. Navy Special Devices Center), New York, Mar. 15–16, 1951.
5. Mengel, A. S., and W. S. Melahn: "RAND REAC Manual, RM-525," pp. 13–15, The RAND Corporation, Santa Monica, Calif., Dec. 1, 1950.

CHAPTER 5

MULTIPLYING AND RESOLVING SERVOS

5-1. Introduction. In the previous chapters, the discussion of components and problems has been restricted primarily to the requirements of the solution of linear systems. Fortunately, the analog computer is capable of solving problems other than those arising from the study of linear systems. The availability of function multipliers allows the solution of systems involving nonlinear equations and nonconstant coefficients.

An entirely new field of investigation has thus been opened for the engineer. In the past, system nonlinearities were undesirable obstacles in the path of the design engineer. The only practical approach, in most cases, was to linearize the system equations and hope the actual system was adequately represented. With the aid of the analog computer, however, an engineer is able to introduce nonlinear effects intentionally into system equations and to study, rapidly and conveniently, the effects of these nonlinearities upon the system behavior. To be able to set up nonlinear systems on the analog computer, the operator needs only to understand the capabilities and limitations of a few more tools than have already been introduced. Of greatest importance among these is the function multiplier.

In the early phase of the rapid growth of the analog computer, the design of function-multiplier equipment was a greater problem for the design engineers than was the design of linear computer components. This caused a lag of several years in the development of electronic-multiplier gear that is truly compatible with the best linear computing elements available. Many types of multipliers have been proposed and built in the past few years, but all of these had major disadvantages until recently. In fact, it was as recently as 1953 that the first stabilized high-speed function multipliers became commercially available.[1] The new all-electronic multipliers have accuracies of 0.1 per cent or better and frequency-response characteristics compatible with the linear components. These new multipliers are the

65

first to provide high-accuracy and high-speed operation in the same multiplier.

Since one of the oldest multiplying devices, and as yet the one most commonly used, is the servomultiplier, it will be treated in the greatest detail. Other common multipliers will be described in Chap. 8 with a brief discussion of the theory of operation and advantages and disadvantages of each type. The new electronic multiplier mentioned above is described in that chapter.

5-2. Servomultipliers. The servomultiplier is a device which operates by the positioning of identical potentiometers proportional to a voltage applied to the input of the servo. The accuracy of the device is limited only by the linearity of the potentiometers which may be obtained. The present limitation, due to manufacturing tolerances, is approximately 0.025 per cent of full scale for 10-turn potentiometers.

Fig. 5-1. Multiplier symbol.

The frequency-response characteristic of high-precision servomultipliers is quite poor and, in most instances, provides an upper limit to the speed of solution of problems. The frequency response of servomultipliers may be improved appreciably, with some sacrifice of linearity, by using single-turn potentiometers and eliminating the indicator dials that permit servomultipliers to double as high-accuracy voltmeters.

A commonly used symbol for a multiplier is shown in Fig. 5-1, where x and y are the inputs and z is proportional to the product of x and y. The constant of proportionality k is determined by the design of the multiplier and by the choice of scale factor made for the problem. A choice of 1 volt = 1 unit in the problem setup will produce a different proportionality constant from a choice of 10 volts = 1 unit. It is for this reason that the author earlier suggested that a fixed scale factor be adopted and used for all problems, linear or nonlinear. Fewer mistakes will be made by the beginner if this is done.

While the above symbol for a multiplier is adequate for electronic multipliers, it has been found desirable to use more detailed symbolism when using servomultipliers. This is due to the ever-present need to consider loading effects. The beginner will find that fewer mistakes will be made if a more detailed symbolism is used, such as is shown in Fig. 5-2. The servomultiplier consists of a servoamplifier and servomotor driving, by a mechanical connection, the wiper of two or more identical precision potentiometers. In Fig. 5-2, these potentiometers are indicated as F, A, B, and C. The first potentiometer F is used as an error-sensing device or follow-up potentiometer. The remaining potentiometers are used as multiplier potentiometers.

The operation of servomultipliers in performing function multiplication is easily understood if the reader attempts to visualize the operation when a constant voltage is applied to the servo input. If a constant voltage w is applied to the input of the servomultiplier, the servomotor will drive the follow-up potentiometer, by a system of gearing, to such a position that w volts is picked up by the wiper of the follow-up potentiometer. At that time, the servomotor will cease running, as the error signal, generated by a null-detecting network at the input of the servoamplifier, is zero.

Consider now the follow-up potentiometer. Since the follow-up potentiometer is linear, $+100$ and -100 volts are applied to the ends

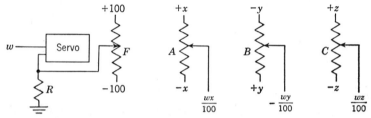

FIG. 5-2. The symbolism commonly employed to represent a servomultiplier.

of the potentiometer, and no current is drawn from the potentiometer wiper at the null position; the only position the potentiometer wiper can have and pick up $+w$ volts is $w/100$ of the distance from the center to the positive end of the potentiometer. This is easily visualized if the reader keeps in mind that the voltage at the geometrical center of the potentiometer is zero because of the equal but opposite in sign, ± 100, voltages placed at the ends of the follow-up potentiometer. The multiplier potentiometers are connected, by means of a common shaft or by gearing, to the follow-up potentiometer. Each of the wipers of the multiplier potentiometers is thus positioned to a position $w/100$ from the center to an extremity of the potentiometer. If equal but of opposite sign voltages, $\pm x$, $\pm y$, and $\pm z$ are placed at the ends of the multiplier potentiometers, the voltages at the respective potentiometer wipers are $w/100$ of the voltages x, y, and z.

The signs of the multiplier output voltages are determined by the sign of the servo input voltage w and the manner of connection of the voltages $\pm x$, $\pm y$, and $\pm z$. As can be seen in Fig. 5-2, to change the sign of the product voltage obtained at the wiper of a particular multiplier potentiometer, it is only necessary to interchange the connections of the inputs to that potentiometer.

The description of the servomultiplier given above is for a constant input voltage w. The operation of the device is identically the same, however, if w is a continuous time-varying function. The major requirement placed on the input function w is that it must vary sufficiently slowly that the servo may, at all times, remain accurately positioned proportional to the voltage representing the function w.

The multiplier, as described above, is capable of four-quadrant multiplication; in other words, the inputs w, x, y, and z may take on either positive or negative values and the proper sign will be affixed to the product. The circuit does require, however, that $\pm x$, $\pm y$, and $\pm z$ be available. If four-quadrant multiplication is not necessary, as in the case where w can take on only positive values, then only the positive or negative value of the quantities need be available if the multiplier potentiometers are center-tapped and the center tap is grounded. This arrangement is desirable, as one amplifier can often be saved for each multiplication. It is important to emphasize that the more slowly varying quantity should be chosen to drive the servo, as the satisfactory operation of the device is based entirely upon the ability of the servo to follow the input signal w accurately and continuously.

To achieve the accuracy of operation that a servomultiplier is capable of delivering, the loading of the potentiometers must be considered just as in the use of any potentiometers. Fortunately, a very simple scheme may be used to compensate for the loading errors. To compensate for loading errors, it is necessary to load the follow-up potentiometer identically to the load on the multiplier potentiometers. The identical error is then induced on the follow-up potentiometer as is present on the multiplier potentiometers provided the load on each multiplier potentiometer is identical. With a load applied to the follow-up potentiometer, the servopotentiometers will no longer be displaced the geometrical distance $w/100$ from the center but they will be displaced $w/100$ of the *electrical* length of the potentiometers and the multiplication will be performed correctly. It is important to note that indicator dials on the servomultipliers *do not* read properly when the follow-up potentiometer is loaded.

In the setup of some problems on a computer, it would be desirable to be able to load the multiplier potentiometers of a servomultiplier with different loads, as would be done if the multiplier outputs were introduced to different gain inputs of computing amplifiers. Unfortunately, this cannot conveniently be done by any scheme with which the author is familiar. One method of compensation that the reader should be cautioned against is the indiscriminate use of coefficient potentiometers as isolation of multiplier potentiometers to permit the use of different gains on the inputs of amplifiers fed by the multiplier. This scheme is shown in Fig. 5-3. A careful analysis of the loading reveals that the loading of the multiplier potentiometers is not uniform, and for some combinations of potentiometer settings, the multiplier errors due to the unequal loading are very appreciable. A sound rule for the beginner to follow is never to load a potentiometer with a second potentiometer without first considering the errors introduced into the computer results by the loading effects.

In Fig. 5-3, if coefficient potentiometers 1 and 2 have a total resistance of 30,000 ohms each, and if potentiometer 1 is set at 0.9 and

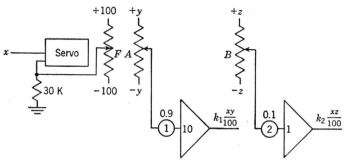

FIG. 5-3. The *improper* use of coefficient potentiometers to achieve a common servomultiplier potentiometer loading.

potentiometer 2 is set at 0.1, then the actual loads on the multiplier potentiometers A and B are 24,260 and 29,910 ohms, respectively. This difference in loading is sufficient to induce appreciable errors into the computer results.

5-3. Division. To many it may appear obvious, on superficial examination, that the servomultiplier can be easily converted to a device capable of performing division by replacing the fixed $+100$ and -100 reference voltages at the ends of the follow-up potentiometer with variable voltages $+u$ and $-u$, respectively. If this is done, the output of the A multiplier potentiometer of Fig. 5-2 becomes wx/u. In actual practice, this method of division is seldom used, since satisfactory operation of the servomechanism is not easily achieved while using this scheme.

The open-loop gain, and thus the stability and sensitivity of the servomechanism, is a function of the voltage applied to the ends of the follow-up potentiometer. If the voltage u, applied to the follow-up potentiometer, is varied over a wide range of values, no constant setting of the servoamplifier gain can give satisfactory operation. If the servoamplifier is provided with an automatic gain-controlling device, fairly good operation using this division scheme can be achieved except when very low values of the voltage u are used. For low values of u, the operation, even with an automatic-gain-controlled servoamplifier, is marginal and other division schemes commonly employed will produce better results. For this reason, most servomultipliers are not provided with an automatic-gain-control amplifier and should never be used for division by replacing the follow-up voltages by variable functions.

Several schemes of performing division are available which will work satisfactorily with any multiplying device. These schemes are all

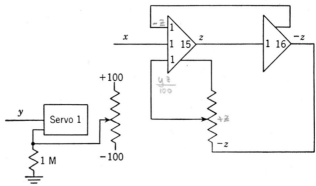

FIG. 5-4. Division circuit.

based upon the solution of an implicit equation of the form

$$x + kyz(x,y) = 0 \tag{5-1}$$

where x = dividend
  y = divisor
  z = quotient
  k = scale-factor constant

One of the most commonly used circuits to perform division is illustrated in Fig. 5-4. Equating the unknown output of amplifier 15 in Fig. 5-4 to the amplifier inputs gives

$$-z = -z + x + \frac{yz}{100} \tag{5-2}$$

$$z = -\frac{100x}{y} \tag{5-3}$$

Division by the quantity y has thus been accomplished. In the circuit, as drawn in Fig. 5-4, the quantity y driving the servo must be positive. If y is negative, satisfactory operation may be achieved by interchanging the high and the low connections of the multiplier potentiometer.   Division by a quantity y which approaches zero will eventually cause an overload of amplifier 15 or 16, since for $x \neq 0$

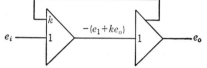

$$\lim_{y \to 0} \frac{x}{y} = \infty \qquad (5\text{-}4)$$

Fig. 5-5. An *infinite*-gain amplifier formed by using positive feedback.

Even if both x and y approach zero simultaneously, trouble will be encountered for sufficiently small values of y.

An improved division circuit may be formed from the circuit of Fig. 5-4 by noting that the portion of the circuit involving the two amplifiers with feedback forms an amplifier of infinite gain *only* if the gain-1 inputs of the amplifiers are exactly unity.   This may be seen by considering Fig. 5-5.   If the gain of the feedback is k, then

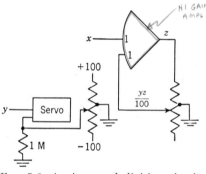

$$e_o = e_i + k e_o \qquad (5\text{-}5)$$
$$\frac{e_o}{e_i} = \frac{1}{1 - k} \qquad (5\text{-}6)$$

If $k = +1$,

$$\frac{e_o}{e_i} = \infty \qquad (5\text{-}7)$$

Assume that an error of 0.1 per cent is present in the gain of the feedback loop; then, for a value of $k = 0.999$,

Fig. 5-6. An improved division circuit using only a single high-gain amplifier. The reader is again reminded that the use of numbers designating gains at the inputs of the symbol for a high-gain amplifier implies the presence of input resistors having values that are the inverse of the gains in megohms.

$$\frac{e_o}{e_i} = \frac{1}{1 - 0.999} = \frac{1}{0.001} = 1,000$$
$$(5\text{-}8)$$

The gain has been reduced by the small error from a theoretical value of infinity to only 1,000.   Most high-quality computing amplifiers have gains of the order of magnitude of 100,000 to 60,000,000.   Certainly then, in general, improved operation will result from the use of a single high-gain amplifier to replace the "infinite"-gain amplifier formed by the use of two amplifiers with positive feedback.   This circuit is shown in Fig. 5-6.

The analysis of this circuit proceeds in a similar manner if it is noted that the gain of the amplifier is very high.   Then, for z to remain within the operating range of the amplifier, the sum of the inputs must differ from zero by only a very small amount. The unknown output z can then be determined by equating the sum of the inputs to zero as in Eqs. (5-9) and (5-10):

$$x + \frac{yz}{100} = 0 \qquad (5\text{-}9)$$

$$z = \frac{-100x}{y} \qquad (5\text{-}10)$$

An analysis of the effect of finite amplifier gain on the operation of the division circuit is of interest, as it emphasizes the desirability of keeping the voltage driving the servo as large as possible. Assume the high-gain amplifier to have a gain $-A$; then, from Fig. 5-6,

$$z = -A\left(x + \frac{yz}{100}\right) \qquad (5\text{-}11)$$

$$z = \frac{-100x}{100/A + y} \qquad (5\text{-}12)$$

It is readily seen that errors due to a finite gain result in an error term in the divisor. Any alignment error present in the servomultiplier potentiometers appears as a similar term. The effects of these errors may be minimized by keeping the divisor as large as possible.

Stability must always be considered when generating functions by implicit techniques. A criterion for stability which has been developed is that the circuit will be stable with plus $F(z)$ as the amplifier input if $\partial F/\partial z > 0$ and plus z is the output of the high-gain amplifier. If $\partial F/\partial z < 0$, minus $F(z)$ must be fed back to the high-gain amplifier to ensure stability.[2]

A simple analysis of the circuit is normally all that is required to ensure that this condition is satisfied. Consider the division circuit of Fig. 5-7. Assume that the sign of the divisor is always positive and the numerator θ may take on both positive and negative values. Arbitrarily, assign a positive value to θ as indicated in Fig. 5-7. Then the output of the high-gain amplifier must be negative. Since the input δ of the servo was assumed to be always positive, the wiper of the multiplier potentiometer must be picking up a negative voltage. The concept of operation of the division circuit is based upon the sum of the inputs of the high-gain amplifier being equal to zero. This condition can be satisfied with the connections as shown. Assume, however, that the connections at the ends of the servomultiplier potentiometer are interchanged; the voltage at the wiper of the potentiometer will then be positive. Obviously, two positive voltages applied to the input of the high-gain amplifier cannot add up to give zero, and the circuit must be unstable. This simply applied test can prove that a system is unstable but does not prove stability. Most often this is the only test needed, however, as the computer operator usually remembers the form of a circuit which has previously proved useful but may not remember the exact connections.

The circuit illustrated above is wasteful of equipment in that connections to both ends of a multiplier potentiometer need never be made simultaneously in a division circuit if a center tap is available on the multiplier potentiometer.

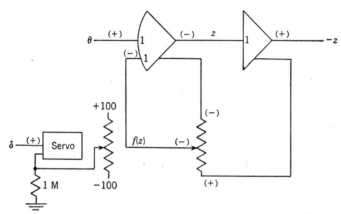

FIG. 5-7. Division circuit demonstrating a practical method of checking stability.

Occasionally, it is necessary to perform a division by a quantity which is zero at the start of the computation but is finite at all other times in the computation. This can often be accomplished with negligible error by adding a small error signal to the divisor at $t = 0$. The nature of the error must be such that it rapidly becomes zero for $t > 0$.

Example 5-1. A problem setup requires the division of a dependent variable $x(t)$ by the independent variable t. The setup of this portion of the problem might be satisfactorily accomplished as in Fig. 5-8. The input ϵ is supplied from a circuit generating

$$\epsilon = Ae^{-t/\tau} \tag{5-13}$$

where the time constant can be made arbitrarily short by adjusting potentiometer 2 and the magnitude of ϵ can be changed by adjusting the initial condition of integrator 2. In operation, ϵ should be made only large enough to prevent overloads. If a slight increase in the magnitude and duration of ϵ will produce no appreciable change in the problem results, then it can be assumed that the solution is satisfactory.

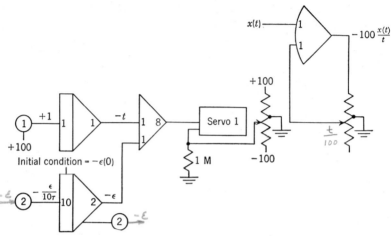

Fɪɢ. 5-8. Method of performing division by a function that is zero at $t = 0$.

5-4. Square Root. The generation of square-root circuits by implicit function techniques follows a similar line of reasoning to that involved in the division circuit. The equation solved is

$$x - \frac{z^2}{100} = 0$$

Since the output of the high-gain amplifier (Fig. 5-9) must remain finite, the equation for the circuit can be written by equating the sum of the inputs to zero, giving

$$x - \frac{z^2}{100} = 0 \tag{5-14}$$

or

$$z = -10 \sqrt{x} \tag{5-15}$$

As in the division circuit, difficulty will be encountered in the vicinity of $x = 0$. Negative values of x are prohibited, since again instability would arise.

If it is desired to use $-x$ as the input of the square-root circuit, this may be accomplished by interchanging the connections at the ends of the multiplier potentiometer. The proper connection of the high and low of the multiplier potentiometer, for stable operation, can easily be determined by the same procedure as was applied to the division circuit.

In many cases, it is desirable to produce the square root of a quantity which is zero at some time during the computation. More satisfactory results will normally be obtained in these instances by generating $\sqrt{x}$

with arbitrary-function-generating equipment of the types to be discussed in Chap. 8.

It should be apparent to the reader by this time that other functions involving roots and powers, such as $x^{3/2}$, can be generated by similar methods. The amount of equipment needed, however, should be weighed carefully against the possibility of using arbitrary-function-generating equipment to generate the desired function.

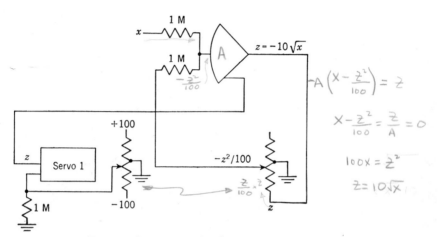

FIG. 5-9. Square-root circuit.

To further clarify the use of multiplying equipment in the solution of differential equations, an illustrative problem will be set up. The example combines the use of multiplication, division, and square-root circuits into a single problem. Particular attention should be paid to the use of amplifiers to avoid loading effects on the potentiometers.

Example 5-2. The system of equations is

$$\frac{dx}{dt} = y + \frac{x}{\sqrt{x^2 + y^2}} [1 - (x^2 + y^2)] \tag{5-16}$$

$$\frac{dy}{dt} = -x + \frac{y}{\sqrt{x^2 + y^2}} [1 - (x^2 + y^2)] \tag{5-17}$$

The initial conditions are

$$x(0) = a \qquad y(0) = b \tag{5-18}$$

The circuit diagram is shown in Fig. 5-10. A plot of x vs. t and y vs. t is given in Fig. 5-11. Of additional interest is the plot of x vs. y of Fig. 5-12. Regardless of the magnitude of the initial conditions, the system is seen to oscillate in a sinusoidal manner with a maximum magnitude of unity.

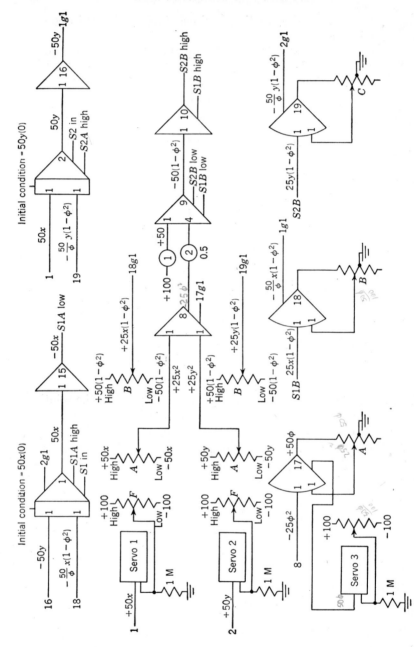

Fig. 5-10. Circuit to solve the system described by Eqs. (5-16) to (5-18). In the diagram $\phi = \sqrt{x^2 + y^2}$.

76

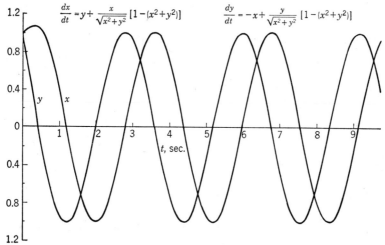

Fig. 5-11. The computer plot of x vs. t and y vs. t produced by the circuit of Fig. 5-10. The initial conditions are $x(0) = y(0) = 1$.

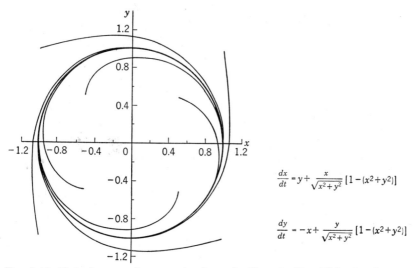

Fig. 5-12. Plot of y vs. x for several values of $x(0)$ and $y(0)$. This plot demonstrates the nature of the steady-state solution of the problem solved by the circuit of Fig. 5-10.

5-5. Resolving Servos. Frequently there arises a need for the inclusion of the trigonometric functions in the solution of problems. The need may arise from the requirement to transform vector quantities from one reference axis to another, as is often necessary in the evaluation of guided-missile systems. It may also arise from a great variety of other systems, mechanical or electrical, for which small-angle assumptions are not valid.

The trigonometric transformations required are normally of two types: polar to rectangular, or rectangular to polar. Of these, the first transformation is by far the simpler to mechanize, as will be seen in the following pages.

The polar-to-rectangular transformation—or, being consistent with common terminology, the "rectangular" transformation—is illustrated by the geometry of Fig. 5-13. If the vector r and the angle θ are

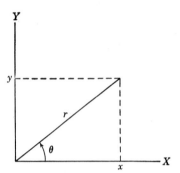

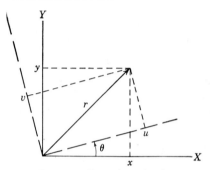

Fig. 5-13. Geometry of the polar-to-rectangular transformation. If r and θ are known, x and y can be determined.

Fig. 5-14. Rotation of axis.

known, then the vector quantities along the x, y coordinate axes are expressable as in Eq. (5-19):

$$x = r \cos \theta \qquad y = r \sin \theta \qquad (5\text{-}19)$$

Correspondingly, rotation of axis of one rectangular coordinate system to a second rectangular coordinate system with a common origin (Fig. 5-14) is accomplished by the equations

$$\begin{aligned} u &= x \cos \theta + y \sin \theta \\ v &= -x \sin \theta + y \cos \theta \end{aligned} \qquad (5\text{-}20)$$

where θ is the angle between the coordinate axis.

Problems involving the rotation of axis arise most frequently in the field of guided-missile studies. In the simulation of guided missiles the nature of the equations is such that axis transformations are used extensively. A complete three-dimensional study of problems of this type requires the use of the Euler angle transformations[3] requiring more resolver capacity than that available at many computing installations throughout the country. As an illustration of the importance of Euler angle transformations in three-dimensional missile studies, it may be noted that the Typhoon computer* has one section of the machine devoted solely to this transformation, with all connections permanently wired. The Typhoon computer is a large-scale analog computer designed specifically for missile-simulation studies.

The second transformation, rectangular to polar, or simply the "polar" transformation, arises when the rectangular coordinates are known and it is necessary to determine the magnitude and angle of the resultant vector. The problem is identical to finding

$$\theta = \tan^{-1}\frac{y}{x} \qquad r = \sqrt{x^2 + y^2} \tag{5-21}$$

as in Fig. 5-13.

The generation of the functions $\sin \theta$ and $\cos \theta$ can be accomplished by using only summing and integrating amplifiers and multipliers. The generation of the sine and cosine functions is treated in Sec. 6-2. The necessity of generating $\theta = \tan^{-1}(y/x)$ can sometimes be avoided by expressing the equations in polar form. Most tasks can therefore be accomplished without resolver equipment, but only at the expense of using considerable multiplying and linear equipment. Problems such as missile-simulation problems would be virtually prohibitive without resolvers, however. Resolvers have become a very important item in a computing laboratory and frequently provide the simplest problem setup even when their use could be avoided.

There are two main types of resolving servos in use today: those using a-c resolvers and demodulators, and those employing d-c sine and cosine potentiometers. Of these, the a-c resolver servos presently used in computer installations are definitely inferior. The difficulty encountered is the drift associated with the demodulator circuit. While using a-c resolvers it is ordinarily very difficult to maintain accuracy better than 1.0 per cent without frequent recalibration. The d-c resolvers, on the other hand, are superior in that they are free from drift and consequently require calibration infrequently. As there are no a-c resolver servos being produced today for analog computer use, the remainder of the section will be devoted to the d-c resolvers.

A relatively low-cost resolver can be constructed, utilizing a rectangular-card sine-cosine potentiometer[4] (Fig. 5-15). The potentiometer consists of a linearly wound card with four wiper contacts accurately positioned at right angles. The distance between diametrically opposite wipers is exactly half the length of the winding of the card. As the card is rotated the wipers pick up voltages as indicated

* Typhoon computer—U.S. Naval Air Development Center, Johnsville, Pa.

in Fig. 5-15.   Exact centering of the axis of rotation is unimportant, as any constant voltage will be canceled upon subtracting the two components of the sine and cosine.   The accuracy of such devices is limited to approximately 0.6 per cent.

More precise trigonometric functions may be developed, using tapered potentiometers.   The arrangement of such devices, as used in resolvers marketed by Reeves Instrument Corporation and Electronic Associates, Inc., is shown in Fig. 5-16.   Each potentiometer consists of four tapered windings connected together and has two wiper contacts spaced 90° apart.   The potentiometers are connected in pairs to

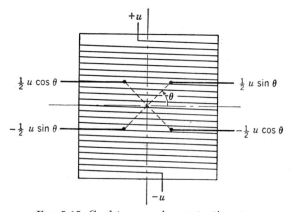

FIG. 5-15. Card-type resolver potentiometer.

a servo in such a manner that the wipers of the two potentiometers are oriented 90° apart.   One pair of contacts pick up voltages proportional to $+ \cos \theta$ and $- \sin \theta$ while the wipers of the second potentiometer pick up voltages proportional to $+ \cos \theta$ and $+ \sin \theta$.   These are the voltages necessary to mechanize the equation $\theta = \tan^{-1}(y/x)$.

To understand the operation of the polar resolvers, consider the geometry of Fig. 5-17.   From the figure it is seen that

$$R = A \cos \theta + B \sin \theta \qquad (5\text{-}22)$$
$$B \cos \theta - A \sin \theta = 0 \qquad (5\text{-}23)$$

From the geometry of Fig. 5-17, it can be seen that Eq. (5-23) is valid only if

$$\theta = \tan^{-1} \frac{B}{A} \qquad (5\text{-}24)$$

If an error exists in the angle θ, Eq. (5-23) becomes

$$B \cos \theta - A \sin \theta = \epsilon \qquad (5\text{-}25)$$

where ϵ is an error signal which may be used to drive the servo to the null position. A block diagram of the complete polar resolver is shown in Fig. 5-18. The connections shown in dotted lines must be wired externally in order to make the automatic-gain-control feature operative. The functioning of the automatic gain control is to make the servo gain approximately constant for ranges of A and B of 0 to 100 volts. This feature is necessary, since for A and B both small, the error signal derived from a given error in θ is small compared to the error signal for A and B large. Very poor servo operation would result if no automatic gain control were provided.

The A and B amplifiers in Fig. 5-18 are wired internally in the resolver unit; however, since they

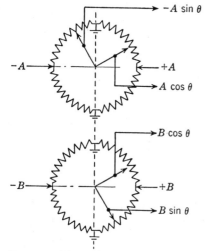

Fig. 5-16. Tapered sine-cosine potentiometers.

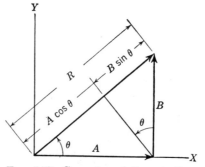

Fig. 5-17. Geometry of the equations mechanized in a polar resolver.

are standard computer amplifiers, provision has been made whereby they may be used as inverting amplifiers in problems not requiring the use of resolvers.

The functioning of the resolver servos in the rectangular transformation is much the same as the servo operation for multiplication. This is true at least in that the angle θ is brought to the input of the servo and the normal feedback potentiometer is used as the error-sensing device. A switch is provided on the servo chassis to interconnect the internal components in the proper manner for either rectangular or polar operation.

Attention should be brought to the importance of loading resolver potentiometers in rectangular operation. The REAC and Electronic Associates computer resolver potentiometers are wound with a correction for a 1-megohm load. If loadings other than 1 megohm are used, an error will be present.

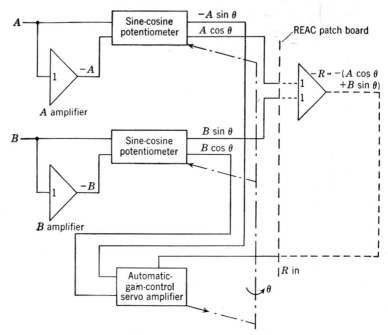

Fig. 5-18. Block diagram of a REAC resolver.

5-6. Choice of Rectangular or Polar Coordinates. The equations of motion of a system can be expressed in either polar or rectangular coordinates. The computer circuit diagram can correspondingly be prepared from either set of equations. Question may be raised, then, regarding the advantages or disadvantages of preparing equations in either coordinate system for computer solution. Experience has shown that there are very definitely strong arguments in favor of the polar form of the equations. These arguments may be listed as follows:

1. The polar form of the equations ensures the knowledge of the vector and angle, requiring only the rectangular transformation to find the x and y components of the vector. The rectangular form of the equations requires the polar transformation to be performed in order to find the resultant and angle. In general, it will be found that greater accuracy may be attained in determining $\sin \theta$ and $\cos \theta$ rather than $\theta = \tan^{-1} (B/A)$ and $r = \sqrt{x^2 + y^2}$.

2. When using the rectangular transformation, resolvers need not be used. Any of the other means of generating the sine and cosine of an angle may be employed, as discussed in Chap. 6.

3. Ordinarily, appreciably less equipment will be required for the

setup of a system expressed in polar coordinates than for one expressed in rectangular coordinates.

It would seem, then, that the very first step in the setup of a system is to ensure that the equations are expressed in polar form. Doing this will often simplify the preparation of circuit diagrams. A typical example of a problem where there is much to be gained by proper choice of coordinate system is the computation of bomb trajectories.

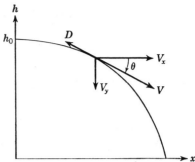

FIG. 5-19. Geometry of the bomb-trajectory problem.

Example 5-3. It is desired to determine the trajectory of a bomb dropped from an aircraft. The geometry of the system is as illustrated in Fig. 5-19.

The equations of motion of the system are

$$M \frac{dV_x}{dt} = -D \cos \theta \tag{5-26}$$

$$M \frac{dV_y}{dt} = W - D \sin \theta \tag{5-27}$$

$$D = \tfrac{1}{2} V^2 \rho s c_D \tag{5-28}$$
$$\rho = 0.002378(1 - 0.135 \times 10^{-4} h)^2 \tag{5-29}$$
$$V_x = V \cos \theta \tag{5-30}$$
$$V_y = V \sin \theta \tag{5-31}$$
$$h = h_0 - \int V_y \, dt \tag{5-32}$$
$$x = \int V_x \, dt \tag{5-33}$$

where
M = mass of bomb
W = weight of bomb
V_x = x component of velocity
V_y = y component of velocity
V = velocity of bomb
D = drag $\tag{5-34}$
θ = angle from horizontal to velocity vector
ρ = density of air
s = characteristic area of bomb
C_D = coefficient of drag
h_0 = launch altitude
V_0 = initial velocity

The physical constants of the bomb are

$$\begin{aligned} W &= 5,000 \text{ lb} \\ S &= 10 \text{ ft}^2 \\ C_D &= 0.18 \end{aligned} \tag{5-35}$$

The launch conditions are

$$h_0 = 20,000$$
$$V_0 = 500 \text{ ft/sec} \tag{5-36}$$
$$\theta_0 = 0°, 10°, 20°$$

The first step to take in the preparation of this system of equations for computer solution is to perform the transformation from rectangular to polar coordinates. (It is suggested that the reader set up the system in rectangular coordinates as a comparison of the methods.)   The transformation to polar coordinates may best be carried out in the manner demonstrated below.

Differentiating Eqs. (5-30) and (5-31) produces Eqs. (5-37) and (5-38):

$$\frac{dV_x}{dt} = \frac{dV}{dt} \cos \theta - V \sin \theta \frac{d\theta}{dt} \tag{5-37}$$

$$\frac{dV_y}{dt} = \frac{dV}{dt} \sin \theta + V \cos \theta \frac{d\theta}{dt} \tag{5-38}$$

Substituting Eqs. (5-37) and (5-38) in Eqs. (5-26) and (5-27), respectively, gives

$$M \frac{dV}{dt} \cos \theta - MV \sin \theta \frac{d\theta}{dt} = -D \cos \theta \tag{5-39}$$

$$M \frac{dV}{dt} \sin \theta + MV \cos \theta \frac{d\theta}{dt} = W - D \sin \theta \tag{5-40}$$

Solving for $d\theta/dt$ and dV/dt from Eqs. (5-39) and (5-40) by using determinants gives Eqs. (5-41) and (5-42):

$$\frac{d\theta}{dt} = \frac{\begin{vmatrix} M \cos \theta & -D \cos \theta \\ M \sin \theta & W - D \sin \theta \end{vmatrix}}{\begin{vmatrix} M \cos \theta & -MV \sin \theta \\ M \sin \theta & MV \cos \theta \end{vmatrix}} = \frac{g \cos \theta}{V} \tag{5-41}$$

$$\frac{dV}{dt} = \frac{\begin{vmatrix} -D \cos \theta & -MV \sin \theta \\ W - D \sin \theta & +MV \cos \theta \end{vmatrix}}{\begin{vmatrix} M \cos \theta & -MV \sin \theta \\ M \sin \theta & +MV \cos \theta \end{vmatrix}} = -\frac{D}{M} + g \sin \theta \tag{5-42}$$

By means of Eqs. (5-28) to (5-33) and Eqs. (5-41) and (5-42) the circuit diagram may be prepared.

For convenience in determining proper scale factors throughout the problem, it is wise at this point to tabulate the range of the parameters in the system.   For this problem the approximate ranges are

$$0 \le \theta \le 1.57 \text{ radians}$$
$$V_x \le 500 \text{ ft/sec}$$
$$V_y \le 1,136 \text{ ft/sec}$$
$$V \le \sqrt{V_x^2 \text{ (max)} + V_y^2 \text{ (max)}} = 1,240 \text{ ft/sec} \tag{5-43}$$
$$\frac{d\theta}{dt} \le \frac{g}{V_0} \cong 0.06 \text{ radian/sec}$$
$$h \le 20,000 \text{ ft}$$
$$x \le 17,620 \text{ ft}$$
$$t \le 35.24 \text{ sec}$$

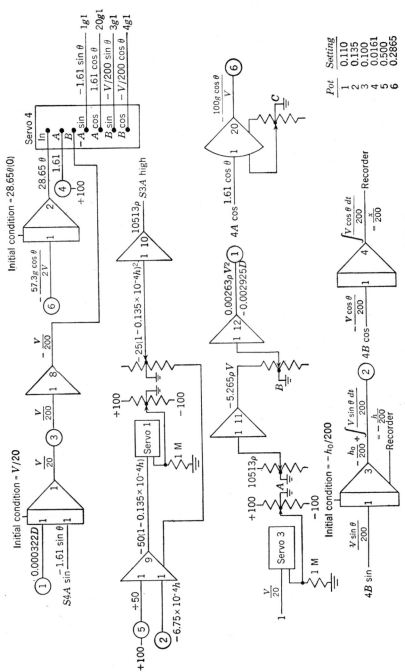

FIG. 5-20. Circuit for the bomb-trajectory calculation.

85

All the above information is available from the problem statement if a little reason is applied.   Very helpful in arriving at the above approximate limits of V_x, V_y, V, x, and t is the calculation of the vacuum trajectory.   This calculation is important for another reason, as it provides a check of the machine solution if the drag is set equal to zero.   The time spent in analysis of this type will ordinarily pay large dividends in time saved, as has been previously emphasized.

Keeping in mind the maximum range of the variables, the circuit diagram can now be prepared as in Fig. 5-20.   Resolvers have been used in this circuit diagram, but it should be pointed out that the circuit might just as well be prepared using

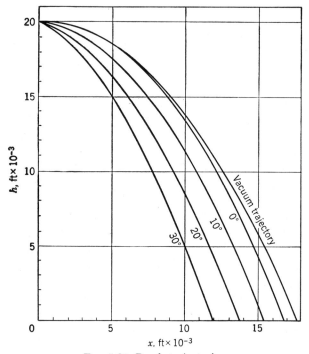

FIG. 5-21. Bomb trajectories.

any other means of generating the sine and cosine functions.   The results obtained with this circuit diagram for launch angles $\theta = 0°$, $10°$, $20°$, and $30°$ are included in Fig. 5-21.

PROBLEMS

5-1. In Fig. 5-3, if the input to the servo x is 60 volts and the loads on the multiplier potentiometers A and B, respectively, are 24,260 ohms and 29,910 ohms, what is the error in each output of the multiplier?   HINT: Calculate the loading correction for each of the potentiometers F, A, and B.   Do not consider second-order effects.

5-2. It is occasionally desirable to perform the operation of division with the servomultiplier driven by the quotient rather than the divisor.   (a) Show that the circuit of Fig. P 5-2 is capable of fulfilling this requirement.   (*b*) What, if any, restrictions are placed upon the magnitude and sign of the inputs x and y by the circuit?

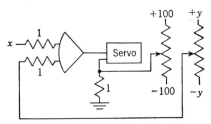

FIG. P 5-2. Resistance values are given in megohms.

5-3. Determine the output z of the circuit of Fig. P 5-3.   What restrictions are placed upon x?

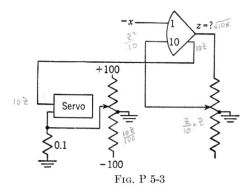

FIG. P 5-3

5-4. Determine the output z of the circuit of Fig. P 5-4.   What restrictions are placed upon x and y if $|z| < + 100$ volts?

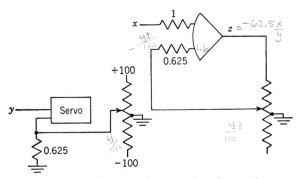

FIG. P 5-4. Resistance values are given in megohms.

5-5. Show a circuit capable of generating the cube root of a variable.   HINT: The equation solved is $x = z^3/10^4$.

5-6. Devise a circuit diagram for the computer solution of the nonlinear equation

$$\frac{d^2x}{dt^2} - \alpha(1 - x^2)\frac{dx}{dt} + x = 0$$

where $\alpha = 1$ and where the system is excited by initial conditions on x and dx/dt. NOTE: The solution of this equation will reach a steady-state sustained oscillation regardless of the values of the initial conditions used in the problem. Examination of the damping term will permit the reader to estimate the approximate magnitude of the sustained oscillation in order to choose properly the amplitude-scale factor of the problem. A plot of x vs. dx/dt illustrates the nature of the solution of this equation very effectively.

5-7. For the circuit of Fig. 5-9, what is the error present if the impedance of the lower gain-1 input of the amplifier is 0.99 megohm instead of 1.0 megohm? Is the percentage error greater or smaller for large values of the input x?

REFERENCES

1. Morrill, C. D., and R. V. Baum: "A Stabilized High-speed Multiplier," GER-4952, Goodyear Aircraft Corporation, Akron, Ohio, Aug. 25, 1952.
2. Mengel, A. S., and W. S. Melahn: "RAND REAC Manual, RM-525," p. 78, The RAND Corporation, Santa Monica, Calif., Dec. 1, 1950.
3. Rauscher, M.: "Introduction to Aeronautical Dynamics," p. 495, John Wiley & Sons, Inc., New York, 1953.
4. Korn, G. A., and T. M. Korn: "Electronic Analog Computers," p. 282, McGraw-Hill Book Company, Inc., New York, 1952.

CHAPTER 6

ADDITIONAL COMPUTER TECHNIQUES

6-1. Introduction. In the earlier chapters, with the exception of Chap. 4, the main emphasis was on the introduction of the basic computer components. In this chapter an effort will be made to expand the usefulness of these tools by the introduction of new techniques.

In the earlier sections of this chapter, methods of generating functions internally in the computer will be described. Greatest emphasis will be placed on the trigonometric functions, although other functions submit themselves to similar techniques. The later portion of the chapter will be devoted to methods of overcoming one of the shortcomings of the d-c electronic analog computers, namely, electronic instabilities.

6-2. Analytic-function Generation. Analytic functions needed in the solution of systems of differential equations are themselves often the solution of a differential equation. Typical examples of this type of function are sin βt, cos βt, and $e^{-\alpha t}$, where α and β are constants and t is the independent variable. A similar group of functions posing a somewhat more difficult setup problem are sin x, cos x, and e^{-x}, where x is a dependent variable of the problem.

The setup of functions that are the solution of differential equations is best achieved by repeatedly differentiating the function to obtain the differential equation representing the desired function. This technique is illustrated by the following examples.

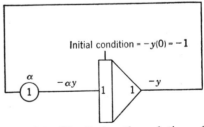

Initial condition $= -y(0) = -1$

α $-\alpha y$ $-y$

Example 6-1. Generate the function

$$y = e^{-\alpha t} \qquad (6-1)$$

Differentiating Eq. (6-1) gives

Fig. 6-1. Circuit for the solution of $y = e^{-\alpha t}$. Scale factor has been neglected.

$$\frac{dy}{dt} = -\alpha e^{-\alpha t} = -\alpha y \qquad (6-2)$$

The machine diagram for the generation of $y = e^{-\alpha t}$ can therefore be represented as in Fig. 6-1.

In this example the problem voltage level has not been considered but as always should be included in any final setup. It may be noted here that, to change the amplitude-scale factor of the setup, it is necessary to change only the initial condition applied to the system, since the system is linear.

Example 6-2. Generate the functions $\sin \beta t$ and $\cos \beta t$ where β is a constant. Differentiating each of the functions gives

$$\frac{d}{dt} \sin \beta t = \beta \cos \beta t \tag{6-3}$$

$$\frac{d}{dt} \cos \beta t = -\beta \sin \beta t \tag{6-4}$$

Next, integrating Eqs. (6-3) and (6-4) above gives

$$\sin \beta t = \beta \int \cos \beta t \, dt \tag{6-5}$$
$$\cos \beta t = -\beta \int \sin \beta t \, dt \tag{6-6}$$

From these equations, the circuit diagram may be prepared as in Fig. 6-2.

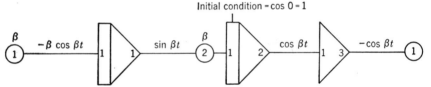

FIG. 6-2. Generation of $\sin \beta t$ and $\cos \beta t$, where β is a constant.

Again, scale factors should be considered before placing the problem on the machine. As in the previous example, the amplitude scale factor can be changed simply by multiplying the initial conditions and all terms of the equations by a constant. In this example, either potentiometer 1 or potentiometer 2 could be eliminated; however, they are usually both retained for convenience in altering the frequency β.

Example 6-3. Generate the function

$$y = e^{-x} \tag{6-7}$$

where $x = x(t)$. Differentiating Eq. (6-7) gives

$$\frac{dy}{dt} = -\frac{dx}{dt} e^{-x} \tag{6-8}$$

$$\frac{dy}{dt} = -\frac{dx}{dt} y \tag{6-9}$$

In this example, the differential equation is nonlinear, so that the technique of adjusting scale factor by changing the initial conditions of the system no longer applies. The scale factor should, therefore, be considered before attempting to prepare the circuit diagram. An estimate of the magnitude of y is necessary. Assume $y(\max) = 10$ units; then multiplying Eq. (6-9) by a factor of 5, to give a maximum voltage of 50 volts at the output of integrator 1 (Fig. 6-3), gives

$$5\frac{dy}{dt} = -5\frac{dx}{dt}y \qquad (6\text{-}10)$$

From Eq. (6-10), the circuit diagram of Fig. 6-3 is easily prepared. In the circuit, it is assumed that 10 dx/dt is available at some other point in the circuit not considered here.

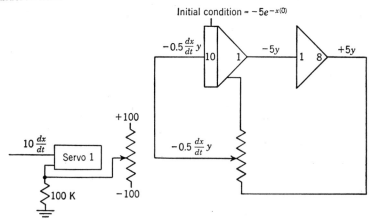

FIG. 6-3. Generation of $y = e^{-x}$ where y and x are dependent problem variables.

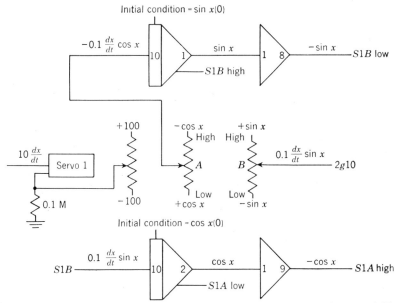

FIG. 6-4. Generation of sin x and cos x where x is a dependent problem variable.

Example 6-4. Generate the function sin x where $x = x(t)$. As in Example 6-2, the procedure is to differentiate sin x and cos x, giving Eqs. (6-11) and (6-12):

$$\frac{d}{dt} \sin x = \frac{dx}{dt} \cos x \qquad (6\text{-}11)$$

$$\frac{d}{dt} \cos x = -\frac{dx}{dt} \sin x \qquad (6\text{-}12)$$

Integrating both sides of Eqs. (6-11) and (6-12) gives

$$\sin x = \int \frac{dx}{dt} \cos x \, dt \qquad (6\text{-}13)$$

$$\cos x = -\int \frac{dx}{dt} \sin x \, dt \qquad (6\text{-}14)$$

Neglecting scale factor, the circuit diagram is shown in Fig. 6-4. Again, $10 \, dx/dt$ is assumed to be available.

Other functions that may be generated internally on a computer by similar techniques to those illustrated in the previous examples are exponential, logarithmic, and hyperbolic functions. A few of the many possible circuits generating functions of these types are illustrated in subsequent examples.

Example 6-5. Generate the function

$$y = A(t + a)^n \qquad (6\text{-}15)$$

Here the best approach is to first take the logarithm of both sides of Eq. (6-15) and

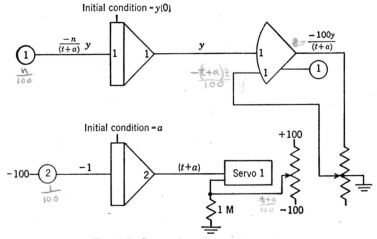

Fig. 6-5. Generation of $y = A(t + a)^n$.

then differentiate to form a differential equation. Carrying out these operations gives

$$\ln y = \ln A + n \ln (t + a) \qquad (6\text{-}16)$$

$$\frac{1}{y} \frac{dy}{dt} = \frac{n}{t + a} \qquad (6\text{-}17)$$

$$\frac{dy}{dt} = \frac{n}{t + a} y \qquad (6\text{-}18)$$

$$y(0) = Aa^n \qquad (6\text{-}19)$$

The circuit diagram for the generation of the function of Eq. (6-15) can therefore be drawn as in Fig. 6-5.

The technique used in this example, taking the logarithm of each side of the equation, is particularly useful in the generation of functions involving exponents.

Example 6-6. Generate the function

$$z = \ln (t + a) \tag{6-20}$$

Differentiation produces the new equation

$$\frac{dz}{dt} = \frac{1}{t + a} \tag{6-21}$$

where
$$z(0) = \ln a \tag{6-22}$$

It is possible to proceed from Eqs. (6-21) and (6-22) to generate the function z by obtaining the function $1/(t + a)$ by the process of division. One amplifier can be saved in generation of z, however, if it is noted that

$$\frac{dz}{dt} = y = \frac{1}{t + a} \tag{6-23}$$

can be generated by differentiating Eq. (6-23) to produce

$$\frac{dy}{dt} = - \frac{1}{(t + a)^2} = -y^2 \tag{6-24}$$

where
$$y(0) = \frac{1}{a} \tag{6-25}$$

A further advantage obtained by proceeding in this manner is that more precise results can usually be obtained by the process of multiplication than by the process of division. The circuit diagram for the generation of the function defined by Eq. (6-20) and utilizing the results of Eqs. (6-24) and (6-25) is shown in Fig. 6-6.

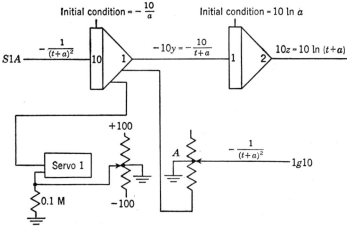

FIG. 6-6. Generation of $z = \ln (t + a)$.

Example 6-7. Generate the function

$$z = a^t \tag{6-26}$$

Differentiating Eq. (6-26) produces the equation

$$\frac{dz}{dt} = a^t \ln a = z \ln a \tag{6-27}$$

where $$z(0) = 1 \tag{6-28}$$

The setup of Eq. (6-27) can take on two forms, depending upon the value of $\ln a$.

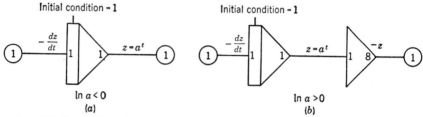

FIG. 6-7. Generation of $z = a^t$ for (a) values of $\ln a < 0$, (b) values of $\ln a > 0$.

If $\ln a < 0$, the circuit will be as shown in Fig. 6-7a. For values of $\ln a > 0$, the circuit will be as shown in Fig. 6-7b.

Example 6-8. Generate the function

$$y = e^{ax^2} \tag{6-29}$$

Proceeding as in the previous examples, the function can be differentiated to

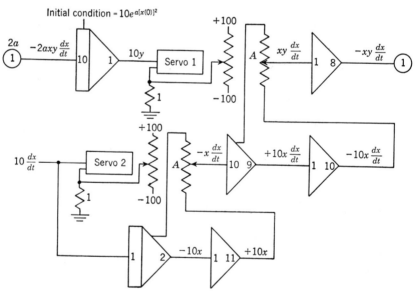

FIG. 6-8. Generation of $y = e^{ax^2}$.

give

$$\frac{dy}{dt} = 2ax\frac{dx}{dt}e^{ax^2} = 2ax\frac{dx}{dt}y \tag{6-30}$$

where

$$y(0) = e^{a[x(0)]^2} \tag{6-31}$$

In the setup of this function the quantity dx/dt must be available from some other source. Assuming that $10\ dx/dt$ is available, the setup of $y = \exp ax^2$ is given in Fig. 6-8.

Example 6-9. As a final example of the generation of functions that are the solution of differential equations, the generation of the function

$$y = \cosh at \tag{6-32}$$

will be demonstrated. The similarity of the hyperbolic functions to the trigonometric functions suggests that a similar technique to that used for the generation of the trigonometric functions can be applied. Following the procedure used in the setup of the trigonometric functions, the hyperbolic sine and hyperbolic cosine can each be differentiated once, as in Eqs. (6-33) and (6-34):

$$\frac{d}{dt}\sinh at = a\cosh at \tag{6-33}$$

$$\frac{d}{dt}\cos at = a\sinh at \tag{6-34}$$

Next, integrating both sides of Eqs. (6-33) and (6-34) gives the new equations

$$\sinh at = a\int\cosh at\,dt \tag{6-35}$$
$$\cosh at = a\int\sinh at\,dt \tag{6-36}$$

As before, the integration of the right side of the equations is only indicated, as the computer will perform the actual integrations. From Eqs. (6-35) and (6-36),

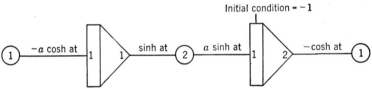

Initial condition $-\,-1$

Fig. 6-9. Generation of sinh at and cosh at.

the circuit diagram for the generation of the hyperbolic functions can easily be drawn (Fig. 6-9).

In many instances, a quantity $y = f(x)$ can be approximated by an analytic function over the region of interest. Parabolas, hyperbolas, exponentials, and polynomials of higher order are very useful in the internal generation of this group of functions. A word of caution should be inserted at this point regarding the use of polynomials in fitting the curves. If the polynomial required to fit a particular function is composed of alternatingly large positive and negative terms, the polynomial will, in general, be inadequate for REAC use. The magnitude of such a polynomial at any point is dependent upon the

small differences of large quantities.   A small error in the setting of
the parameters of the polynomial can therefore completely destroy the
fit of the polynomial.

6-3. Generalized Integration.   The nature of the analog computer
is such that it permits the solution of problems having only one independent variable, since time is the variable of integration of all the
computer integrators.   The question may arise then as to the ability
of the computer to integrate with respect to a variable other than the

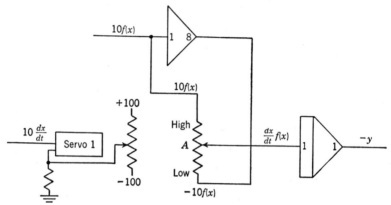

Fig. 6-10. Circuit for the solution of the equation $y = \int f(x)\, dx$, where $x = x(t)$.

independent variable.   This can be, and often is, accomplished in the
setup of problems.   Consider Eq. (6-37), where t is the independent
variable and $x = x(t)$:

$$y = \int f(x)\, dx \qquad\qquad (6\text{-}37)$$

This equation can be rewritten as

$$y = \int f(x)\, \frac{dx}{dt}\, dt$$

It should be apparent to the reader that this equation can readily be
set up on the computer if dx/dt is available.   The setup is shown in
Fig. 6-10.   Here again, for convenience, it is assumed that $10\ dx/dt$
and $10\ f(x)$ are available from other portions of the circuit.   This
circuit diagram has the disadvantage of requiring that dx/dt, or some
multiple thereof, be available.   If dx/dt is not available, it is usually
possible to avoid differentiating on the computer by modifying the
problem equations prior to setup so that dx/dt is available.   In a few
problems, however, it is not practical to rewrite the system equations
in order to allow the explicit generation of dx/dt.   Such is the case

when x must be introduced into the problem by the use of arbitrary-function-generating equipment or when x is an output of actual hardware forming part of a physical simulation problem. If dx/dt cannot be formed explicitly in the computer, it is necessary to differentiate x in order to form dx/dt. The method of approximate differentiation discussed in the next section is useful when differentiation must be performed.

6-4. Approximate Differentiation. As was pointed out in the previous section, the situation does arise where it is absolutely necessary to differentiate on an analog computer. In an earlier chapter it was

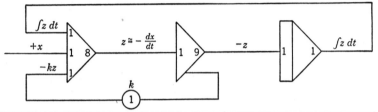

FIG. 6-11. Circuit for approximate differentiation. As k is increased, $-z$ approaches the true derivative dx/dt.

shown that differentiation could easily be performed by using a condenser and resistor as the input and feedback impedance, respectively, of an operational amplifier. It was indicated at that time that differentiation was a noise-amplifying process and was very undesirable. In those applications where differentiation is necessary, satisfactory results can usually be obtained by an approximate differentiation which can be made to approach arbitrarily close to a true derivative at the discretion of the operator. In actual use, it is adjusted to be as close to a true derivative as the noise level in the problem will permit.

The circuit for approximate differentiation is based on the solution of the implicit equation

$$z = -x - \int z \, dt + kz \qquad (6\text{-}38)$$

Rearrangement of Eq. (6-38) gives

$$\int z \, dt + z(1 - k) = -x \qquad (6\text{-}39)$$

It may be readily observed from Eq. (6-39) that

$$\lim_{k \to 1} z = -\frac{dx}{dt} \qquad (6\text{-}40)$$

The circuit diagram for producing the approximate derivative is shown in Fig. 6-11. The potentiometer setting k is adjusted as near to unity as the noise level permits.

6-5. A One-amplifier Circuit Representation of a Second-order System. In the investigation of the behavior of physical systems, it is frequently convenient to represent a portion of a system by differential equations and the remainder of the system by introducing actual hardware, such as an autopilot, into a computer setup of the system. When actual hardware is introduced, the major problem is usually in providing adequate transducers to change shaft rotations or other forms of intelligence into d-c voltages compatible with the computer requirements. Similarly, the inverse process of changing d-c voltages into shaft rotations or other forms of inputs compatible with the physical components must be implemented. For a well-equipped laboratory, these obstacles can usually be overcome.

Physical simulation, using actual hardware in the system, places greater demands upon a computer than does the simulation of systems represented entirely by mathematical equations. The added requirement placed on the computer is that the problem must be solved in natural time. Fortunately, the frequencies encountered in the simulation of most mechanical systems are often compatible with the useful frequency range of the analog computer. However, this is not always the case, as some systems have very high natural frequencies. If sufficiently high frequencies are encountered, the portion of the problem simulated on the computer can become unstable because of the high gains necessary in the circuit and the accumulative phase shift of the amplifiers.

Instabilities of the type that will be encountered here can be easily demonstrated by placing on the computer the circuit for the solution of the differential equation

$$\frac{d^2y}{dt^2} + \omega_n{}^2 y = 0 \tag{6-41}$$

where
$$y(0) = A \tag{6-42}$$

The computer solution for this system should be

$$y = A \cos \omega_n t \tag{6-43}$$

For small values of ω_n the results will check well with the theoretical solution. For sufficiently high values of ω_n the computer results show a divergence due to the phase shift in the computer amplifiers.* In effect, the divergence will be similar to that normally expected if a negative damping term is present in the system.

---

* A more precise treatment of the causes of the instability discussed here is given in Chap. 10.

One method of extending the useful frequency range of the computer is to set up the system to be generated and arbitrarily add damping into the system to produce a known response. This method is not very practical for some systems, however. A second alternative is to reduce the number of amplifiers in the circuits and thus reduce the cumulative phase shift. Since most systems of differential equations are combinations of second- and first-order equations, to be able to represent a second-order differential equation with a single operational amplifier is a very powerful method of extending the usable frequency range of the computer. Such a circuit has been successfully used in simulation problems to extend the useful frequency range of

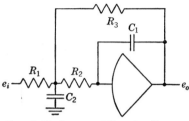

Fig. 6-12. One-amplifier circuit representation of a second-order system.

the computer. A circuit which permits a one-amplifier representation of a second-order system is shown in Fig. 6-12. It is apparent that this is only another application of complex input and feedback techniques.

The transfer function for this circuit can be expressed as

$$\frac{e_o}{e_i} = -\frac{R_3/R_1}{R_2R_3C_1C_2p^2 + R_2C_1p(1 + R_3/R_1 + R_3/R_2) + 1} \quad (6\text{-}44)$$

In the equation it can be seen that by changing the magnitude of R_1, R_2, R_3, C_1, and C_2 any combination of frequency and damping ratio can be represented. From the equation it can also be observed that the least amount of calculation is necessary if the resistors are held constant and only C_1 and C_2 are varied. Convenient values for high-frequency systems are obtained by letting

$$R_1 = R_3 = 0.05 \text{ megohm}$$

and $R_2 = 1$ megohm. Equation (6-44) then can be expressed as

$$\frac{e_o}{e_i} = -\frac{1}{0.05 \times 10^{12}C_1C_2p^2 + 2.05 \times 10^6C_1p + 1} \quad (6\text{-}45)$$

The most convenient manner to use this circuit, if the frequency and damping ratio must be varied frequently, is to prepare a nomograph giving values of C_1 and C_2 for the interesting range of frequencies and damping ratios. This chart (see Fig. 6-13) together with the use of decade condensers for C_1 and C_2 provides a very rapid and convenient method of varying the parameters of the problem.

The circuit of Fig. 6-12 has been used successfully on REAC equipment at natural frequencies above 25 cps. This is considerably above the normal useful frequency range of the REAC and has permitted the successful completion of problems that otherwise would have proved troublesome.

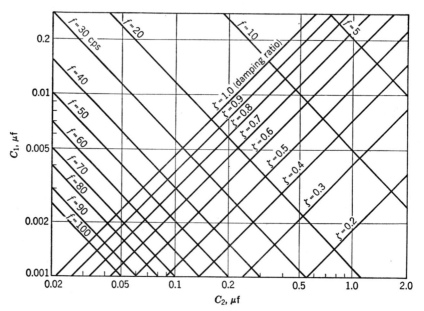

Fig. 6-13. Condenser nomograph for use with the circuit of Fig. 6-12.

6-6. Computer Instability. Occasionally problems arise that produce violent electronic amplifier instabilities when set up on an analog computer. This is true even of problems that have stable mathematical representations. To be able to cope with all types of problems, it is necessary that the computer operator be able to recognize problems that can cause electronic instability. Further, it is essential that the operator understand the cause of computer instability when it occurs in a problem in order that he can modify the system equations in such a manner as to permit a satisfactory computer solution of the problem. The remainder of this section will be devoted to a discussion of the nature of the instability induced in a computer and the form of presentation of equations that can lead to an unstable computer setup.

A plot of amplifier gain and phase shift vs. frequency for a typical high-gain d-c amplifier is shown in Fig. 6-14. For stability, the gain of the amplifier must drop below unity at a frequency less than that which induces 180° phase shift in the amplifier. For a single amplifier this condition is easily satisfied while designing the amplifier.

In Chap. 2, the transfer function of a high-gain d-c amplifier with negative feedback was shown to be

$$\frac{e_o}{e_i} = -\frac{z_f}{z_i}\frac{1}{1 + 1/A(z_f/z_i + 1)} \tag{6-46}$$

where z_f and z_i are the feedback and input impedances, respectively. Examination of Eq. (6-46) reveals that for $A \gg 1$ the ratio e_o/e_i is influenced little by any change in amplifier gain. Therefore, when summing amplifiers are arbitrarily connected in a series manner in a

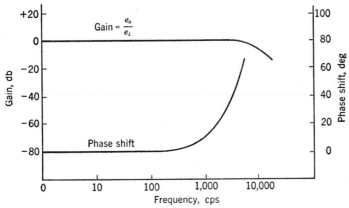

Fig. 6-14. Logarithmic plot of feedback amplifier characteristic.

closed-loop system, the phase shift is additive but the gain e_o/e_i is relatively constant over a large range of A (and frequencies); therefore, no design criterion can ensure that the stability conditions are satisfied for all possible connections of the equipment.

If an even number of amplifiers are connected in a closed-loop manner, the stability of the system is dependent solely upon the open-loop gain of the system. The system is stable if the open-loop gain is less than unity and is unstable if the open-loop gain is equal to or greater than unity.

If amplifier phase shift is disregarded, a simplified analysis of an odd number of summing amplifiers connected in a closed loop indicates that the circuit is stable for all values of gain. Unfortunately the simplified analysis is not valid. If the open-loop d-c gain in a circuit is sufficiently great to provide a gain of unity at frequencies producing a total phase shift of 180°, then instability will result. In actual practice it is found that instability will result at d-c open-loop gains only slightly greater than unity for closed-loop circuits containing as few as three summing amplifiers in series. The resulting high-frequency oscillation that occurs in the amplifiers of the loop is independent of any forcing function or initial conditions applied to the system. The noise present in the amplifiers is sufficient to excite the system if the conditions are such as to permit instability in the system.

The presence of an integrator in a closed-loop system effectively eliminates the possibility of instabilities at loop gains normally used in d-c analog computers. The integrator in the circuit serves as a low-pass filter and, therefore, reduces the loop gain at high frequencies sufficiently to prevent instability from occurring.

From the foregoing discussion, it is easily seen that violent amplifier instability can arise if two or more summing amplifiers are connected in a closed-loop path providing an integrator is not present in the path. When a loop containing only summing amplifiers is present on a computer, then the total gain and phase shift will determine the circuit stability or instability.

Recognition of electronic instability in a problem setup is relatively easy. The high-frequency oscillation that always results is independent of the position of the computer operate-reset control, as no integrating amplifiers can be involved in the unstable circuitry. Whenever amplifier oscillation occurs independent of the position of the operate-reset control, it is probably due to the presence of a closed loop or loops containing summing amplifiers only.

In the solution of differential equations on a computer, the only condition that requires two or more summing amplifiers to be connected in a closed-loop path is the presence of the highest-order derivative of two or more problem variables in each of two or more of the equations representing the system. A system of equations that illustrates this condition is given in Eqs. (6-47) and (6-48):

$$\frac{d^2x}{dt^2} + a_1 \frac{d^2y}{dt^2} + a_2 \frac{dx}{dt} - a_3 \frac{dy}{dt} + a_4x = 0 \qquad (6\text{-}47)$$

$$\frac{d^2y}{dt^2} + b_1 \frac{d^2x}{dt^2} + b_2 \frac{dy}{dt} - b_3 \frac{dx}{dt} + b_4y = 0 \qquad (6\text{-}48)$$

In the setup of this system of equations (Fig. 6-15) the highest-order derivative of each equation must be formed explicitly at the output of an amplifier, as the highest derivative of each variable is necessary in forming the setup of the other equation. The feedback in the amplifier loop is very apparent from the setup of the equations.

In this example, the system of equations is mathematically stable; however, machine instability can still result. Satisfactory operation will result from low values of the parameters a_1 and b_1, but high values of a_1 and b_1 will surely result in unsatisfactory operation of the circuit.

The proper treatment of a system of this type requires that the equations be algebraically manipulated to eliminate the highest-order derivative from one of the equations of the system. For the system under discussion, this can most easily be accomplished by substituting

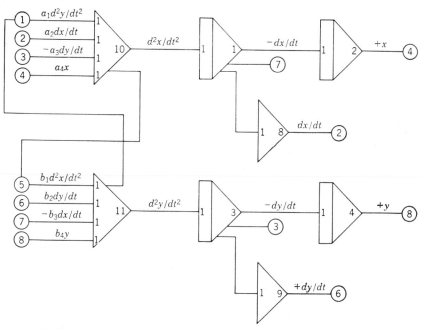

FIG. 6-15. Setup of system having a closed loop including only summing amplifiers.

the value of d^2y/dt^2 obtained from the second equation for d^2y/dt^2 in the first equation, giving the new equations

$$\frac{d^2x}{dt^2} - a_1\left(b_1\frac{d^2x}{dt^2} + b_2\frac{dy}{dt} - b_3\frac{dx}{dt} + b_4y\right)$$

$$+ a_2\frac{dx}{dt} - a_3\frac{dy}{dt} + a_4x = 0 \quad (6\text{-}49)$$

$$\frac{d^2y}{dt^2} + b_1\frac{d^2x}{dt^2} + b_2\frac{dy}{dt} - b_3\frac{dx}{dt} + b_4y = 0 \quad (6\text{-}50)$$

or $\qquad \frac{d^2x}{dt^2} - C_1\frac{dy}{dt} + C_2\frac{dx}{dt} - C_3y + C_4x = 0 \quad (6\text{-}51)$

$$\frac{d^2y}{dt^2} + b_1\frac{d^2x}{dt^2} + b_2\frac{dy}{dt} - b_3\frac{dx}{dt} + b_4y = 0 \quad (6\text{-}52)$$

The setup of the latter equations no longer can produce electronic instability, as the offending loop made up of summing amplifiers has been broken (Fig. 6-16).

In actual practice, if the system of equations is composed of several second-order equations, each containing all the highest-order derivatives, the elimination of terms may require considerable labor.   In those cases, it is usually wise to proceed with the problem setup of the original equations.   Occasionally, the range of coefficients will be such as to produce satisfactory results.   If a high-frequency oscillation

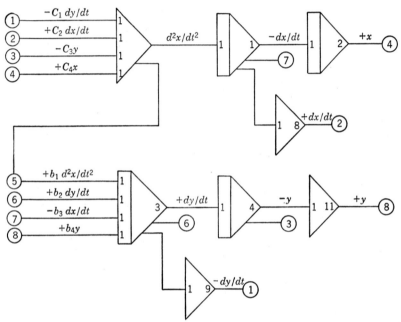

Fig. 6-16. Setup of system shown in Fig. 6-15 after the closed loop consisting of summers only has been broken by algebraic manipulation of the system equations.

occurs, it is sometimes possible that it will occur in only a single loop. After eliminating the offending loop, all may be well.   Often considerable time is saved by proceeding in this manner.

Fortunately, the most frequently used methods of deriving differential equations seldom permits the highest-order derivative of each variable to occur in more than one equation.   The notable exception is Lagrange's equations.[1]   Very frequently the application of Lagrange's equations in the derivation of a system of differential equations leads to the inclusion of each of the highest-order derivatives in each equation of the system of equations.   This method of deriving differential equations that are to be solved on an analog computer should, therefore, be avoided whenever possible.

6-7. Concluding Remarks. Many of the circuit diagrams demonstrated in this chapter under the topic of Analytic-function Generation have been in common use at analog-computer installations for some time. It is very difficult in many cases to attempt to give credit for the origination of the individual circuits. The first comprehensive tabulation of analytic functions that can be readily generated on analog computers was made by The RAND Corporation.[2]

The circuits for generalized integration and approximate differentiation given in Secs. 6-3 and 6-4 were first seen by the author in a letter distributed by Reeves Instrument Corporation.

The circuit described herein for the single-amplifier representation of a second-order system was described in a Boeing computer manual.[3]

PROBLEMS

For each of the Probs. 6-1 to 6-10, prepare a circuit diagram to generate the function. In each case perform any time-scale or amplitude-scale adjustments that are necessary to permit the circuit to operate with the maximum magnitude of the voltage at the output of each amplifier in the range 10 to 100 volts.

6-1. $\qquad y = \sin\left(5t + \dfrac{\pi}{3}\right)$

6-2. $\qquad y = 0.5e^{-0.1t}$

6-3. $\qquad y = e^{-10t}\sin 5t$

6-4. $\qquad y = 5(1 - 2e^{-0.2t})$

6-5. $\qquad y = 2^t \qquad$ assume $0 < t < 10$

6-6. $\qquad y = e^{-0.2t^2}$

6-7. $\qquad y = 5 + t + 0.1t^2 + 0.05t^3$

Do not use multipliers in setting up this function.

6-8. $\qquad y = \sinh 0.2t \qquad$ assume $0 < t < 10$

6-9. $\qquad y = \ln(t + 2) \qquad$ assume $0 < t < 10$

6-10. $\qquad y = \cos\left(5x + \dfrac{\pi}{4}\right)$

where $y = y(t)$ and $x = x(t)$. Assume that $10\, dx/dt$ is available.

6-11. It is desired to use only one amplifier to solve, in real time, the transfer function

$$\frac{e_o}{e_i} = -\frac{1}{0.0001p^2 + 0.01p + 1}$$

Determine the values of R_1, R_2, R_3, C_1, and C_2 needed in the circuit of Fig. 6-12 to solve this equation.

REFERENCES

1. Page, L.: "Introduction to Theoretical Physics," pp. 213–215, D. Van Nostrand Company, Inc., New York, 1928.
2. Mengel, A. S., and W. S. Melahn: "RAND REAC Manual, RM-525," p. 85, The RAND Corporation, Santa Monica, Calif., Dec. 1, 1950.
3. Frantz, W. J.: "The Operation of the Boeing Electronic Analog Computer, Document D-12209," p. 47, Boeing Airplane Company, Seattle, Wash., Sept. 25, 1951.

CHAPTER 7

THE REPRESENTATION OF NONLINEAR PHENOMENA

7-1. Introduction. In this chapter two new tools will be introduced, the differential relay and the vacuum diode. Both are capable of performing similar tasks of function generation, although in specific applications superiority may lie with one or the other of the devices.

Commonly encountered nonlinear effects adequately representable by the techniques to be presented include hysteresis, gear backlash, dry friction, and displacement limiting. A complete tabulation of nonlinearities occurring in nature would be very great in scope. Fortunately most, if not all, of these functions may be reasonably well represented on the analog computer.

7-2. Differential Relays and Diodes—General. The differential relays most useful with an analog computer must satisfy two main requirements. First, the relays must be capable of very high-speed operation so that the switching time in a particular problem is negligible as compared to the time delays in the problem. Relay switching times of the order of 1 msec are satisfactory for most problems. A second requirement is high sensitivity. A sensitivity such that the relays switch on an input voltage difference of 10 or 20 mv is adequate for the majority of applications.

Satisfactory differential relay design and the early use of these devices in analog computation were pioneered independently by Hughes Aircraft Corporation under the direction of R. R. Bennett[1] and the Computation Section of the Flight Research Laboratory at Wright Field, Ohio, under the direction of L. M. Warshawsky.[2] The circuit designed at the Flight Research Laboratory consists of a high-speed, sensitive, single-pole, double-throw, polarized relay driven by a two-stage balanced d-c amplifier (see Fig. 7-1).

The two controlling voltages are applied directly to the grids G and G' of the twin triode. If the input voltages are equal, each section will carry half the total current. If an inequality exists, the plate voltages of the two sections of the tube will vary correspondingly.

The action of the pentode in the cathode circuit of the input double

107

triode is to cause the total current flow in the two sections to remain approximately constant. Thus the device remains *in balance* regardless of the voltage level of the inputs, since the triodes always operate on the same portions of their characteristic curves. Once the circuit is balanced for a particular set of tubes, little further adjustment need be made to ensure its proper operation.

The plates of the twin triode are direct-coupled to the grids of two pentodes. The two windings of a sensitive polarized relay form the

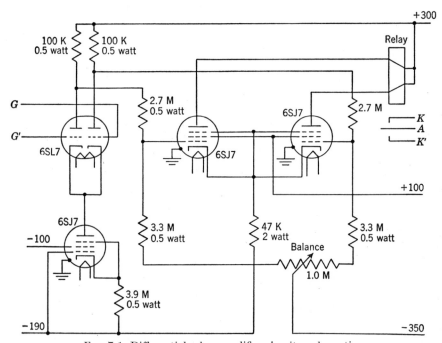

FIG. 7-1. Differential relay amplifier circuit—schematic.

plate impedances of the pentodes. An unbalanced voltage applied to the grids G and G' causes a greater unbalance to be present across the relay windings and thus causes the relay to switch to the proper position. A balancing potentiometer in the grid circuits of the pentodes is provided to compensate for inequalities in tube characteristics.

Relays which have proved satisfactory for use with this circuit are the British-made Carpenter relay, model 3J12, and the German-made Siemens relay. More recently, American-made relays have been developed that will fulfill the operating requirements of the circuit.

A diagrammatic representation of the differential relays that is commonly used is shown in Fig. 7-2. In the figure, G and G' represent the grid inputs of the twin triode, K and K' represent the two contacts of the relay, and A is the relay arm. The arrangement is such that if G becomes more positive than G', the relay is caused to switch, making contact between the arm and K. If G' becomes more positive than G, the converse is true and the arm will close with contact K'.

Diodes commonly used in computer installations are of the vacuum-tube type. Crystal diodes are, in most applications, unsatisfactory because of their finite back resistance. An exten-

FIG. 7-2. Symbolic representation of a differential relay.

sive discussion of the use of diodes in analog computers may be found in a paper by C. D. Morrill and R. V. Baum[3] of Goodyear Aircraft Corporation. A few of the more important circuits will be discussed here.

7-3. Applications of Relays and Diodes to Simple Limiting. As an introductory example, consider the case of simple limiting. It is desired to generate a function e_2, defined as

$$e_2 = -a \qquad e_1 < -a$$
$$e_2 = e_1 \qquad -a < e_1 < b \qquad (7\text{-}1)$$
$$e_2 = b \qquad e_1 > b$$

This can be accomplished using the diode limiters supplied on most of the commercially available computers. The basic limiter circuit provided in the REAC computer is of the input-shunt type and can be used as illustrated in Fig. 7-3. The portion of the circuit enclosed in dotted lines is wired internally in the

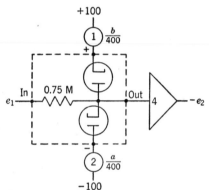

FIG. 7-3. The series limiter circuit provided in the REAC computer. The circuitry enclosed in dotted lines is wired internally in the computer.

REAC computer. The diodes have been drawn inverted in order that the labeling of the + and − terminals will agree with their location on the REAC patch board.

Recalling that the input impedance corresponding to a gain-4 input of an amplifier is 0.25 megohm and that the grid of the amplifier is effectively at zero, it is easy to visualize the operation of the circuit. Suppose e_1 is in the linear region (that is, $-a < e_1 < b$); then neither of the diodes can conduct, and the voltage appearing at the OUT terminal of the limiter is $-e_1/4$. The amplifier output $-e_2$ is then equal to $-e_1$. If e_1 is less than $-a$, the plate of the diode associated with the negative input is more positive than its cathode and the diode conducts, holding the OUT terminal at $-a/4$ volts. The output $-e_2$, therefore, remains at

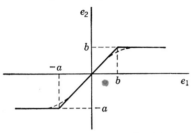

FIG. 7-4. Limiting achieved with the circuit of Fig. 7-3. The solid lines show the desired limiting. The dotted lines show the actual limiting characteristics.

$$-e_2 = a \qquad e_1 < -a$$

If the input e_1 is more positive than b, the diode associated with the positive limit conducts and the output of the amplifier is clamped at the voltage $-b$. The negative of the desired function has, therefore, been achieved.

In actual operation, this circuit does not give too good results, as the limiting is not sharp. Figure 7-4 shows the desired and actual limiting achieved with the circuit of Fig. 7-3. The actual limiting is shown in dotted lines and has a rounded characteristic due to the contact potential[4] of the diodes.

A diode circuit that has sharper limiting characteristics than the circuit of Fig. 7-3 is shown in Fig. 7-5, where the diodes are utilized in the amplifier feedback path. As long as $-a < e_1 < b$, where $-a$ and b are the desired lower and upper limits, neither diode in Fig. 7-5 will conduct, as the cathodes remain more positive than the corresponding plates. If e_1 is made increasingly positive, the voltage appearing at the cathode of T_1, which is a function of $-e_2$ and the potentiometer setting, will eventually become negative. At the time the cathode of T_1 becomes negative, T_1 will commence conducting and will serve as a low-impedance feedback path, reducing the gain of the amplifier until the output remains at the desired voltage level. If the input e_1 becomes increasingly negative, the plate of diode T_2 eventually becomes positive, clamping the amplifier output to the desired level. The simplest method of setting the potentiometers involved in this limiting circuit is to adjust them by trial and error.

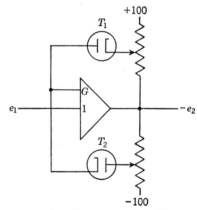

FIG. 7-5. Output shunt limiting.

The potentiometers required for this application must have both ends available for external connection; therefore, coefficient potentiometers that have one end permanently grounded cannot be used. On a REAC the initial-condition potentiometers, if not needed to set initial conditions on the integrators, may be conveniently used in this application, since all their terminals are brought out to the patch board. The diodes supplied in the REAC limiters may likewise be utilized directly in this circuit by ignoring the input terminal (see Fig· 7-3) and using only the terminals labeled $+$, $-$, and OUT. The results achieved using this circuitry again exhibit some lack of sharpness, but for many purposes the circuit is entirely adequate. In general, the

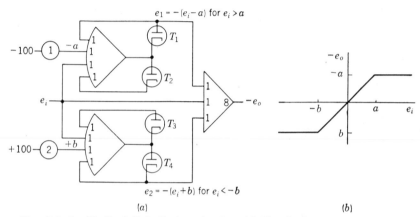

FIG. 7-6. An *idealized*-diode limiter circuit.   (*a*) Circuit diagram; (*b*) output.

utilization of diodes in amplifier feedback paths produces sharper results than does input shunt limiting.

It is possible to prepare circuit diagrams employing so-called *idealized diodes*, or circuits giving an output response that does not exhibit the effect of diode contact potential. The circuit of Fig. 7-6 illustrates an idealized-diode circuit having the same limiting characteristic as the previous circuits. Here e_i and $-e_o$ are the input and output voltages respectively. The limiting provided by this circuit is exceedingly sharp.

The operation of the circuit of Fig. 7-6 is easily understood as soon as the operation of the so-called idealized-diode circuit is understood. Consider only the circuitry associated with the upper high-gain amplifier of Fig. 7-6a. If e_i is negative, diode T_2 will conduct and T_1 will remain cut off. The voltage at point e_1 will be very close to zero, since the grid of the amplifier always remains close to zero. At the time that the potential of the input e_i becomes slightly greater than

$+a$, the diode T_2 will cease conducting and T_1 will commence conducting. The voltage at e_1 is thus $-(e_i - a)$ for $e_i > a$. The resulting output of amplifier 8, due to the voltages e_1 and e_i, is $-e_i$ for $e_i < a$ and is $-a$ for $e_i > a$.

It will help the reader to visualize the operation of the circuit if he considers the diode T_1 to be a portion of the high-gain amplifier. This concept is satisfactory, since the presence of the diode in its conducting state affects the over-all gain of the high-gain amplifier only slightly.

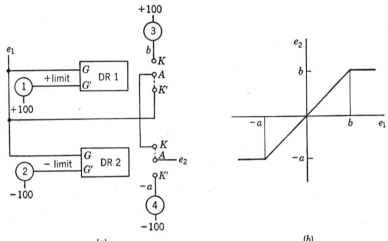

(a)   (b)

FIG. 7-7. Differential relay limiter circuit. (a) Circuit; (b) output.

The feedback around the amplifier is then the path from the point labeled e_1 through the 1-megohm resistor indicated as a gain-1 input of the high-gain amplifier. During the period of conduction of T_1, the voltage e_1 is thus the output of a summing amplifier with the inputs $-a$ and e_i.

The operation of the lower high-gain amplifier circuit is similar. If $e_i > -b$, then T_4 cannot conduct and e_2 remains at zero potential. If e_i becomes more negative than $-b$, then T_4 conducts, causing the voltage e_2 to be $-(e_i + b)$.

The use of idealized-diode circuitry normally requires more equipment than the simpler diode limiters. This is not true in all cases, however, as will be illustrated in an absolute-value circuit to be described later in this chapter.

Differential relays may be utilized to perform the same type of limiting as performed by the previous circuits of this section. The circuit of Fig. 7-7 is commonly used in this application.

In the region where $-a < e_1 < b$, the relay associated with DR 1 is switched to the K' position and DR 2 is closed to the K position, as indicated in the diagram.   The output e_2 is, therefore, equal to e_1. If e_1 becomes more positive than the positive limit b, DR 1 will close to the K position and e_2 will be equal to b.   If e_1 becomes more negative than $-a$, DR 2 closes to K' position, and e_2 is equal to $-a$.   It is obvious that the limiting will be perfect except for the transient occurring during the switching.   Since the relays have a switching time of the order of 1 msec, the transient is negligible for most applications.

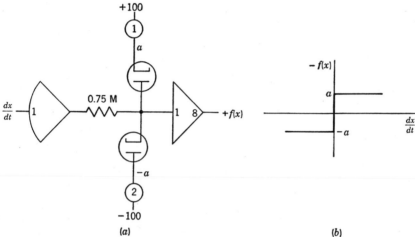

FIG. 7-8. Dry-friction simulator using diodes.   (a) Circuit; (b) output.

It may be well to point out again that three conditions are satisfied in generating this simple limiting function defined by e_2; that is,

$$\begin{aligned} e_2 &= b & e_1 &> b \\ e_2 &= e_1 & -a &< e_1 < b \\ e_2 &= -a & e_1 &< -a \end{aligned} \qquad (7\text{-}2)$$

Two relays are needed in the generation of the function.   In general, $n - 1$ double-throw, single-pole relays are required to generate a particular function, where n is the number of conditions which must be satisfied.   When designing a relay circuit to perform a nonlinear operation, either parallel or series connection of the relay outputs can usually be used.   The reader will find that a series connection, as used above, will normally lead to a circuit requiring the minimum amount of equipment.

7-4. Other Diode and Relay Circuits.   Dry friction is another physical phenomenon which must occasionally be simulated on an analog computer.   In equation form, dry friction can be represented as

$$f(x) = a \qquad \frac{dx}{dt} < 0$$

$$f(x) = -a \qquad \frac{dx}{dt} > 0 \tag{7-3}$$

A shunt limiter may well be used for this application (see Fig. 7-8). If dx/dt becomes only slightly positive, the output of the high-gain amplifier is a very large negative voltage.   Conversely, if the input dx/dt is slightly negative, the high-gain amplifier will produce a very large positive output.   Either T_1 or T_2 will conduct, depending upon whether the output of the high-gain amplifier is positive or negative. Only if the input is identically zero or differs only negligibly from zero will the high-gain amplifier operate in the linear region.   The amplifier goes almost immediately from its maximum negative output to its maximum positive output, and therefore, since the current drawn from the diodes is a constant for most of the range of operation, the circuit will give very sharp limiting.

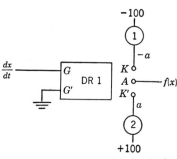

Fig. 7-9. Relay circuit for simulating dry friction.

In this circuit when using amplifiers with an automatic-balance system, such as are used on the REAC and the L-3 model GEDA, the automatic-balance system must be disabled, as the amplifier operates at saturation much of the time.   The long-time constant associated with the automatic-balance system would otherwise prohibit satisfactory operation.

The simulation of dry friction using differential relays may be accomplished as in Fig. 7-9.   In the circuit of Fig. 7-9, if dx/dt is positive, $f(x) = -a$.   If dx/dt is negative, $f(x) = a$.   The only error present in the system is in the vicinity of $dx/dt = 0$; here $f(x)$ will be zero over a small region.   If the speed of the relays and sensitivity of the differential amplifier are high, the operation will be satisfactory.

Dead Space.   Another nonlinear effect that frequently must be represented on a computer is dead space.   Mathematically, this may be represented as

$$f(x) = 0 \qquad\qquad -C < x < C$$
$$f(x) = (x - C) \qquad x > C \tag{7-4}$$
$$f(x) = (x + C) \qquad x < -C$$

Graphically, dead space is represented by the solid line of Fig. 7-10b. Figure 7-10a is a circuit capable of generating this function.

The broken lines on the graph of $f(x)$ vs. x represent the actual output of this circuit; the solid lines, the ideal output. It is necessary, in the use of the circuit, to compensate for this imperfection. A much more satisfactory diode circuit for the simulation of dead space is given

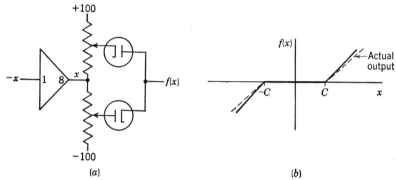

FIG. 7-10. Diode circuit for the simulation of dead space.   (a) Circuit; (b) output.

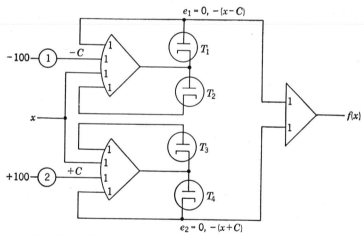

FIG. 7-11. Excellent diode circuit for dead-space simulation.

in Fig. 7-11. It can be seen that this circuit is formed by a simple rearrangement of the circuit of Fig. 7-6.

The operation of the circuit can be analyzed by considering only one-half the circuit at a time. It is apparent that T_1 will conduct only when x is more positive than C. During the time T_1 conducts, the voltage at e_1 is $-(x - C)$ and at the same time $e_2 = 0$. When $x < C$, T_1 cannot conduct and $e_1 \cong 0$. During the time the input potential is in the region $-C < x < C$, neither T_1 nor T_4 conducts and the output remains at zero potential. When x falls below the potential $-C$, the output of the lower high-gain amplifier becomes positive and e_2 becomes $-(x + C)$. The operation is, therefore, as described by Eqs. (7-4).

A relay circuit for the simulation of dead space is given in Fig. 7-12. Since the circuit is slightly more complex than those previously attempted with relays, it may again be beneficial to analyze the operation in detail. If $-C < x < C$, DR 1 and DR 2 will be switched as

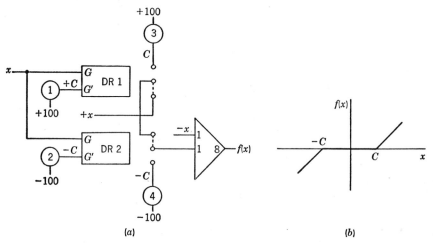

Fig. 7-12. Relay dead-space simulator.

shown in the diagram. The quantities feeding amplifier 8 are x and $-x$, so that $f(x)$ is zero. If $x > C$, DR 1 will close to the K position and $f(x) = x - C$. If $x < -C$, DR 2 will close to the K' terminal and consequently the output will be $f(x) = x + C$. The prescribed function is thus satisfied identically by the above circuit. It should be apparent to the reader that the dead space need not be symmetrical about $x = 0$ as in this example.

Backlash. Gears, involved so frequently in mechanical systems, are subject to backlash unless extreme care is taken in the design and assembly of the gear trains. The use of spring-loaded antibacklash gears in devices such as the mechanical differential analyzer, or in high-precision servomultiplying equipment for an electronic analog computer, is almost mandatory to prevent the backlash from affecting the operation of the mechanism. In most applications, however, the requirements of mass production completely preclude the possibility of using precision gearing. In some gear applications the effects of backlash are unimportant, but in other instances its presence can completely change the dynamic reponse of the system. The analog-computer design phase of a system study must, in many instances, include an investigation of the effects of backlash in order to provide tolerances to allow the economical construction of the system. Backlash, as present in gear trains, is illustrated in Fig. 7-13. In this diagram θ_1 represents the position of the driving gear and θ_2 is the position of the driven gear. Correspondingly, $\Delta\theta$ is the backlash present in the gears. A diode circuit for producing this function is given in Fig. 7-14a.

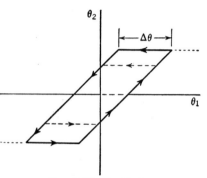

Fig. 7-13. Backlash.

The potentiometers associated with T_1 and T_2 in Fig. 7-14a are adjusted to allow T_1 or T_2 to conduct as the output of summer 8 reaches $-\Delta\theta/2$ or $\Delta\theta/2$, respectively. If θ_1 starts from the zero reference point and increases positively, neither diode will conduct until $\theta_1 - \theta_2 = \Delta\theta/2$. At that instant T_1 will begin conducting and integrator 1 will commence integrating. The junction of the triodes is taken directly to the grid input of the integrator, so that the input impedance of the integrator is very small. The integrator time constant is correspondingly very small, and the integrator output θ_2 rises almost instantaneously to the voltage representing $\theta_1 - \Delta\theta/2$. The output of integrator 1, therefore, follows the input, lagging it a quantity $\Delta\theta/2$. If θ_1 reverses its direction of travel, neither T_1 nor T_2 will conduct and the output level of integrator 1 will remain essentially constant until such time as

$$\theta_1 - \theta_2 = -\frac{\Delta\theta}{2}$$

At that instant T_2 will begin conducting and again the output θ_2 follows θ_1, lagging a quantity $\Delta\theta/2$.

The circuit shown in Fig. 7-14a operates best when the input θ_1 varies in such a manner that the output θ_2 does not remain in the backlash region very long at a time. The output of integrator 1 tends to drift slightly rather than hold a constant value, and this may cause the operation of the circuit to be unsatisfactory in some applications.

A relay circuit capable of simulating backlash can be constructed that operates best under the conditions that give the poorest operation of the diode circuit. The first step in preparing the relay cir-

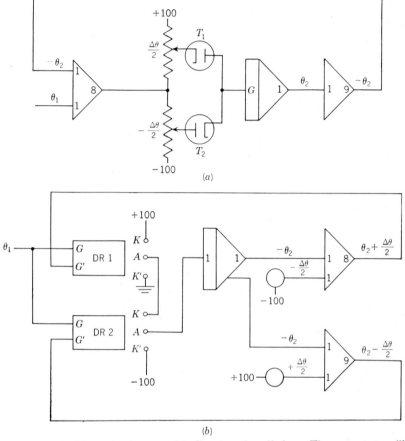

FIG. 7-14. Backlash simulators. (*a*) Circuit using diodes. The output θ_2 will drift slightly in the backlash region. (*b*) Circuit using differential relays. This circuit operates best for a slowly varying input voltage.

cuit for the generation of any function is to state the conditions that must be satisfied by the function. Backlash must satisfy the following conditions:

1. If θ_1 increases,

$$\theta_1 \leq \theta_2 + \frac{\Delta\theta}{2}$$

2. If θ_1 decreases,

$$\theta_1 \geq \theta_2 - \frac{\Delta\theta}{2}$$

3. If $\theta_2 - \dfrac{\Delta\theta}{2} < \theta_1 < \theta_2 + \dfrac{\Delta\theta}{2}$,

$$\theta_2 = \text{constant}$$

Since three conditions must be satisfied, the relay circuit requires at least two single-pole double-throw relays. It is apparent from the stated conditions that these relays must distinguish the conditions

$$\theta_1 > \theta_2 + \frac{\Delta\theta}{2} \quad \text{and} \quad \theta_1 < \theta_2 - \frac{\Delta\theta}{2}$$

If θ_1 becomes greater than $\theta_2 + \Delta\theta/2$, then θ_2 must increase until the inequality is no longer satisfied. If θ_1 becomes less than $\theta_2 - \Delta\theta/2$, θ_2 must decrease until the inequality is no longer satisfied. These conditions lead the computer operator to the configuration shown in Fig. 7-14b.

This circuit has certain limitations in its usefulness. The relays DR 1 and DR 2 have a finite switching time, so that the output of

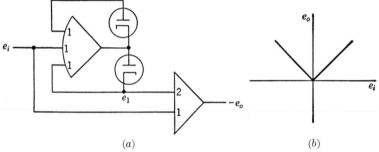

(a) (b)

Fig. 7-15. Diode absolute-value circuit. (a) Circuit; (b) output.

integrator 1 $(-\theta_2)$ changes in incremental steps. In order to prevent an excessive overshoot of the output voltage, it is necessary to restrict the rate of change of θ_2 to a value that will give the relays time to open before an excessive error is made. An integrating rate of 100 volts/sec, when using relays having a switching time of 1 msec, therefore produces a maximum overshoot of 0.1 volt. If the integrating rate is reduced, the overshoot is reduced proportionately.

The integrating rate of the amplifier producing $-\theta_2$ limits the rate of change of the input θ_1 that the circuit can be expected to follow. For slowly varying input signals, the circuit operation is excellent. The circuit will cause θ_2 to remain constant over long periods of time if the problem input remains in the backlash region.

An approximate representation of magnetic hysteresis may be achieved by a simple modification of the circuit in Fig. 7-14a. If magnitude limiting is applied to the output of integrator 1, the resulting output has the form shown in dotted lines in Fig. 7-13.

Absolute Value. Either diodes or relays can be used to form the absolute value of a quantity. The generation of this function can be very economically accomplished using idealized-diode techniques. A circuit for the absolute value is given in Fig. 7-15.

The operation of the circuit in Fig. 7-15 is quite simple. Point e_1 is zero when e_i is positive. Correspondingly, e_1 is equal to $-e_i$ when e_i is negative. Since the voltage e_1 is multiplied by a factor of 2 and added to e_i at the input of the summing amplifier, the output is equal to $-(2e_1 + e_i)$ or

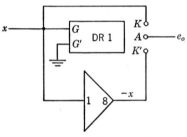

$$e_o = e_i \qquad e_i > 0$$
$$e_o = -e_i \qquad e_i < 0 \qquad (7\text{-}5)$$

A circuit using differential relays may also be used to form the absolute value of a quantity. Both the relay and diode methods give excellent results. The circuit for

FIG. 7-16. Relay absolute-value circuit.

forming the absolute value, using relays, is given in Fig. 7-16.

7-5. Limiting the Output of an Integrator. Very often limiting of the output of an integrator is necessary in the proper application of an analog computer. A typical example wherein an integrator output must be limited is the simulation of guided-missile control surface that reaches a limit stop. A second common example is the piston of a hydraulic actuator reaching the end of its cylinder.

Superficial examination of this limiting problem leads the computer operator to the conclusion that the requirements are very simply satisfied. Unfortunately this is not the case, and the problem requires much deeper consideration. The proper analysis of this type of limiting will be demonstrated by the consideration of the simple mechanical system illustrated in Fig. 7-17.

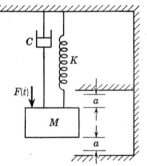

FIG. 7-17. Simple mechanical system with displacement limiting.

The system consists of a simple mass, spring, and viscous damper driven by a forcing function

$$F(t) = b \sin \omega_1 t \qquad (7\text{-}6)$$

Inelastic limit stops are provided to restrain the movement of the mass to a region $-a < x < a$. To illustrate the pitfall that may be readily encountered in the setup of this problem, the simple but *incorrect* setup will be demonstrated. The equation of motion of the system is

$$M \frac{d^2x}{dt^2} + C \frac{dx}{dt} + Kx = b \sin \omega_1 t \qquad (7\text{-}7)$$

with the restriction $-a < x < a$ at all times. The equation is first divided by M, giving

$$\frac{d^2x}{dt^2} + \frac{C}{M} \frac{dx}{dt} + \frac{K}{M} x = \frac{b}{M} \sin \omega_1 t \qquad (7\text{-}8)$$

The circuit diagram, neglecting scale factor, is represented in Fig. 7-18.

The output of amplifier 8 is properly restricted to remain in the region $-a < x < a$, but the circuit *does not* represent the physical

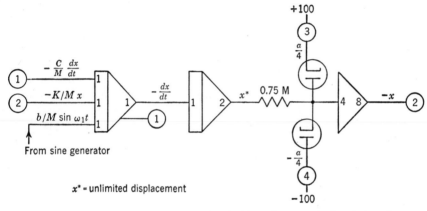

FIG. 7-18. *Incorrect* circuit diagram for limiting the output of an integrator.

problem, as will be presently shown. Assume that the system is placed in operation, and further assume that the forcing function is of such magnitude that x always operates in the linear region. In this case the circuit will operate satisfactorily, since the diodes are always cut off. If b, the coefficient of the forcing function, is increased until the mass reaches its limit stops, the operation of the circuit is no longer satisfactory.

Suppose x increases until finally it reaches the limit stop. At that time the output of amplifier 8 will be correct, but if dx/dt is still positive, the unlimited output of integrator 2 will continue to increase. At the time dx/dt becomes negative, x should commence decreasing in magnitude as in the physical system. This is impossible, though, as x^* is greater than the limit value of x and dx/dt must remain negative an appreciable time before x^* will again fall below the limit value of x and allow the output of amplifier 8 to decrease. It is apparent from this analysis that the circuit introduces a time lag in the problem that completely changes the nature of the solution.

A correct setup of the system will now be. undertaken. Of utmost importance in the setup of this problem is the recognition of the fact that the differential equation of motion applies only during the period of linear operation of the system. During the time that the mass is motionless against either limit stop, the differential equation of motion does not apply. Instead, a static-force equation is satisfied by the physical system. The complete system equations can be expressed as

$$\frac{d^2x}{dt^2} + \frac{C}{M}\frac{dx}{dt} + \frac{K}{M}\,x = \frac{b}{M}\sin\omega_1 t \qquad -a < x < a \qquad (7\text{-}9)$$

$$F_s = -\frac{K}{M}\,x + \frac{b}{M}\sin\omega_1 t \qquad x = \pm a \qquad (7\text{-}10)$$

where F_s = force on the stop.

In other words, the force equation simply expresses the condition that the force on the stop is the algebraic sum of the spring force, attempting to restore the system to the neutral position, and the forcing function holding the system against the stop. During the time $b/M \sin \omega_1 t > Kx/M$, the mass will remain motionless and dx/dt will be zero. As soon as $b/M \sin \omega_1 t$ becomes less than Kx/M, the mass leaves the limit stop and the system again operates as described by the differential equation of motion. It is important to note that, while the mass is motionless against a limit stop, the form of the expressions for d^2x/dt^2 and F_s are identical, since dx/dt is zero in the differential equation. The force equation and the equation of motion can, therefore, be represented by the same circuit.

Instead of operating on x, it is possible to force dx/dt to zero and thus cause x to remain at the limit value. A relay circuit for properly controlling dx/dt is given in Fig. 7-19. The operation of the circuit may be analyzed as follows: If $-a < x < a$, the relays DR 1 and DR 2 will be positioned as indicated in the diagram. The feedback around integrator 1 is broken, and the circuit will operate in the linear region. If x becomes slightly more positive than the upper limit a, DR 1 will switch, closing to K. In order for x to increase, dx/dt must be positive; consequently, since the output of integrator 1 is negative, diode T_1 will conduct, forming a low-impedance feedback path around the integrator and forcing the output of the integrator essentially to zero. The output of integrator 2 remains approximately constant, and the physical-system behavior has been approximated to this point.

As soon as the restoring force, due to the spring, exceeds the force holding the mass against the limit stop, the input to integrator 1 changes sign and dx/dt becomes negative. The diode T_1 ceases conducting, and immediately x falls below the limit value, allowing DR 1 to return to its original state. As x becomes increasingly negative, DR 2 switches to the K' position when the negative limit is reached. At this time dx/dt is negative, and thus, since the output of integrator 1 is positive, T_2 will conduct, reducing the output of integrator 1 to approximately zero. The mechanics of operation of the remainder of the cycle is similar to that described for the positive limit. As may

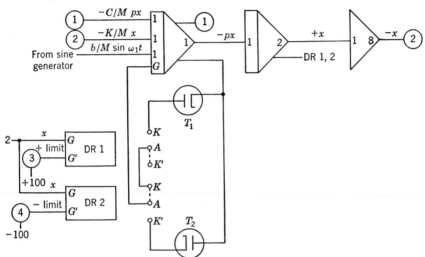

Fig. 7-19. A relay circuit for *properly* limiting the output of an integrator.

be seen from the foregoing discussion, the only purpose of the diodes T_1 and T_2 is to allow the circuit to *back off* from the limit position.

In this circuit it is important that the output of integrator 1 feed to a gain 1 or lower gain of the following integrator. This is important because the output of integrator 1 is not driven to identically zero but to a small finite value. Integrator 2, therefore, drifts slightly above its limit value a. If gains greater than unity are used, the drift will be increased by the magnitude of the gain used. Gains other than unity may be applied at other points in the circuit with less detrimental effect on the operation. This circuit, although subject to some imperfections, produces a very satisfactory representation of displacement limiting in most applications.

7-6. Representation of a Unit Impulse. The analytic analysis of many systems is facilitated by the use of the unit impulse. Similarly, the unit impulse is occasionally useful in the solution of problems on an analog computer. In the past, many engineers have been "stopped" by the apparent difficulty of representing this function on an analog computer. This should not be the case, however, as this function is really quite simple to simulate.

The unit impulse $u_1(t)$ is defined as the limit of a rectangular pulse of unit area where the limit is taken as the width of the pulse approaches zero. This may be expressed mathematically in Laplace transform notation as

$$u_1(t) = \lim_{a \to 0} \frac{u(t) - u(t - a)}{a} \qquad (7\text{-}11)$$

The geometrical interpretation is shown in Fig. 7-20. This limit process defines $u_1(t)$ in the limit as a rectangular pulse of infinite height and zero width.

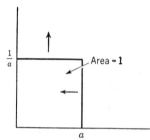

FIG. 7-20. The unit impulse function $u_1(t)$.

There are two ways in which a unit-impulse function may enter into a computer problem. The unit impulse can be used as a forcing function that is applied only at $t = 0$, or it can be used as a repetitive disturbance occurring periodically throughout the solution of the problem. A physical example of a problem of the latter type is the study of the dynamics of a rapid-fire cannon or machine gun.

The basic approach to the simulation of the two types of unit impulse functions mentioned is quite different. The unit impulse occurring at $t = 0$ can be treated analytically by means of the Laplace transform, whereas a repetitive impulse must be generated by nonlinear function-generation techniques.

In this section only the unit impulse occurring at $t = 0$ will be considered. The repetitive impulse will be demonstrated in Sec. 7-7. The analysis to be used here is to show that the Laplace transform of the unit impulse is completely analogous to a velocity initial condition in a second-order system.

Consider the differential equation

$$m \frac{d^2x}{dt^2} + a \frac{dx}{dt} + bx = u_1(t) \qquad (7\text{-}12)$$

where $u_1(t)$ is the unit-impulse function. The Laplace transform of Eq. (7-12) is

$$m \left[s^2 X(s) - x(0)s - \frac{dx}{dt}(0) \right] + a[sX(s) - x(0)] + bX(s) = 1 \qquad (7\text{-}13)$$

If, in Eq. (7-12), the initial value of dx/dt and x are defined as zero, Eq. (7-13) becomes

$$ms^2X(s) + asX(s) + bX(s) = 1 \qquad (7\text{-}14)$$

Consider now the case of the homogeneous equation, $u_1(t) = 0$, with initial conditions

$$\frac{dx}{dt}(0) = \frac{1}{m} \qquad x(0) = 0$$

For these conditions Eq. (7-13) becomes

$$ms^2X(s) - 1 + asX(s) + bX(s) = 0$$

or $\qquad ms^2X(s) + asX(s) + bX(s) = 1 \qquad (7\text{-}15)$

Comparison of Eqs. (7-14) and (7-15) reveals that they are identical. Since the transform of the second-order system with a unit impulse applied as a forcing function is identically equal to the transform of the same equation with an initial condition on velocity, it is readily apparent that an initial condition on velocity can be used on an analog computer to represent the unit impulse.

A word of caution should be entered here regarding the effect of a time-scale change when representing the unit impulse in this manner. The equation should be changed to a differential equation with the equivalent initial condition stated before applying the time-scale change. Less frequent errors will result from this procedure.

An alternate method of representing the unit impulse that has frequently been used is to approximate it with an exponential function. The function most commonly used is

$$f(t) = \alpha e^{-\alpha t} \qquad (7\text{-}16)$$

In order to obtain an adequate representation of the unit-impulse function, two requirements must be satisfied: (1) the duration of the impulse must be short compared to the time constants of the problem in which it is to be used; and (2) the area under the function must be unity.

Integrating Eq. (7-16) shows that the function can satisfy the requirements placed upon the unit-impulse function, since performing the integration gives

$$\int_0^\infty f(t)\, dt = \int_0^\infty \alpha e^{-\alpha t}\, dt = 1$$

If α is made arbitrarily large, the function $f(t)$ becomes arbitrarily short in duration, but the area or integral of the function remains unity.

Since the unit-impulse function is normally applied as a forcing function, it is usually applied to the input of an integrator as one of the terms which, when added together, are equivalent to the highest-order derivative of the equation being solved. As will be shown in detail in Sec. 10-5, the inputs to an integrator are disconnected from the integrator during the time that the computer controls are in the RESET position. The actual voltage applied to the integrator input is thus zero until the computer controls are placed in the OPERATE position. Although the initial value of $f(t)$ in Eq. (7-16) is α, the integrator sees it as a sudden jump from zero to α volts at $t = 0$ and then as an exponential decay to zero with a time constant $1/\alpha$.

The first method presented for representing a unit impulse function is certainly the preferred method, since it requires no equipment and represents the desired function exactly. The exponential method of generating the unit-impulse function was described here as a comparison of existing techniques.

7-7. The Repetitive Unit Impulse. In the preceding section two methods were presented for representing a unit-impulse function applied at $t = 0$. In this section a means of approximating a repetitive forcing function in the form of a unit impulse will be discussed. The definition of the unit impulse is important here, as it leads to a justification of the techniques to follow.

The limit process of Eq. (7-16) defined $u_1(t)$ as a rectangular pulse of infinite height and zero width. Obviously, this cannot be represented exactly on the computer, but a good approximation can be made by generating rectangular pulses of unity area and increasing the height and decreasing the width until no change in the system response is observed.

Differential relays provide a particularly easy means of generating just such a function. The necessary circuitry includes a sinusoid generator to establish the periodicity of the function, and relays to turn a voltage on and off. Such a circuit is shown in Fig. 7-21. In the region where $-b/2 < \cos \omega t < b/2$, the differential relays are positioned so that the output is $1/a$. The duration of the pulse a is a function of the setting of potentiometers 3 and 4. As the settings of potentiometers 3 and 4 are decreased, the pulse becomes narrower, and as potentiometer 5 is increased, the pulse becomes greater in magnitude. Since it is very difficult to measure the exact width of the narrow pulses, the output of the circuit should be checked by integration. When properly adjusted, each pulse should add unity to the output of an integrator used in the check.

In actual use, it is usually found that the pulse width can remain quite appreciable and still give satisfactory computer results. The limiting pulse width for satisfactory operation can easily be determined by increasing the pulse width slightly (keeping the area unity).   If no significant change in the system response is observed, the representation is adequate.

The illustrative problem of Chap. 3, involving the automobile suspension system, employed the same method of generating a forcing function as is employed here.   The only difference is that in the previous example the pulse width and height were assigned arbitrary values rather than a pulse area of unity as required for the unit impulse.

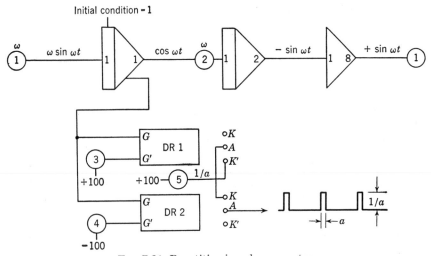

FIG. 7-21. Repetitive impulse generator.

7-8. Approximation of a True Time Lag.   The setup of problems on computers occasionally requires the representation of a "true time lag," or an expression of the form $f(t - \tau)$.   The brute-force approach to the solution of this problem, and one that has been used in the past, is to generate $f(t)$ in the computer and plot $f(t)$ vs. t on a specially equipped recording device.   The special equipment necessary is a reticle, coupled to a function-generating device such as a potentiometer, that can be manually positioned to $f(t)$ at some fixed time interval τ after $f(t)$ is generated and plotted.   This scheme has proved to be workable for some problems, but it has several limitations and disadvantages.   First, this method of generating a true time lag requires manual tracking of the function $f(t - \tau)$ and thus introduces human error into the problem.   Second, and most important, there is an upper and lower limit to the magnitude of the time lag that can be introduced into a function by this means.   These limits are imposed by the physical design of the manual tracking device. Third, the necessity of using manual tracking places a severe limit upon the speed of solution of the problem involved.

A better scheme of producing a true time lag has been devised.[5] This scheme is based upon the mathematical approximation to the Laplacian shift operator $e^{-s\tau}$ and allows a good representation of the true time lag for value of τ even as great as a minute or longer, if necessary.

The Laplace transform of $f(t - \tau)$ is

$$\mathcal{L}[f(t - \tau)] = F(s)e^{-s\tau} \tag{7-17}$$

if $f(t - \tau) = 0$ for $0 < t - \tau$. In Eq. (7-17), $e^{-s\tau}$ is commonly called the Laplace shift operator. The problem of generating a function $f(t - \tau)$ can therefore be reduced to the problem of generating the function $e^{-s\tau}$.

The best known approximation to the function e^x is the Taylor series expansion

$$e^x = 1 + x + \frac{x^2}{2!} + \frac{x^3}{3!} + \cdots + \frac{x^n}{n!} \tag{7-18}$$

This expansion is convergent for all values of x, but unfortunately the rate of convergence is small for x large. For this reason the Taylor series is not well suited to the generation of a fixed time lag for problems involving high frequencies or for long time constants. This can be seen by replacing s by $j\omega$ in the expression for $e^{-s\tau}$.

An approximation of $e^{-s\tau}$ that is superior to the Taylor series expansion for the generation of a true time lag is the Padé[6] approximation

$$e^x = \lim_{(u+v) \to \infty} \frac{F_{u,v}(x)}{G_{u,v}(x)} \tag{7-19}$$

where

$$F_{u,v}(x) = 1 + \frac{vx}{(u + v)1!} + \frac{v(v - 1)x^2}{(u + v)(u + v - 1)2!}$$
$$+ \cdots + \frac{v(v - 1) \cdots 2 \cdot 1x^v}{(u + v)(u + v - 1) \cdots (u + 1)v!} \tag{7-20}$$

$$G_{u,v}(x) = 1 - \frac{ux}{(v + u)1!} + \frac{u(u - 1)x^2}{(v + u)(v + u - 1)2!}$$
$$+ \cdots + (-1)^u \frac{u(u - 1) \cdots 2 \cdot 1x^u}{(v + u)(v + u - 1) \cdots (v + 1)u!} \tag{7-21}$$

The convergence for this series expansion is quite rapid, and often values of u and v of 2 will give good accuracy for short time lags and low frequencies.   The Padé approximation of $e^{-s\tau}$ for $u = v = 2$ is given in Eq. (7-23).

$$e^{-s\tau} \simeq \frac{1 - 2/4(s\tau) + 2/4!(s^2\tau^2)}{1 + 2/4(s\tau) + 2/4!(s^2\tau^2)} \qquad (7\text{-}22)$$

$$e^{-s\tau} \simeq \frac{s^2\tau^2 - 6s\tau + 12}{s^2\tau^2 + 6s\tau + 12} \qquad (7\text{-}23)$$

In terms of the original problem, generating $f(t - \tau)$ when $f(t)$ is known, the equation for the second-order Padé approximation can be expressed in transfer-function notation as

$$\frac{f(t - \tau)}{f(t)} \simeq \frac{p^2\tau^2 - 6p\tau + 12}{p^2\tau^2 + 6p\tau + 12} \qquad (7\text{-}24)$$

The justification of the validity of Eq. (7-24) is easily demonstrated as follows:

$$\mathcal{L}f(t - \tau) = F(s)\, e^{-s\tau} \qquad (7\text{-}25)$$
$$\mathcal{L}f(t - \tau) = \mathcal{L}f(t)\, e^{-s\tau} \qquad (7\text{-}26)$$

Substituting Eq. (7-23) into Eq. (7-26) gives

$$\frac{\mathcal{L}f(t - \tau)}{\mathcal{L}f(t)} \simeq \frac{s^2\tau^2 - 6s\tau + 12}{s^2\tau^2 + 6s\tau + 12} \qquad (7\text{-}27)$$

Rewriting Eq. (7-27) gives

$$(s^2\tau^2 + 6s\tau + 12)\mathcal{L}f(t - \tau) = (s^2\tau^2 - 6s\tau + 12)\mathcal{L}f(t) \qquad (7\text{-}28)$$

Performing the inverse Laplace transformation upon Eq. (7-28) gives

$$(p^2\tau^2 + 6p\tau + 12)f(t - \tau) = (p^2\tau^2 - 6p\tau + 12)f(t) \qquad (7\text{-}29)$$

Comparison of Eqs. (7-29) and (7-27) reveals that the equations are identical.   This is, of course, a logical conclusion, as the Laplacian operator and the differential operator may be used interchangeably providing the initial conditions in a system are identically zero.   This is true in the system described above.

In setting up the transfer function of Eq. (7-24) for computer solution, the technique presented in Sec. 4-3 is most useful.   Proceeding as in Sec. 4-3 by dividing the numerator and denominator of Eq. (7-24) by $p^2\tau^2$ gives

$$\frac{f(t - \tau)}{f(t)} = \frac{1 - 6/p\tau + 12/p^2\tau^2}{1 + 6/p\tau + 12/p^2\tau^2} \qquad (7\text{-}30)$$

Solving the equation for $f(t - \tau)$ and collecting terms according to

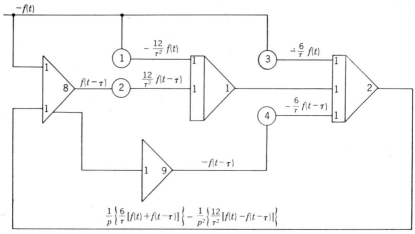

FIG. 7-22. Circuit for the generation of the second-order Padé approximation of a true time lag.

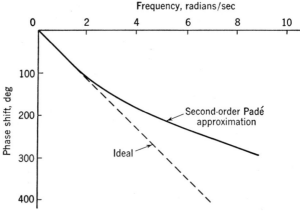

FIG. 7-23. Phase characteristics of the second-order Padé approximation to $e^{-s\tau}$.

powers of p gives

$$f(t - \tau) = f(t) - \left[\frac{6}{\tau} f(t) + \frac{6}{\tau} f(t - \tau) \right] \frac{1}{p}$$
$$+ \left[\frac{12}{\tau^2} f(t) - \frac{12}{\tau^2} f(t - \tau) \right] \frac{1}{p^2} \quad (7\text{-}31)$$

The setup of the second-order approximation to a true time lag can easily be prepared from this equation and is shown in Fig. 7-22.

The range of frequencies and time lags for which the second-order approximation to $e^{-s\tau}$ is useful is shown in Fig. 7-23 as a plot of the phase shift in degrees vs. the frequency in radians per second.   In order to use this chart it is necessary to substitute $j\omega$ for s in the expression for $e^{-s\tau}$ and use for ω the highest value of the frequency that will be encountered in a particular problem.

The fourth-order Padé approximation to $e^{-s\tau}$ is

$$e^{-s\tau} = \frac{(s\tau)^4 - 20(s\tau)^3 + 180(s\tau)^2 - 840s\tau + 1{,}680}{(s\tau)^4 + 20(s\tau)^3 + 180(s\tau)^2 + 840s\tau + 1{,}680} \qquad (7\text{-}32)$$

The setup of the fourth-order Padé approximation to a true time lag can be made in a manner analogous to that for the second-order Padé

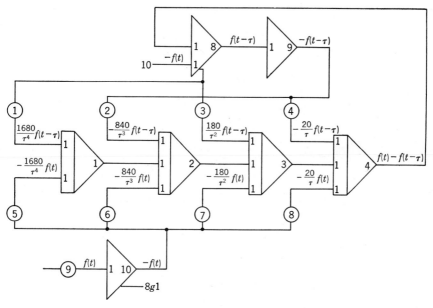

Fig. 7-24. Circuit for the generation of the fourth-order Padé approximation of a true time lag.

approximation.   The setup for the fourth-order Padé approximation is shown in Fig. 7-24.   Scale-factor adjustment for particular values of τ has been left to the reader.

The plot of the frequency vs. phase shift for Padé approximations to $e^{-s\tau}$ using values of $u = v = 2$, 4, and 6 is shown as Fig. 7-25.

The fidelity of representation of the second- and fourth-order approximations to $e^{-s\tau}$ is quite good.   A plot of frequency vs. phase shift for the sixth-order approximation reveals that the approximation deviates quite considerably from the desired values (see Fig. 7-25). This fact led Morrill[5] to suggest that a better method of extending the accuracy of the approximation beyond that obtainable from the fourth-order approximation is to devise a "mop-up" equalizer network to be applied to the results of the fourth approximation. The method of designing a "mop-up" equalizer, as suggested by Morrill, is:

1. Plot the phase-shift characteristics of the fourth-order Padé approximation to $e^{-j\omega\tau}$.

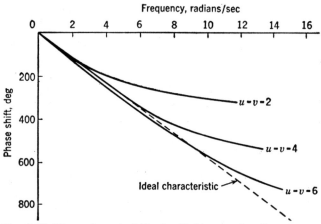

Fig. 7-25. Phase characteristics for Padé approximations to $e^{-s\tau}$.

2. Plot an error curve determined by the difference between the above curve and the desired straight-line function.

3. Determine the network having a phase characteristic which most nearly follows the error curve.

PROBLEMS

7-1. There are usually several ways that particular functions can be generated on an analog computer. Show that the circuit of Fig. P 7-1 is an additional method of generating the absolute value of a function.

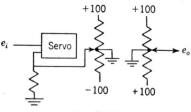

Fig. P 7-1

7-2. An aircraft landing-gear strut has a dump valve mounted in its oil passage so that when the aircraft is moving downward (compressing the strut) the damping force ϕ is

$$\phi = f_1\left(x, \frac{dx}{dt}\right)$$

When the motion is in the opposite direction the dump valve opens, reducing the damping force to

$$\phi = f_2\left(x, \frac{dx}{dt}\right)$$

Assume that $f_1(x, dx/dt)$, $f_2(x, dx/dt)$, x, and dx/dt are available in another portion of the circuit. Assume that dx/dt is positive when the aircraft is moving downward. Show a circuit diagram to produce ϕ.

7-3. It is necessary to generate a particular forcing function δ, where δ is defined as

$$
\begin{aligned}
\delta &= a & 0 < t < t_1 \\
\delta &= a[1 - c(t - t_1)] & t_1 < t < t_2 \\
\delta &= b & t_2 < t < t_3 \\
\delta &= f(x, t) & t_3 < t
\end{aligned}
$$

The forcing function is illustrated graphically in Fig. P 7-3. Show a circuit to generate this function. Do not use in excess of three differential relays and two integrators in the circuit.

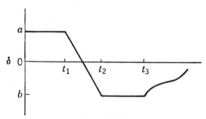

FIG. P 7-3

7-4. A relay circuit to simulate velocity limiting and displacement limiting in the output of a servomechanism is shown in Fig. P 7-4. The equation simulated is

$$\frac{d^2x}{dt^2} + a\frac{dx}{dt} + bx = f(t)$$

with the limits

$$-e < x < e \qquad -d < \frac{dx}{dt} < c$$

Describe in detail the operation of that portion of the circuit producing the velocity limiting.

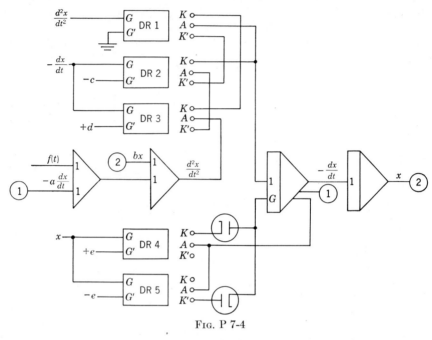

FIG. P 7-4

7-5. Describe the operation of the diode circuit of Fig. P 7-5 and plot e_o vs. e_i for the circuit.

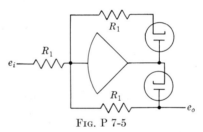

FIG. P 7-5

7-6. It is desired to simulate a regulator which controls the speed according to whichever of two controlled variables is the smaller. Draw a diode circuit to perform the selection

$$e_3 = e_1 \qquad e_1 < e_2$$
$$e_3 = e_2 \qquad e_2 < e_1$$

HINT: Connect diodes, properly oriented, from the output of amplifiers generating e_1 and e_2 to a junction that is supplied a positive voltage through a dropping resistor.

7-7. Show a computer circuit diagram to solve the equation

$$25 \frac{d^2x}{dt^2} + 10 \frac{dx}{dt} + 15x = u_1(t)$$

where $u_1(t)$ is defined as the unit-impulse function.

REFERENCES

1. Bennett, R. R.: The Generation of Straight Line Transfer Relationships, "Project Cyclone Symposium I on REAC Techniques," Reeves Instrument Corporation (under contract with the U.S. Navy Special Devices Center), New York, Mar. 15–16, 1951.
2. Warshawsky, L. M., and W. G. Braun: Applications of Differential Relays to Solutions of REAC Problems, "Project Cyclone Symposium II on Simulation and Computing Techniques, Part 2," pp. 187–196, Reeves Instrument Corporation (under sponsorship of the U.S. Navy Special Devices Center and the U.S. Navy Bureau of Aeronautics), New York, Apr. 28–May 2, 1952.
3. Morrill, C. D., and R. V. Baum: Diode Limiters Simulate Mechanical Phenomena, *Electronics*, vol. 25, no. 11, pp. 122–126, November, 1952.
4. Chance, Britton, et al.: "Waveforms," p. 61, McGraw-Hill Book Company, Inc., New York, 1949.
5. Morrill, C. D.: A Sub Audio Time Delay Circuit, *Trans. IRE (Professional Group on Electronic Computers)*, vol. EC-3, no. 2, June, 1954.
6. Perron, O.: "Die Lehre von den Kettenbruchen," p. 459, Chelsea Publishing Company, New York, 1950.

CHAPTER 8

MULTIPLIERS AND FUNCTION GENERATORS

8-1. Introduction. During the period of time that has elapsed since the construction of the first electronic analog computer, many function multipliers have been built and many others proposed for use in computing installations. The large variety of multipliers that have been built is due to the varied requirements placed on function multipliers by different computer laboratories. Some laboratories require maximum accuracy from their function multipliers, while other laboratories need multipliers capable of high-speed operation. The type of problems most frequently encountered in a laboratory is the primary consideration in choosing the proper multipliers for the installation.

Most function multipliers can be classified as having good frequency-response characteristics or as being capable of producing results of relatively high precision. In general, speed of response can be obtained only at the cost of precision, and vice versa. Recently, however, function multipliers that combine the characteristics of high-speed and high-accuracy operation into a single device have been introduced to the computing industry. The basic principle of operation of the new multipliers is described in Sec. 8-2.

A few of the other more common multipliers will be described in subsequent sections of this chapter; however, no further mention will be made of the servomultiplier, as it has been treated in some detail in an earlier chapter.

Simultaneously with the development of function-multiplying equipment, there has been carried out the development of arbitrary-function-generating equipment. As in the case of function multipliers, the function generators can be classed as high-precision or high-speed devices. The distinction is somewhat more difficult to make here, however, as several of the function-generating devices in use today combine high-speed operation with reasonably good accuracy. None of the existing function-generating equipment is without faults, however, and better equipment will undoubtedly be introduced in the coming years. A description of a few of the more important arbitrary-function generators presently in existence will be the chief topic of the latter half of this chapter.

8-2. The Time-division Multiplier. The device which seems to have the greatest possibility of replacing the servomultiplier for accurate, high-speed analog computation is the stabilized time-division multiplier.[1] The first commercially available models of this type of function multiplier were produced by Goodyear Aircraft Corporation in 1953. This multiplier is all-electronic and is capable of producing static accuracies of the order of 0.1 per cent of full scale. The dynamic characteristics of the GEDA N-3 multiplier, as described by Baum and Morrill[2] of Goodyear Aircraft Corporation, are (1) frequency response:

flat to about 200 cps, with a 3-db rise at 1,000 cps; (2) phase shift: 16° at 200 cps and 0.7° at 10 cps. This excellent dynamic response has never previously been available in a precision function multiplier.

For some time Goodyear has produced a time-division multiplier; however, the earlier model was not nearly so attractive a device from

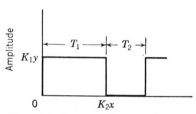

Fig. 8-1. Rectangular waveform of unfiltered time-division multiplier output.

the standpoint of use as is the stabilized N-3 model. The earlier model was unstabilized and, therefore, was subject to drift. Because of the drift, it lacked somewhat in repeatability and convenience of operation. A further advantage of the stabilized multiplier is the ease with which an adequate overload warning system can be incorporated in its design. The overload warning system used on the stabilized multiplier is similar to the system used on stabilized d-c amplifiers. The operation of overload warning systems will be discussed in Sec. 10-3.

The time-division multiplier forms the algebraic product of two variables by averaging several cycles of a *quasi-rectangular waveform*. To describe the principle of operation of the multiplier and to make clear the meaning of quasi-rectangular waveform, it is most convenient to describe the logic of the multiplier in terms of the multiplication of constants rather than variables.

Consider the waveform shown in Fig. 8-1. The duration of the first portion of the rectangular wave of Fig. 8-1 is proportional to the constant x, and the amplitude of the rectangular wave during time T_1 is proportional to the magnitude of the input constant y. Since the second half of the rectangular wave has zero amplitude, the average amplitude of the rectangular wave is proportional to the product xy if the time $T_1 + T_2 = T$ is assumed to be constant.

If the duration T of the complete waveform cycle shown in Fig. 8-1 is made very short and the process of generating a pulse of magnitude and duration proportional to y and x, respectively, is repeated at a sufficiently high rate, then if x and y are variable quantities the incremental change in x and y during the period T is small. The waveform can, therefore, be defined as *quasi-rectangular*. The average magnitude of the quasi-rectangular waveform obtained with the variable inputs x and y is a very close approximation to kxy, where k is some proportionality constant, if x and y vary slowly in comparison to the time T of a single cycle of the rectangular wave.

The components necessary to demonstrate the principle of the time-division process, as described above, are:

1. Two electronic switches
2. An integrator
3. A bistable multivibrator
4. An output amplifier and filter

The manner of interconnection of these components is indicated in the block diagram, Fig. 8-2. Frequent reference to Fig. 8-2 will be made during the detailed description of the multiplier contained in the remainder of this section.

In Fig. 8-2 consider the bistable multivibrator. The output of the multivibrator is of rectangular waveform as shown in the block diagram. The durations of the first and second portions of the rectangular wave are T_1 and T_2, respectively. The bistable multivibrator is caused to switch from its first stable state to its second stable state when the output of the integrator reaches a reference voltage e_1, and it switches back to the first stable state when the integrator output falls to the voltage level e_2.

The stabilized electronic switches 1 and 2 are controlled by the output of the multivibrator, and they conduct when the multivibrator is in state 1. Examination of Fig. 8-2 reveals that the input to the summing integrator during state 1 is

$$\frac{x}{c} + \frac{z}{2ab} - \frac{z}{ab} = \frac{x}{c} - \frac{z}{2ab} \qquad (8\text{-}1)$$

where a, b, and c are constants. Since the output of the integrator must be increasing in a positive sense during this period, it is required that

$$\frac{z}{2ab} > \frac{x}{c} \qquad (8\text{-}2)$$

The output of the integrator is, therefore, caused to increase linearly with time and the duration of state 1 is established by Eq. (8-3):

$$k \int_0^{T_1} \left(\frac{x}{c} - \frac{z}{2ab} \right) dt = e_2 - e_1 \tag{8-3}$$

where k is the gain of the integrator.

The basic assumption made in the multiplier is that the output of

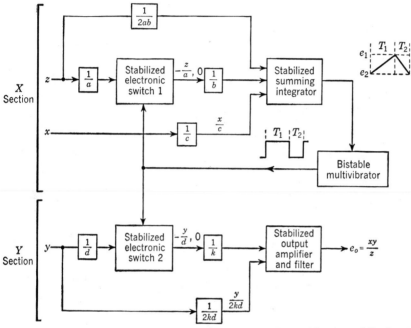

FIG. 8-2. Block diagram of a stabilized electronic multiplier. (*Courtesy of Goodyear Aircraft Corporation.*)

the multivibrator is of quasi-rectangular waveform. To satisfy this requirement, it is necessary that the cycle rate of the multivibrator be sufficiently high to ensure that the inputs x, y, and z remain essentially constant over several cycles of operation. Equation (8-3) can, therefore, be treated as though x and z are constants, giving

$$T_1 = \frac{e_1 - e_2}{k(z/2ab - x/c)} \tag{8-4}$$

As soon as the output of the integrator reaches the voltage level e_1, the switches 1 and 2 open and the input to the integrator becomes $z/2ab + x/c$. The duration T_2 of the second portion of the cycle is established by Eq. (8-5):

$$k \int_0^{T_2} \left(\frac{z}{2ab} + \frac{x}{c} \right) dt = e_1 - e_2 \tag{8-5}$$

Again x and z can be assumed constant and the equation gives

$$T_2 = \frac{e_1 - e_2}{k(z/2ab + x/c)} \tag{8-6}$$

Returning again to Fig. 8-2, it is seen that during period T_1 the output of electronic switch 2 is $-y/d$ and that it is zero for period T_2. The average input to the output amplifier and filter is then

$$-e_o \,(\mathrm{avg}) = \frac{y}{2kd} - \frac{y}{kd} \frac{T_1}{T_1 + T_2} = \frac{y}{kd} \left(\frac{1}{2} - \frac{T_1}{T_1 + T_2} \right) \tag{8-7}$$

Substituting values of T_1 and T_2 obtained in Eqs. (8-4) and (8-6) into Eq. (8-7) gives

$$e_o \,(\mathrm{avg}) = \frac{ab}{kcd} \frac{xy}{z} \tag{8-8}$$

The gain of the output amplifier is made equal to kcd/ab so that the output voltage is xy/z.

From Eqs. (8-4) and (8-6), it is readily seen that the duration of T_1 and T_2 are functions of z as well as x. Further, it is apparent that, as z is reduced, the repetition rate of the bistable multivibrator is reduced. This creates a filtering problem and imposes a lower limit on the value of z. For this reason z is usually chosen as a fixed reference voltage. If the reference voltage is $+100$ volts, then the output of the multiplier is $xy/100$.

The multiplier is supplied in two forms: a master multiplier consisting of an X section and two Y sections, and slave multipliers consisting only of Y sections. If it is desired to multiply the variable x by more than two variable quantities, it is necessary to connect the timing pulse from the X section to additional Y channels that can be purchased separately. In this manner, considerable economy of equipment is achieved.

The stabilized electronic switch used in the multiplier circuit is of considerable interest. The heart of the switch (see Fig. 8-3) is a stabilized d-c amplifier. The switching action is obtained by alternately connecting different feedback impedances into the circuit. During the period T_1, tube V3-A is allowed to conduct and V3-B is cut off. V1, therefore, is cut off and V2 conducts, connecting R_2 into the feedback path. The output from the electronic switch is taken from the junction of R_2 and V2. The amplifier gain is correspondingly R_2/R_i. During the last half of the cycle, T_2, V3-A is cut off and V3-B conducts. V2 is, therefore, cut off and V1 is allowed to conduct, connecting R_1 into the feedback path. In this condition, the output of the switch is maintained at zero, since it is connected through R_2 to the grid input of the amplifier.

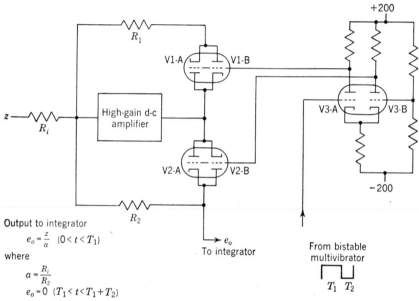

Output to integrator

$$e_o = \frac{z}{a} \quad (0 < t < T_1)$$

where

$$a = \frac{R_i}{R_2}$$

$$e_o = 0 \quad (T_1 < t < T_1 + T_2)$$

FIG. 8-3. Basic principle of operation of one form of electronic switch. (*Courtesy of Goodyear Aircraft Corporation.*)

The stabilized electronic multiplier has been realizable for some time. Goldberg[3] first demonstrated a circuit stabilizing a d-c amplifier prior to 1947, but it was not until Ingerson[4] succeeded in stabilizing a large number of d-c amplifiers with a single pulse amplifier that the stabilized time-division multiplier circuit was developed. The incorporation of the Ingerson stabilization system allows a very appreciable reduction in the number of vacuum tubes required in the circuit, and in addition it eliminates the necessity of a costly chopper for each amplifier. The Ingerson scheme will be discussed in more detail in the section on stabilized d-c amplifiers (Sec. 10-2). Subsequent to the production of the first stabilized electronic multiplier, rapid development of similar devices has taken place. Multipliers using either the Goldberg or Ingerson stabilization system are available at present.

8-3. Quarter-square Multipliers.   A multiplier that is relatively important because of the number in use, rather than because of the high quality of the results produced, is the quarter-square multiplier. This multiplier has been used extensively with repetitive-type computing equipment (see Chap. 12), as it has good frequency-response characteristics.

The name quarter-square multiplier comes from the equation that is mechanized in performing the multiplication.   The equation mechanized is the identity

$$x_1 x_2 \equiv \tfrac{1}{4}[(x_1 + x_2)^2 - (x_1 - x_2)^2] \tag{8-9}$$

It is apparent from Eq. (8-9) that, if a device can be constructed that

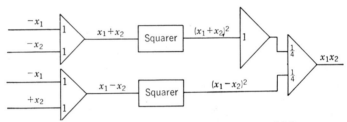

Fig. 8-4. Block diagram of a quarter-square multiplier.

is capable of performing the operation of squaring, a quarter-square multiplier can be readily constructed.   The block-diagram representation of a quarter-square multiplier is shown in Fig. 8-4.

Philbrick computing equipment* utilizes a multiplier of this type. The squaring circuit used in the Philbrick multiplier takes advantage of the nonlinear characteristics of a triode.   The nonlinear characteristic of interest is the variation of the plate current i_b *approximately* proportional to the square of the plate voltage applied, **or**

$$i_b = k e_b{}^2 \tag{8-10}$$

Since the equivalent plate resistance of a vacuum tube is

$$R_b = \frac{e_b}{i_b} \tag{8-11}$$

dividing Eq. (8-10) through by e_b produces the equation

$$\frac{1}{R_b} = \frac{i_b}{e_b} = k e_b \tag{8-12}$$

* George A. Philbrick Researches, Inc., Boston, Mass.

Inverting Eq. (8-12) gives the expression

$$R_b = \frac{1}{ke_b} \qquad (8\text{-}13)$$

which makes possible the ready understanding of the squaring circuit of Fig. 8-5.

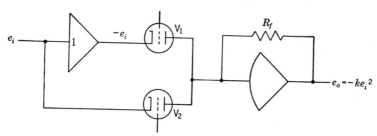

FIG. 8-5. Squaring circuit utilizing the nonlinear characteristics of vacuum tubes. Tubes V_1 and V_2 serve as the input impedance of the high-gain amplifier.

Vacuum tubes V_1 and V_2 serve as the input impedance of the high-gain amplifier. Since R_f is a constant, the gain of the circuit is

$$\frac{e_o}{e_i} = -\frac{z_f}{z_i} = \frac{R_f}{R_b} = ke_b \qquad (8\text{-}14)$$

Figure 8-5 shows, however, that $e_b = |e_i|$, for e_i either positive or negative, so that Eq. (8-14) can be written as

$$e_o = -ke_i^2 \qquad (8\text{-}15)$$

The grid inputs of V_1 and V_2 are supplied by constant voltages that must be adjusted to give operation on the proper portion of the characteristic curve. Needless to say, a multiplier constructed with a squaring device of this type can never be expected to achieve the accuracy obtainable from the servomultiplier or time-division multiplier.

8-4. The Crossed-fields Multiplier. Another multiplier that is capable of very-high-frequency response is the crossed-fields multiplier. The crossed-fields multiplier was developed by Macnee,[5] and like the quarter-square multiplier it is well suited for use with repetitive computer installations.

Figure 8-6 shows the basic components of a crossed-fields multiplier. The basic components are an electrostatic deflection cathode-ray tube, two photocell pickups, and a differential amplifier to amplify the difference of intensity between the signals produced by the photocells.

A magnetic deflection coil, placed around the neck of the cathode-ray tube, completes the essential components of the multiplier.

In operation, a current I_1 is passed through the magnetic deflection coil. A voltage V_1 applied to the vertical deflection plates of the tube then deflects the electron beam, causing it to cut lines of magnetic force produced by the current I_1 in the magnetic deflection coil. The magnetic field causes the electron beam to be deflected horizontally. A light barrier placed vertically along the face of the cathode-ray tube divides the face into two halves. If a greater intensity of light from the cathode beam falls on the photocell associated with either half of the tube face, an unbalanced condition exists in the voltages produced by the photocells. The unbalanced photocell voltages are amplified by the differential amplifier and applied to the horizontal deflection plates of the cathode-ray tube. Equilibrium conditions are reached when the voltage V_2, produced by the differential amplifier, is just sufficient to restore the beam to its neutral position. In the equilibrium condition the voltage V_2 is approximately proportional to the vertical deflection voltage V_1 and the current I_1 in the magnetic deflection coil.

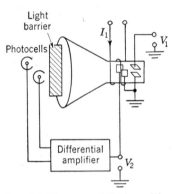

Fig. 8-6. The crossed-fields multiplier.

If V_1 and I_1 are made proportional to quantities x_1 and x_2, then the voltage V_2, developed across the horizontal deflection plates, is proportional to the product x_1x_2.

8-5. Other Multiplying Devices. There are several other multiplying devices currently in use, or proposed for use, with analog computers. All these devices have some undesirable features, just as have the devices previously discussed. In general, either accuracy or speed has been sacrificed in the design, depending upon the use to be made of the multiplier.

A partial list of multipliers and their capabilities is given in Table 8-1. The type of multiplier, its developer or manufacturer, type of operation, and principle of operation are given in the table. The table is not intended to be complete but indicates, to some extent, the availability of several multipliers.

8-6. Function-generating Equipment. Frequently it becomes necessary to introduce arbitrary functions into a problem. The requirement may arise from the need to represent nonlinear effects or to intro-

duce a particular forcing function into a problem. A listing of all
phenomena easily simulated by means of arbitrary-function-generating

TABLE 8-1

Multiplier	Developer or manufacturer (if commercially available)	Principal characteristics	Comments
Servomulti-plier	Reeves Instr. Corp., New York, N.Y.; Goodyear Aircraft Corp., Akron, Ohio; others	Capable of high accuracy, but poor frequency response	Presently the most common multiplying device in *real-time* computer installations
Time-division multiplier	Goodyear Aircraft Corp., Akron, Ohio; Beckman Instr. Corp., Richmond, Calif.; Reeves Instr. Corp., New York, N.Y.; Electronic Associates, Inc., Long Branch, N.J.	Relatively high-speed, high-accuracy operation	At present the most promising multiplier for high-precision, high-speed analog-computer operation
Quarter-square multiplier	Geo. A. Philbrick Researches, Inc., Boston, Mass.	Low-accuracy, high-speed operation	Used extensively with repetitive computers
Crossed-fields multiplier	A. B. Macnee	High-speed operation, moderate accuracy	Very satisfactory for repetitive computer installations
Electrodyna-mometer multiplier	Specialties, Inc., Skunk's Misery Rd., Syosset, N.Y.	Moderate accuracy, relatively low frequency response (0.5 cps)	Originally developed as compact packaged component for aircraft applications
Step-relay multiplier	RCA Research Laboratories, Princeton, N.J.	Very high accuracy obtainable, speed reduced as accuracy is increased	Developed specifically for the Typhoon computer, a three-dimensional missile simulator; some relay troubles encountered

equipment would be voluminous. A few commonly encountered functions easily represented by means of such equipment are:

1. The nonlinear damping of an aircraft shock strut having a tapered metering pin.

2. The nonlinear spring force needed to represent a pneumatic tire under load.

3. The torque-vs.-rpm characteristic curve of a turbojet engine.

4. The variation with altitude of the index of refraction of a non-homogeneous air mass such as the earth's atmosphere.

5. The variation of the coefficient of drag with Mach number for a missile in flight.

6. Any arbitrary forcing function that might be desired. Typical might be the gust loading of a structure in the path of an atomic explosion.

7. The load distribution placed on a structural member.

8. The change in thrust of a rocket as it nears burnout.

9. The variation of density with altitude in the earth's atmosphere.

10. The generation of sinusoids, squares, cubes, square roots, cube roots and exponentials, etc.

Some of the functions mentioned here may be generated relatively easily internally in the computer. Others of the functions are extremely difficult to represent mathematically and almost hopeless to attempt to generate internally on an analog computer. The inclusion of arbitrary-function-generating equipment as part of a computer installation thus considerably extends the ability of the computer installation to handle any problems that may arise.

The function-generating equipment available for analog-computer use is extremely varied. The devices vary considerably in fidelity of reproduction and in frequency response. In many cases the ease of operation or setup of a particular function generator may be its most attractive (or unattractive) characteristic. In the following pages a brief discussion of some of the more common function generators is presented.

8-7. The Input Table. In the early days of the electronic analog computer the natural trend was to borrow techniques previously established for use with mechanical differential analyzers. The most common procedure for generating arbitrary functions when using a mechanical differential analyzer is to plot the required function, say $f(x)$ vs. x, on a graph sheet and by *hand-tracking* the function on an input table, cause the function $f(x)$ to be introduced into the problem. The essential components of a manually operated input table are shown in Fig. 8-7. The input shaft is driven proportional to a problem variable x, and the operator, by means of the hand crank, keeps the reticle at all times positioned on the curve representing $f(x)$. In the case of the mechanical differential analyzer, incremental changes of the generated function are introduced into the problem as a rotation of the output shaft $\Delta f(x)$. The input tables used with electronic analog computers differ from the system illustrated in Fig. 8-7, as the input and output shaft positions are controlled by servomechanisms positioned by d-c voltages. The principle of operation is the same, however.

The manual-tracking method of arbitrary-function generation is relatively satisfactory for the mechanical differential analyzer, as problem operating speeds are low and little difficulty is encountered in keeping the reticle properly positioned. Even for a mechanical differential analyzer, however, an imaginative person makes a very poor "tracker," as he tends to attempt to compensate for errors he has

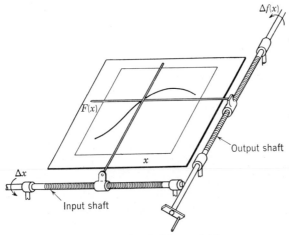

Fig. 8-7. Mechanical input table.

made previously. In this manner he unconsciously introduces a bias into the problem.

With the higher problem speeds of the electronic differential analyzer, the hand-tracking method was found to be unsatisfactory. It was no longer possible to track sufficiently accurately and with sufficient repeatability at the higher speeds required. To slow the problem speed sufficiently to allow hand tracking is unsatisfactory, as integration errors are then increased.

It was not long after the introduction of the electronic analog computer that a satisfactory solution to the problem of function generation was reached. The first major improvement over manual tracking was the introduction of servo-driven function potentiometers. The *function potentiometer* consists of a linear potentiometer mandrel in contact with a conductor affixed permanently to a plastic drum. The conductor is positioned on the drum in such a manner that it contacts the mandrel at a point having a potential proportional to $f(x)$ when the drum is positioned proportional to x.   The disadvantage of function potentiometers is that the preparation of a drum to generate a function requires a special lathe.   Economical use of this technique of function generation is, therefore, restricted to those functions which are to be used many times.

Fig. 8-8. REAC input–output table.

The servo-driven arbitrary-function-generating device finally came of age when it was determined that a wire could be cemented on a graph sheet and used in much the same manner as the function potentiometers.   The scheme is particularly attractive since all existing two-axis recording equipment can be easily and economically converted to perform automatic arbitrary-function generation.   The only modification necessary in most cases is the addition of a linear potentiometer mandrel at right angles to one of the driven axes of the recorder.   A photograph of a Reeves input–output table modified for arbitrary-function generation is shown in Fig. 8-8.   The schematic representation of an input table used for automatic function generation is shown in Fig. 8-9.

In Fig. 8-9 the drum is servo-driven to a position proportional to the input signal x.   A wire is cemented to the graph of the function $f(x)$ vs. x, and this graph is attached to the drum.   A linear potentiometer mandrel is attached to the frame of the input table perpendicular to the x axis of the plotted function. The mandrel makes contact with the wire cemented to the graph at the position determined by the input signal x. When suitable reference voltages K_1 and K_2 are placed on the ends of the linear potentiometer mandrel, a voltage proportional to $f(x)$ is present on the wire. This voltage is used as the output of the device.

Experience has shown that the adjustment of the input reference voltages K_1 and K_2 can be accomplished most easily by trial and error. The procedure recommended is to first establish the magnitude of the output $Kf(x)$ desired, then mark two points x_1 and x_2 on the curve $f(x)$ vs. x. One point should be for $f(x_1)$ large and the second for $f(x_2)$ small. Having established the magnitude of the output desired, it is a simple matter to calculate the voltage needed to represent $Kf(x_1)$ and $Kf(x_2)$. The drum is then rotated to the position x_1 and potentiometer 1 is adjusted to give the voltage $Kf(x_1)$ at the output of the function generator. The drum is then moved to position x_2 and $Kf(x_2)$ is adjusted by means of potentiometer 2. Unless one end of the linear mandrel is exactly at the zero position of the graph of $f(x)$ vs. x,

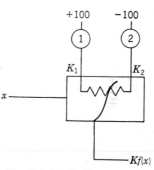

Fig. 8-9. Block-diagram representation of a wire-mandrel type of automatic input table.

the adjustment of K_2 will affect the value of $f(x_1)$ previously set by K_1. It is, therefore, necessary to repeat the procedure until no change is observed. The entire time spent in the calibration of the output will normally not consume more than about five minutes, as three or four adjustments of potentiometers 1 and 2 are usually all that are necessary to give convergence of the output voltages to the desired values.

In Fig. 8-9 the input table is shown with constant inputs at the ends of the potentiometer. The constant inputs can be replaced by $\pm u$ where u is a problem variable. In this manner, a multiplication is saved at another point in the circuit if the product $Kuf(x)$ is needed.

Care should be taken, when using the linear-mandrel type of function generator, to load the output with as high an impedance as possible to minimize loading errors. For a potentiometer approximately 10 in. long and having 20,000 ohms resistance, the maximum error, when loaded by a 1-megohm resistor, is approximately $\frac{1}{20}$ in. on the graph of $f(x)$, or 0.5 per cent of full scale. This error is slightly greater than the maximum error that need be made in laying the wire curve if care is taken. Therefore, using 2 megohms as the input impedance of the amplifier fed by the function generator is justifiable if maximum accuracy is to be achieved.

With a little practice, the wire curves can be prepared in little more than the time necessary to draw the graph from a tabulated set of data. A fairly complex curve can be prepared in about twenty minutes.

A few remarks can be made regarding the preparation of the graphs. The wire should, of course, be straightened by stretching it beyond its yield point to remove all bends and kinks. The consistency of the glue (duco cement or radio service cement) is the key to easy preparation of the graphs. It should be thinned until almost water-thin. It will be necessary to handle the finished graph more carefully if this is done, but more trouble-free operation will result. If heavy glue is used, it has a tendency to shrink upon drying and pull the paper up around the wire, resulting in a poor contact between wire and potentiometer. A second consequence of using heavy glue is the necessity to sand the wire excessively to ensure good contact. The sanding requires too much time if done with crocus cloth and roughens the surface of the wire if done with heavier materials. Needless to say, a roughened wire will very rapidly destroy the linear potentiometer mandrel during operation of the input table.

Several modifications of the wire-mandrel arbitrary-function-generating scheme have been proposed and built. The basic idea behind these modifications is to eliminate the necessity of laying a wire on the graph. Silver paint and other conducting materials have been used, but a frequent difficulty encountered with these materials is that they tend to smudge with prolonged use. Another possibility that has been investigated is the use of a photocell pickup to supply the driving signal necessary to position the reading head to the proper position. So far as is known, none of these devices has been able to provide as trouble-free operation as the simple linear potentiometer and wire. Development work is still being continued.

Another scheme to provide curve-following capability in a servo-driven recorder has recently been developed. The graph of the function to be reproduced is drawn with conducting ink on a graph sheet. Instead of using a brush or potentiometer mandrel to sense the position of the conducting line, as some schemes do, this system avoids physical contact with the line and thus eliminates any possibility of smudging and poor contact.

In this function generator the conducting line is energized by a high-frequency current. The pickup stylus contains a coil which senses the magnetic field radiated from the conducting line. The signal from the pickup head is then demodulated and used to drive the servomotor which keeps the stylus always positioned over the conducting line. The servo also drives a precision potentiometer that supplies the desired output voltage $f(x)$ when suitable reference voltages are placed on its ends.

The magnetic-stylus-pickup scheme of arbitrary-function generation appears to have excellent possibilities of becoming a popular method of function generation. It offers ease of graph preparation and should give good fidelity of reproduction of the required curve.

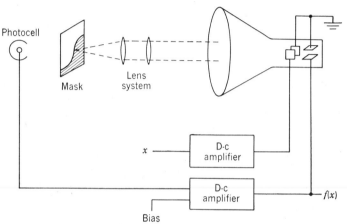

Fig. 8-10. Block diagram of a photoformer function generator.

8-8. The Photoformer. The photoformer[6] is one of the developments brought about by the requirement for a high-speed arbitrary-function generator. It consists of a cathode-ray tube, a mask, an optical system, and a photocell, together with the amplifiers necessary to drive the horizontal and vertical deflection plates of the cathode-ray tube (see Fig. 8-10). A bias voltage is applied to the vertical deflection plates to deflect the beam to the top of the cathode-ray-tube screen. When light falls upon the photocell, the voltage produced is applied to the vertical amplifier and drives the beam toward the bottom of the tube. The resulting vertical position of the electron beam is, therefore, determined by an opaque mask at the focal point of the lens system which serves to cut off the light from the photocell.

The mask is prepared as a plot of the function $f(x)$ vs. x, with the area below the curve made optically black and the upper area transparent. As the electron beam is driven horizontally by an input signal x, the output $f(x)$ is obtained as the voltage across the vertical deflection plates of the cathode-ray tube.

The photoformer is sufficiently fast in response to allow its use with repetitive computers, but it is a relatively low-accuracy device. The usable mask area on many photoformers is approximately $2\frac{1}{2}$ in. square. Needless to say, it is very difficult to prepare a mask for the generation of a function with much detail on this small an area. Two methods of mask preparation are commonly in use. The first is to draw the function to scale directly on the material to be used as the mask and, after trimming the material, use it as the mask. The second and preferred method is to prepare the graph of the function to be generated on the photoformer on a large sheet of paper. The graph is then reduced to the proper size by photographic means. In the latter method of mask preparation, the area underneath the curve representing the desired function should be blackened before photographing the curve so that a positive transparent photographic print can be used directly as the photoformer mask.

Even when the second method of mask preparation is used, distortion of the generated function still results. This distortion results from nonlinearities in the photoformer deflection circuits and from the finite size of the spot formed on the face of the cathode-ray tube. An additional inherent error in photoformers using electrostatic deflection cathode-ray tubes arises in the manufacture of the tubes. The horizontal and vertical deflection plates of such tubes are seldom found to be at exactly right angles. This produces a distortion for which it is difficult to provide compensation.

A method of photoformer-mask preparation that has been proposed as a means of minimizing errors in photoformer function generators is to cause the photoformer to prepare its own mask. This can be accomplished by driving the horizontal deflection plates with x and the vertical plates with the function $f(x)$ produced by some other more precise function-generating equipment. The cathode-ray beam is then used to expose a photographic plate, which in turn is used as a mask after suitable processing. This system of mask preparation is cumbersome but reduces errors arising from nonlinearities in the photoformer. Obviously, this scheme is not very practical for most applications, as the desired function $f(x)$ vs. x first must be generated on some other function-generating equipment in order to prepare the photoformer mask.

A modified version of the photoformer has been built by Armour Research Foundation* that is probably capable of greater fidelity of

* This function generator was constructed under Air Force contract 33(038-12399) by the Armour Research Foundation, Illinois Institute of Technology. It is described in a manual entitled "Instruction Handbook for Generator, Special Function, for Electronic Analog Simulating Equipment," Armour Research Foundation, January, 1952.

reproduction of the desired function than is the conventional photoformer. The advantages of the Armour photoformer are twofold. First, the modified photoformer utilizes magnetic deflection cathode-ray tubes, which allows closer control of the angle between the deflection axes of the tubes than is usually available in electrostatic deflection tubes. Second, the preparation of the mask is easier and can be done more rapidly, because the function to be generated is plotted on a relatively large surface provided for that purpose in the photoformer. The function is plotted directly with white ink on a special black plate of relatively large size. The photoformer optical system causes the cathode-ray tube beam to follow along the white line as the beam is driven horizontally proportional to the argument of the generated function. The generated function is proportional to the voltage developed across the vertical deflection windings of the cathode-ray tube.

8-9. Diode-type Arbitrary-function-generating Equipment. Diode-type arbitrary-function-generating equipment has become increasingly popular. The increased popularity of the diode function generators can be attributed to several desirable features that they possess. These desirable features are:

1. Ease and speed with which they can be set up to generate a function
2. Good frequency response
3. Relatively low cost of the equipment
4. Good fidelity of reproduction of most functions

The diode-type function generator approximates the desired arbitrary function by a series of straight-line segments. The number of straight-line segments usable in the representation varies from 5 to 22, depending upon the manufacturer of the equipment. The diode function generators are supplied in two forms: with variable voltage break points, and with fixed voltage break points. A *break point* is the point of intersection between two straight-line segments comprising a portion of the curve. The variable-break-point function generators have the advantage of greater flexibility and in general closer representation of functions having exceptional curvature. The circuitry of the variable-break-point function generators is slightly more complex, and correspondingly these function generators are more expensive than function generators having fixed-break-point voltages.

The operation of the variable-break-point generator can be demonstrated by using the circuit of the Ease arbitrary-function generator[7] (Fig. 8-11). In the diagram of Fig. 8-11, two stages of the function generator are shown. The Ease function generator consists of 11 similar pairs of diode circuits. If the function to be generated is $f(x)$ vs. x, the portion shown controls one segment of $f(x)$ in the region $x < 0$, and one segment in the region $x > 0$. Since the function generator is symmetrical, it is necessary to place a bias a_1 on the input x, so that one-half the segments of the function to be generated lie in the region $x + a_1 > 0$ and one-half in the region $x + a_1 < 0$ in order to use all 22 straight-line segments in generating a particular function.

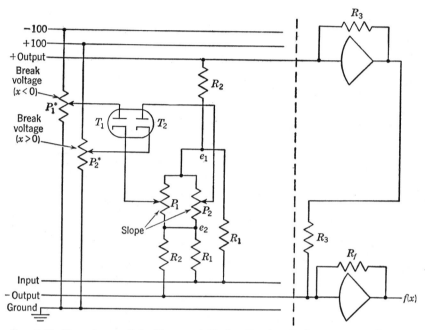

FIG. 8-11. Two stages of the Ease variable-break-point diode function generator.

The actual operation of the function-generator circuit can be more easily visualized if the circuit diagram is further reduced. Consider only the operation of the circuit directly associated with tube T_2 in Fig. 8-11. If, in the circuit of Fig. 8-11, the voltage at the cathode of T_2 is replaced by a constant voltage V whose magnitude is controllable by the setting of potentiometer P_2^*, the circuit can be redrawn as in Fig. 8-12.

In the circuit of Fig. 8-12 as long as

$$\frac{R_2}{R_1 + R_2} x < V \tag{8-16}$$

the diode T_2 will not conduct. (The grids of operational amplifiers are always at zero potential.) With T_2 not conducting, the voltages

e_1 and e_2 are equal and $f(x)$ is zero, since R_2 and R_3 are chosen to be equal.   If

$$\frac{R_2}{R_1 + R_2} x > V \qquad (8\text{-}17)$$

the diode T_2 will commence conducting, and the difference between e_1 and e_2 will be proportional to x providing P_2 is not centered.   If P_2 is set at its exact center, e_1 will equal e_2 for all values of x and $f(x)$

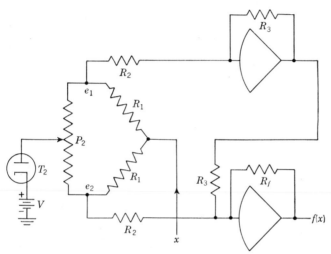

Fig. 8-12. Bridge form of representation of one stage of the Ease diode function generator.

will be zero.   If P_2 is not centered, e_1 will differ from e_2.   For a particular setting of P_2, the output $f(x)$ will vary linearly with x and its slope will be either positive or negative, depending upon the setting of P_2.   The magnitude of the slope is dependent upon the setting of P_2 and on the magnitude of the feedback resistor R_f of the final summing amplifier.   The other stages of the diode function generator operate in a similar manner.   The positive and negative outputs of each are summed in the same amplifiers, so that $f(x)$ is the sum of the output of all the stages in the function generator.

The setup procedure is relatively simple.   The break-point voltages x_i and the magnitude of $f(x_i)$ at each break point must be tabulated. Each break point and the corresponding slope is then set on the potentiometers associated with the proper diode.   The accuracy of the function generator is, of course, determined largely by the function to be generated, as a straight-line representation is used.   If as many as

22 segments are available, quite complex functions may be represented to an accuracy of 1 per cent, or better.

A very simple scheme is available to apply smoothing to the output of a diode function generator and thus to produce rounded corners

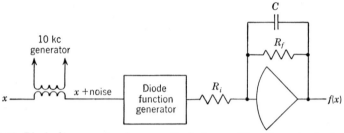

FIG. 8-13. Block diagram showing a method of smoothing the output of a diode function generator.

rather than abrupt changes of slope in the generated function.[8]   Figure 8-13 illustrates the scheme.

A high-frequency noise signal is introduced into the input signal x. The presence of the noise signal causes the diode associated with each break point to start conducting intermittently before the break point is actually reached. As the input approaches closer to the break point, the diode conducts a greater percentage of the time. A small condenser in the feedback path of the output amplifier serves as a filter to average the voltage produced by the intermittent conduction of the diode. The resulting function $f(x)$ has rounded corners rather than points of discontinuity of slope. Figure 8-14 shows the effect of applying noise to the input of a diode.

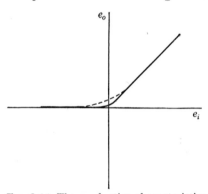

FIG. 8-14. The conduction characteristics of a diode. The solid line shows the conduction characteristic for a *clean* input signal. The dashed line shows the filtered output when noise is present on the input.

A triangular noise signal has been found to be very useful in smoothing the output of a diode function generator, as it gives a predictable smoothing effect.   The use of a triangular-waveform noise signal gives approximately parabolic corners.

In fitting curves when using smoothing it is necessary to choose the break points outside the curve to achieve the best results. A little experience will allow the computer operator to achieve excellent function representation using this scheme.

8-10. Tapped Potentiometers. Tapped potentiometers have frequently been used as function-generating equipment. The principle of operation is illustrated in Fig. 8-15. Other circuit arrangements are in common use, and though superior from the standpoint of requiring less current from the power supply and being self-protected from burning out the main potentiometer, they are less flexible in operation than the circuit shown here.

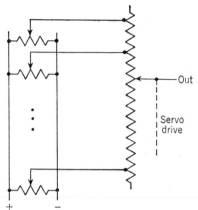

In Fig. 8-15 the main potentiometer may be either a single-turn or helical-type potentiometer with as many as 40 taps. A voltage is connected to each of the taps from low-accuracy calibration potentiometers. The wiper of the tapped potentiometer is driven proportional to the argument x, and the output varies according to the voltages set at each tap. In this

FIG. 8-15. Tapped-potentiometer arbitrary-function generator.

manner a function is represented by as many as 39 straight-line segments.

The earlier models of the tapped-potentiometer function generators had one very important drawback. Although the cost was low, the reliability excellent, and the fidelity of reproduction good, the time required to set up a function was excessive. This one feature limited the usefulness of the devices.

The excessive setup time was due to the interaction between the voltages applied to the individual taps. As the voltage at each tap of the potentiometer was adjusted, it affected the value at every other tap. It was, therefore, necessary to adjust each potentiometer several times in order to arrive at a satisfactory representation of the desired function. Experience in using the device shortened the setup time, however, as the operator learned to compensate for the calibration-potentiometer interaction effect and thus was able to reduce the number of trial adjustments.

Electronic Associates Incorporated contributed considerably toward the usefulness of tapped-potentiometer function generators when they developed a calibration scheme that does away with the interaction between taps during calibration.   This scheme is shown schematically in Fig. 8-16.

The potentiometers provided in the Electronics Associates function generator have 17 taps and, thereby, can represent a function by 16

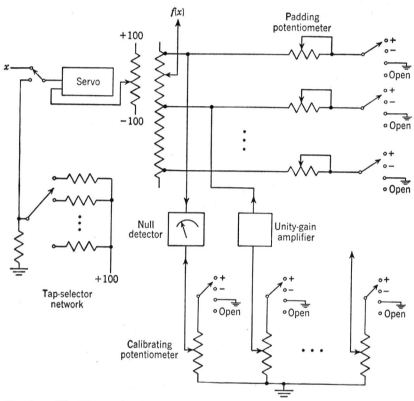

FIG. 8-16. The Electronics Associates, Inc., scheme for setting tapped potentiometers.

straight-line segments.   To each tap of the tapped potentiometer is connected a padding potentiometer controlled by a switch; it is connected to the positive or negative reference voltage, connected to ground, or left open depending upon the switch position.   By varying the resistance in series with each tap, it is, therefore, possible to provide any desired voltage at each tap.

In adjusting the function generator, the desired voltages for each tap are first set on 17 precision potentiometers provided on the control panel.   The particular tap being adjusted is then compared, by means of a null meter, with the voltage previously set on the corresponding precision potentiometer.

To prevent interaction of the taps, the tap voltages are adjusted in sequence starting with the first tap. As indicated in Fig. 8-16, the next tap in the sequence is fed its true tap voltage during the adjustment of the preceding tap. This is accomplished by feeding the voltage from the precision potentiometer through an isolation amplifier of unity gain. Since the isolation amplifier has an output impedance of approximately zero, the tap that it feeds is forcibly held at the proper voltage, thus providing the proper load on the tap being set.

A multiposition switch is provided that allows the convenient selection of the tap that is to be set and also positions the servo so that the wiper of the tapped potentiometer is positioned to the tap that is being set.

The tapped potentiometer is very well suited to the generation of standard functions such as sines, cosines, and exponentials. For these functions, the adjusting potentiometers can be replaced by fixed resistors. A suitable plug-in device then allows the function generated by the tapped potentiometer to be changed by changing a plug-in unit containing the calibrated resistors.

8-11. Resistive Materials as Function Generators. A means of generating arbitrary functions that has recently been exploited is the use of resistive materials. By means of these materials it is possible to represent two-dimensional field effects. The description of a particular problem that has been solved by the method will make clear the techniques involved.

Example 8-1. It is necessary to determine the heat distribution required to de-ice a radome under varying atmospheric conditions   The basic problem is, therefore, to determine the distribution of water droplets striking the radome in a region of precipitation. It is assumed that the radome is symmetrical and that only two-dimensional effects need be represented. The geometry of the problem can, therefore, be represented as in Fig. 8-17. Because of the symmetry, only one-half the radome need be shown, and since icing occurs only at the leading edge, the rear section may be omitted. In the diagram, u_x and u_y are the x and y components of the velocity distribution of the air flow and v_x and v_y are the corresponding components of the velocity of the water droplet. The velocity of the water particle is a function of its mass and the aerodynamic forces acting upon it. From the geometry it is apparent that

$$v_x = f(u_x) \qquad \text{and} \qquad v_y = f(u_y) \tag{8-18}$$

If the velocity distribution of the air around the body is adequately represented in such a manner that the data can be introduced into the computer, it is then a relatively easy task for the computer to calculate the x and y position of the water particle with respect to time. A plotting board is then used to plot the droplet trajectories for various initial distances $y(0)$ from the center line. After plotting families of trajectories for various-sized particles, the icing distribution is determined from statistical studies of droplet size normally encountered under various atmospheric conditions.

The technique of representing the velocity distribution of the air flow around the object is the main point of interest in this discussion. A direct analogy exists between the two-dimensional velocity distribution of the airflow around an object and the potential distribution in a resistive medium of the proper shape. If conducting strips at potential P_1 and P_2 are placed at the ends of the resistive material, lines of constant potential gradient along the resistive material correspond to the

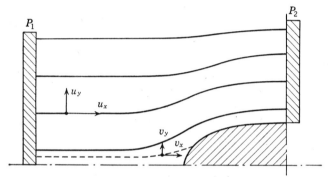

FIG. 8-17. Water-droplet trajectories.

aerodynamic streamlines. A three-pointed probe contacting the resistive material then picks up voltages proportional to u_x and u_y if one pair of contacts, the reference probe and a second probe, are oriented along the x axis and the reference probe and third probe are oriented along the y axis. It is these voltages, u_x and u_y, that are fed to the computer in order to calculate the x and y positions of the water droplet as a function of time.

Early attempts at solving the problem using a solid resistive material were relatively unsatisfactory. The methods of preparing the material were time-consuming, but even more important were the other obstacles encountered. To ensure the safety of laboratory personnel, it was deemed inadvisable to apply a potential difference much in excess of 100 volts across P_1 and P_2. Also, for good accuracy, it was necessary to keep the spacing of the probes small. The result was that only a few millivolts were available at the probes. A very high gain was, therefore, necessary in introducing the signal into the computer. Contact troubles were encountered at the probes, and this together with the high gain required made the system impractical because of the high noise level in the problem.

The use of an electrolytic tank was found to give more satisfactory results. Here, however, d-c voltages had to be abandoned because of polarization effects. It was found to be satisfactory to modulate the voltage applied to the ends of the tank at P_1 and P_2 by means of a commutator and demodulate the resulting probe signals by the same commutator after passing the signals through a-c amplifiers. Good results were obtained by this method.

One point should be kept in mind in designing a system of this type. The orientation of the probes is a very critical factor in the accurate solution of a problem.   The probes should be designed so that they may be adjusted accurately to the proper alignment.   The actual adjustment of the probes in the example discussed here is easily accomplished by moving the probe to a region of constant potential distribution along the y axis (such a region is found near the conductor P_1) and adjusting the probes until u_x is maximum and u_y is zero.

A class of arbitrary functions that are easily generated by using solid resistive materials are those functions of two variables that are represented by n parameter families.   The generation of functions of this class is simpler than is the generation of the velocity gradient described previously in this section. In the generation of functions described by n parameter families, it is not necessary to determine the gradient of the function but only the value of the function itself as determined by two dependent variables of the problem.

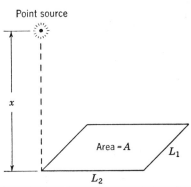

Fig. 8-18. Radiation between a point source and a surface A.

In order to illustrate the techniques of generating arbitrary functions of two variables, a hypothetical problem involving radiant-energy transmission will be considered.

As a portion of a problem it is necessary to determine the net amount of radiant energy received at a rectangular surface of area A from a point source located at a distance x from the surface.   In the problem to be considered, the distance x varies in an arbitrary manner.   A further requirement of the problem is that the point source is located along a line normal to the surface and passing through one corner of the surface.   The geometrical configuration is illustrated in Fig. 8-18.

In the figure L_1 and L_2 are the lengths of the sides of the rectangle of area A.   The *geometrical factor* F is that fractional part of the radiant energy that strikes the area.   Figure 8-19 is a plot of the geometrical factor F as a function of x/L_2 and x/L_1.

In order to generate a function such as is described in Fig. 8-19, it is necessary to generate a voltage proportional to the geometrical factor F.   One medium that has been successfully used in the generation of functions of this type is a resistive material in the form of a thin uniform layer on glass or other nonconducting material.   Lines of constant F are drawn on the resistive plate corresponding to the lines of constant F shown in Fig. 8-19.   These lines are drawn with a conducting material such as silver paint. Each of the conducting lines is connected to a voltage source adjusted to the proper potential corresponding to the particular value of F to be represented by that line.

A servo-driven plotting board is usually used as the positioning device to position a pickup probe on the resistive material. The pickup probe replaces the writing pen, and voltages proportional to x/L_2 and x/L_1 are applied to the servo to drive the probe to the proper position. The probe then picks up a voltage approximately proportional to the proper value of F, as the resistive material provides

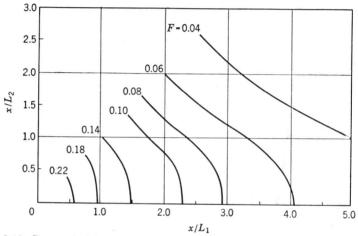

Fig. 8-19. Geometrical factor F for direct radiation between a point source and a rectangular area.

approximately linear interpolation between the lines of constant potential.

The most common material used in the preparation of the resistive plates is a carbon suspension in lacquer. Normally spray-gun application of the material to the glass or plastic plate gives satisfactory results if care is taken to get uniform coverage.

A second method of generating functions of two variables is by the use of a tapped potentiometer similar to those described in Sec. 8-10. This method of generating functions of two variables was perhaps the first method to be used for this purpose at an analog-computer installation, and it was described by Mengel and Melahn[9] in 1950.

Figure 8-20 illustrates the technique of generating a function of two variables, using a tapped potentiometer. A family of curves, say $\phi(x,y_1)$, $\phi(x,y_2)$, . . . , $\phi(x,y_n)$, are generated simultaneously for particular values of the argument y_i where i varies from 1 to n. Each of the $\phi(x,y_i)$ is connected to a tap of a tapped potentiometer. The tapped potentiometer is then positioned proportional to the variable y, and the potential at the potentiometer wiper is the value obtained by linear interpolation between the functions $\phi(y_i)$ and $\phi(y_{i+1})$ where $y_i < y < y_{i+1}$.

The values of y_i at which the functions $\phi(x,y_i)$ are generated (see Fig. 8-21) cannot be chosen in a random manner. The values of

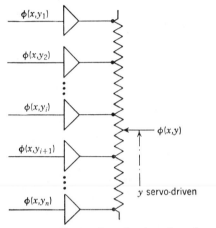

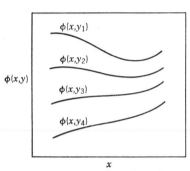

FIG. 8-20. Generation of a function of two variables by using a tapped potentiometer.

FIG. 8-21. Typical function of two variables that can be generated by using a tapped potentiometer.

y_i must be chosen to coincide with the location of the taps on the tapped potentiometer.

The manner of generation of the functions $\phi(x,y_i)$ is relatively unimportant. Any of the function-generating equipment previously described in this chapter can be used for this purpose. It should be pointed out, however, that each of the $\phi(x,y_i)$ must be generated simultaneously when using a tapped potentiometer to generate a function of two variables. For this reason the method is practical only for those functions $\phi(x,y)$ that can be adequately represented by, at most, three or four curves $\phi(x,y_i)$.

8-12. Conclusions. Although many types of function-generating equipment are in use or have been proposed, none of the devices constructed to date is perfect in all respects. There is still a wide-open field for the development of better function-generating equipment. Among the techniques of function generation that need further investigation are magnetic-tape or magnetic-drum recordings. Too little work has been done toward adapting these devices to analog-computer use to date.

In selecting the most desirable function-generating equipment for a particular computer installation, the type of problems to be encountered should be considered. It may be helpful, however, to list some of the more desirable characteristics of function-generating equipment. These are:

1. A high degree of repeatability
2. Good fidelity of representation of functions
3. The ability to represent rapid changes in the function
4. Good frequency response
5. Ease of setup
6. Ease of maintenance

No one function generator will rate as best in regard to all these characteristics. A compromise must be made in choosing any particular function generator.

PROBLEMS

8-1. Draw the circuit diagram for a division circuit using an electronic multiplier.

8-2. Draw the circuit diagram for a square-root circuit using an electronic multiplier.

8-3. Describe how you could generate the cube root of a function using an arbitrary-function-generating device.

8-4. Describe the generation of the function $\sin^{-1} \theta$ using an arbitrary-function generator if $\sin \theta$ is available in the computer setup of a problem.

8-5. The equations for the coefficients of the Fourier-series expansion of a function $f(t)$ are

$$a_n = \frac{1}{p} \int_d^{d+2p} f(t) \cos \frac{n\pi t}{p} \, dt$$

$$b_n = \frac{1}{p} \int_d^{d+2p} f(t) \sin \frac{n\pi t}{p} \, dt$$

where $2p$ is the interval over which the function is to be expanded. If a graphical plot of $f(t)$ is available, show a computer setup to determine the Fourier coefficients a_n and b_n.

REFERENCES

1. Morrill, C. D., and R. V. Baum: A Stabilized Electronic Multiplier, *Trans. IRE* (*Professional Group on Electronic Computers*), December, 1952, pp. 52–59.
2. Baum, R. V., and C. D. Morrill: A Time-division Multiplier for a General Purpose Electronic Differential Analyzer, paper presented at the convention of the IRE, New York, 1951, GER-2939, Goodyear Aircraft Corporation, Akron, Ohio, Dec. 5, 1951.
3. Goldberg, Edwin A.: Stabilization of Wide-band Direct Current Amplifiers for Zero and Gain, *RCA Rev.*, vol. 11, no. 2, pp. 296–300, June, 1950.

4. Ingerson, W. E.: Drift Compensation in D-C Amplifiers for Analog Computers, paper presented at the convention of the IRE, New York, 1951.

5. Macnee, A. B.: An Electronic Differential Analyzer, *Proc. IRE*, vol. 37, p. 1315, 1949.

6. Sunstein, D. E.: Photoelectric Waveform Generator, *Electronics*, vol. 22, part 1, p. 100, 1949.

7. Hussey, J. L., H. Martinez, and A. E. Young, Jr.: "Berkeley Electronic Analog Simulating Equipment," Berkeley Division of Beckman Instruments, Inc., Richmond, Calif., Jan. 10, 1954.

8. Stone, J. J., Jr.: Smooth-curve Function Generation Using Diodes, *IRE Airborne Electronics Digest*, 1954.

9. Mengel, A. S., and W. S. Melahn: "RAND REAC Manual, RM-525," pp. 94–98, The RAND Corporation, Santa Monica, Calif., Dec. 1, 1950.

CHAPTER 9

MISCELLANEOUS APPLICATIONS OF THE
ELECTRONIC ANALOG COMPUTER

9-1. Introduction. The electronic analog computer has proved itself a very powerful tool in the solution of ordinary differential equations. The question naturally arises, "Are there other problems that can adequately be handled on the analog computer?" The answer is, of course, "Yes, but not with as straightforward techniques as are applied in the solution of ordinary differential equations."

A partial list of problems solvable on the electronic analog computer includes simultaneous algebraic equations, partial differential equations, curve-fitting problems, and the determination of the roots of polynomial equations. It will be the purpose of this chapter to summarize some of the methods that have been found useful in the solution of problems in these categories.

9-2. Simultaneous Algebraic Equations. The labor involved in the manual solution of higher-order systems of algebraic equations led engineers to attempt the solution of such systems on analog computers. The most straightforward technique for the setup of linear algebraic equations on an analog computer is to transform the set of simultaneous algebraic equations into a set of linear differential equations having, as a steady-state solution, the solution of the original algebraic equations.

A set of simultaneous linear algebraic equations has the form

$$a_{11}x_1 + a_{12}x_2 + \cdots + a_{1i}x_i + \cdots + a_{1n}x_n + b_1 = 0$$

$$a_{i1}x_1 + a_{i2}x_2 + \cdots + a_{ii}x_i + \cdots + a_{in}x_n + b_i = 0 \quad (9\text{-}1)$$

$$a_{n1}x_1 + a_{n2}x_2 + \cdots + a_{ni}x_i + \cdots + a_{nn}x_n + b_n = 0$$

The differential equations for the analog-computer solution of Eqs. 9-1 are formed by equating each of the n equations to the time derivative of the variable x_i, where $1 \leq i \leq n$ in Eqs. 9-1. The resulting system of differential equations is

$$a_{11}x_1 + a_{12}x_2 + \cdots + a_{1i}x_i + \cdots + a_{1n}x_n + b_1 = -\frac{dx_1}{dt}$$

$$a_{i1}x_1 + a_{i2}x_2 + \cdots + a_{ii}x_i + \cdots + a_{in}x_n + b_i = -\frac{dx_i}{dt} \quad (9\text{-}2)$$

$$a_{n1}x_1 + a_{n2}x_2 + \cdots + a_{ni}x_i + \cdots + a_{nn}x_n + b_n = -\frac{dx_n}{dt}$$

If the computer solution of Eqs. 9-2 is stable, the steady-state values of the computer variables $x_1, \ldots, x_n$ are the solution of Eqs. 9-1, since in the steady state all the derivatives in Eqs. 9-2 are equal to zero. The odds are very great, however, that the solution will not be stable. More specifically, instability will result if the real part of the roots of the characteristic equation of Eqs. 9-2 are not all negative. If instability results, the equations can always be manipulated to obtain a form giving stability,[1] but the amount of labor involved in the manipulation of the equations can be very great. In fact, the labor required to ensure computer stability can be almost as great as that required to solve the algebraic system on a desk calculator by the best available techniques.[2]

A method of setup of algebraic equations that ensures computer stability without algebraic manipulation of the system does exist. The method is described in detail by Gephart[3] and has been applied at the computation section of the Aeronautical Research Laboratory at Wright-Patterson Air Force Base, Ohio. The method is far from perfect, though, as excessive equipment is required in the setup. In general, it required $2n$ potentiometers to adjust the coefficients of the problem, where n is the number of parameters in the algebraic system. Gephart's method ensures stability of the computer solution; however, the accuracy obtainable in using the scheme is to a great extent determined by the system of equations being solved. No attempt will be made here to describe the method in detail; the interested reader will find an adequate description in Gephart's work.[3]

From the experience the author has had in attempting to solve systems of algebraic equations on the electronic analog computer, he strongly recommends against the use of the analog computer for the solution of algebraic equations. Computers such as IBM card-punch machines and other digital devices are very well suited to the solution of simultaneous linear algebraic equations. Indeed, the desk calculator shows up well in comparison with the analog computer for the solution of algebraic equations.

9-3. Partial Differential Equations—Introduction. More success has been encountered in the solution of partial differential equations on an analog computer than in the solution of simultaneous algebraic equations. Here a direct approach to the problem is impossible, as the analog computer is restricted to integrations with respect to one independent variable. In solving systems of partial differential equations, some method must be utilized that will transform the partial differential equations into ordinary differential equations. Two schemes are commonly used: (1) the formation of an eigenvalue problem by the method of separation of variables, and (2) the application of difference techniques to form a *difference-differential equation*. The two techniques will be discussed in some detail in subsequent sections.

9-4. The Solution of Eigenvalue Problems. Frequently linear partial differential equations can be readily reduced to a set of ordinary differential equations of the eigenvalue type by the method of separation of variables. In turn, many eigenvalue problems can be readily solved on the electronic analog computer.

The ordinary differential equations arising from partial differential equations by the applications of the method of separation of variables have both initial and final conditions to be satisfied, rather than initial conditions alone. It is necessary, in the solution of the problems, to determine the eigenvalues, or the characteristic numbers, that permit the end conditions of the problems to be satisfied. The solution of the eigenvalue problem for a particular eigenvalue is termed the *eigenfunction* and is a normal mode of the solution of the partial differential equation from which the eigenvalue problem is derived. The solution of the partial differential equation is formed as a series approximation by the proper combination of the eigenfunctions.

Since the solution of partial differential equations by the method of separation of variables leads to a series-type approximation, it may seem to the reader that the method is quite tedious and of little value. It is very true that the solution is considerably more tedious than the solution of ordinary differential equations on the analog computer, yet there are many partial differential equation problems for which the method of separation of variables, when applied to the computer solution of the problems, proves very useful.

Frequently the analog-computer solution of differential equations involving eigenvalues is practical when it is not practical or possible to solve the systems by analytical means. Conditions that make analytic solution of eigenvalue problems either difficult or impossible are:

1. The high order of the equations
2. The presence of variable coefficients
3. The number of solutions desired for different parameters of the problem

There are several types of eigenvalue problems for which the feasibility of analog-computer solution has been investigated,[4] and these are:

1. Second-order equations with simple homogeneous boundary conditions
2. Complex second-order equations with integral boundary conditions
3. Fourth-order equations with simple homogeneous boundary conditions
4. Eigenvalue problems involving a semi-infinite range of the independent variable

Of these four forms of eigenvalue problems, the first three can usually be solved on the analog computer with little difficulty. The fourth type, problems involving a semi-infinite range of the independent variable, can be handled if an analytic asymptotic solution of the problem is available or if, as sometimes happens, the problem solution approaches its boundary values rapidly even though the range of integration is from zero to infinity. The discussion given below will make clear the limitations of the method of separation of variables for problems in these categories.

The determination of the eigenvalues of a problem on an analog computer is necessarily a process of trial and error. There are always present both initial and final values to be satisfied. The operator has direct control of the initial conditions of the problem but has only indirect control of the problem end conditions. This indirect control is by means of varying the eigenvalues of the problem until a particular set of values of the characteristic numbers is found that causes the end conditions to be satisfied. The process is very simple when only one parameter in the system must be varied in order to satisfy the boundary conditions of the problem. If two parameters must be varied simultaneously to satisfy the problem end conditions, a scheme can usually be found that will permit a rapid determination of the value of the characteristic numbers that will produce a solution.   If three parameters must be determined simultaneously, the end conditions can be determined only with great difficulty, if at all, and with a large expenditure of time.   If four or more parameters or eigenvalues must be varied simultaneously in order to satisfy the boundary or end conditions of the problem, then the task is completely hopeless for the machine operator.   A brief discussion of the four classifications of problems listed above as solvable on the electronic analog computer will enable the reader to visualize the difficulties encountered in the solution of each class of problems.

A second-order equation with simple homogeneous boundary conditions usually has one boundary condition to be satisfied at each end of the interval of integration.   Correspondingly, there is only one eigenvalue or characteristic number to be varied in order to cause the final value of the problem to be satisfied.   The operator can set the initial condition on the computer and can directly see the effect on the problem solution of varying the characteristic number of the eigenvalue problem.   Similarly, a fourth-order eigenvalue problem having simple homogeneous boundary values has two boundary conditions specified at each end of the interval of convergence.   Two problem parameters must then be varied in the system to obtain convergence.   One of these is usually the eigenvalue, and the second is frequently an unspecified initial condition.   Here success of solution can usually be obtained.

If the dependent variable of an eigenvalue problem is a complex function, the number of initial conditions and end conditions in the problem is doubled over the case of a real dependent variable in the problem.   For this reason, a complex second-order eigenvalue problem offers approximately the same order of difficulty in solution on the analog computer as does the fourth-order equation with simple homogeneous boundary values.

The accuracy of solution of eigenvalue problems and the amount of labor required to attain the problem solutions differ widely, depending upon the information that is needed in the problem solution.   The differences of labor that can exist in the solution of eigenvalue problems can be illustrated by pointing out that in many problems only the eigenvalues, or characteristic numbers that allow the boundary conditions to be satisfied, are of interest.   Examples of this type are frequently encountered in vibration and stability studies.   Information as to whether a motion will grow or decay with time is available from the eigenvalues without obtaining the series solution of the partial differential equation. Fortunately also, the first few modes of the vibration are usually the most interesting, so that the characteristic numbers of only a few eigenfunctions need be found.

In other problems it is necessary to determine the series solution of the partial differential equation representing the problem. In these problems, it is necessary that the eigenfunctions or normal modes of the problem be recorded and later combined to form the problem solution. Theoretically, there are an infinite number of normal modes in the solution of a problem. Frequently, however, sufficiently accurate results can be obtained by combining only a few of the normal modes. In general, it is not possible to determine a large number of normal modes on the analog computer, since large values of the characteristic numbers on the computer correspond to marginal computer operation, because of high gains in the computer setup and correspondingly high frequencies in the eigenfunctions. In many problems, an asymptotic solution does exist that will accurately determine the higher normal modes in the problem solution. In these cases the analog computer can be utilized to determine the first few modes of the solution, and these results together with the asymptotic solutions of the higher modes permit a complete determination of the problem. One interesting use that can be made of the analog computer is to determine for which modes of a problem an asymptotic solution of the problem is valid.

No attempt will be made herein to treat the method of separation of variables in any detail. The method is adequately treated in any number of texts concerning themselves with the solution of partial differential equations.[5-7] Similarly, no specific examples of eigenvalue problems will be carried out in this work. The technique of problem setup is very simple once the partial differential equation has been reduced to a form involving only total differential equations. Several illustrative examples of the solution of eigenvalue problems are given in the literature.[4] Also included in the literature are the comparisons of computer results to analytic results obtained for these problems.

9-5. Replacing Partial Derivatives by Finite Differences. Obtaining a series solution of partial differential equations by the method of separation of variables is a fairly effective means of solving partial differential equations on an analog computer. This approach is somewhat tedious, though, and a more direct approach offers some advantage in the solution of some problems. Such an approach has been effectively used and involves the substitution of finite differences for some of the partial derivatives in the problems.[8] The difference-differential equations obtained by replacing some of the partial derivatives by finite differences in the problems are then solvable on the analog computer.

The methods of expressing derivatives in terms of finite differences are very well described in books on the subject of numerical analysis.[9] The expressions for the representation of differentials as finite differences will therefore be stated here without proof.

Assume that a dependent variable $y(x,t)$ is a function of distance x and time t. Utilizing the methods of finite differences, instead of measuring y at all distances x, it is expressed only at certain stations along x, say x_0, x_1, . . . , x_n. For convenience, the stations can be chosen at equal increments of x such that the distance between stations is Δx. An approximate expression for the partial derivative at $x = x_{\frac{1}{2}}$ can be written as

$$\left. \frac{\partial y}{\partial x} \right|_{\frac{1}{2}} \cong \frac{y_1 - y_0}{\Delta x} \tag{9-3}$$

The degree of approximation in the above expansion is readily seen to be a function of the incremental size of Δx, as Eq. (9-3) is, in the limit, the definition of the partial derivative with respect to x as $\Delta x \to 0$. Similarly,

$$\left. \frac{\partial y}{\partial x} \right|_{n-\frac{1}{2}} \cong \frac{y_n - y_{n-1}}{\Delta x} \tag{9-4}$$

and the higher derivatives may be expressed as

$$\left. \frac{\partial^2 y}{\partial x^2} \right|_n = \frac{y_{n+1} - 2y_n + y_{n-1}}{(\Delta x)^2} \tag{9-5}$$

$$\left. \frac{\partial^3 y}{\partial x^3} \right|_{n-\frac{1}{2}} = \frac{y_{n+1} - 3y_n + 3y_{n-1} - y_{n-2}}{(\Delta x)^3} \tag{9-6}$$

$$\left. \frac{\partial^4 y}{\partial x^4} \right|_n = \frac{y_{n+2} - 4y_{n+1} + 6y_n - 4y_{n-1} + y_{n-2}}{(\Delta x)^4} \tag{9-7}$$

Equations (9-4) to (9-7) can be used to replace the corresponding partial derivatives in a system of partial differential equations. In this manner a partial differential equation expressed as a function of distance x and time t can be reduced to a system of ordinary differential equations with time as the independent variable.

For systems restricted to one spatial degree of freedom $y(x,t)$, the partial differential equation will reduce to a system of equations $y_1(t)$, $y_2(t)$, . . . , $y_n(t)$. The initial conditions of each equation $y_1(t)$, . . . , $y_n(t)$ must be specified and are usually known from the physical problem. In order to clarify the application of this technique the setup of the problem of a vibrating string will be demonstrated.   The problem is as specified in Fig. 9-1.   For simplicity, the vibration is restricted

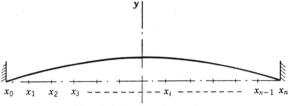

FIG. 9-1. A vibrating string.

to motions along the y direction.   Clearly, the displacement y is a function of x and t.   The equation of motion of the system is

$$a \frac{\partial^2 y}{\partial x^2} = \frac{\partial^2 y}{\partial t^2} \qquad (9\text{-}8)$$

where
$$a = \frac{Tg}{W(x)} \qquad (9\text{-}9)$$

T = tension in string
g = gravity
W = weight of string per unit length

Substituting the value of $\partial^2 y/\partial x^2$ from Eq. (9-5) into Eq. (9-8) gives the differential equation of motion of the point y_i

$$\frac{a_i}{\Delta x^2} (y_{i+1} - 2y_i + y_{i-1}) = \frac{d^2 y_i}{dt^2} \qquad (9\text{-}10)$$

The equations of all interior points have this same form; however, application of the boundary conditions of the problem simplifies the equations of points x_1 and x_{n-1}.   In the problem being considered, both ends of the string are fixed, and therefore the value of y_0 and y_n must be zero at all times.   Applying the end conditions, Eq. (9-8) becomes

$$\frac{a_1}{\Delta x^2} (y_2 - 2y_1) = \frac{d^2 y_1}{dt^2} \qquad (9\text{-}11)$$

and
$$\frac{a_{n-1}}{\Delta x^2} (-2y_{n-1} + y_{n-2}) = \frac{d^2 y_{n-1}}{dt^2} \qquad (9\text{-}12)$$

at stations x_1 and x_{n-1}, respectively.   The circuit diagram of the system can now be prepared from Eqs. (9-10) to (9-12) and is given in general form in Fig. 9-2.

In this problem, if a is constant over the entire length of the string and if the initial displacement of the string is symmetrical, the problem setup can be simplified by considering only those stations to the left or right of the mid-point. The representation of partial differential equations by difference techniques uses a large number of computing amplifiers; thus, all problems should be very carefully checked for symmetry to reduce the size of the computer setup, if possible.

The evaluation of initial conditions at each station of the problem can be a considerable task in some problems. Suppose forces are

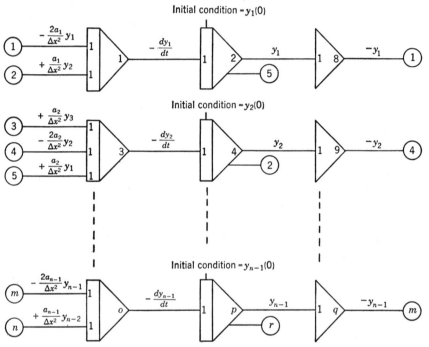

FIG. 9-2. General form of the setup for the simple vibrating-string problem.

applied to various stations along the string and suddenly the forces are released at $t = 0$. For this form of excitation, it is necessary to determine the initial displacements from the force distribution. This may be done analytically in many problems; however, much time can usually be saved by making the determination on the computer. To determine the initial conditions, it is necessary to apply forces to each station corresponding to the conditions at $t = 0$ and adjust the initial displacements until the problem remains in a quiescent state when the computer is placed in operation. This trial-and-error adjustment compares closely to Southwell's relaxation method,[10] used extensively in the numerical solution of partial differential equations.

The technique of replacing some of the partial derivatives of a problem with difference equations has been demonstrated here for a problem having a single spatial degree of freedom. The principle of replacing partial differences with finite differences applies equally well to systems having two or three spatial degrees of freedom. The only complication that arises in the solution of problems having two and three spatial degrees of freedom is the size of the computer setup. For problems having two and three spatial degrees of freedom, the computer setup increases in size approximately as the power of the number of degrees of freedom, as a differential equation must be solved at each point in a lattice formed by replacing the partial derivatives by finite differences at increments in x, y, and z.

The University of Michigan is presently designing an analog computer with a large number of amplifiers specially for the purpose of carrying out an investigation of the solution of partial differential equations of types that are impossible to solve on their existing equipment.

For additional examples of problems involving partial differential equations which have been solved on the computer and a treatment of the accuracy obtained, the reader is referred to an article by Howe and Haneman.[8]

9-6. Computers as Curve-fitting Devices. Occasionally there arises a need for determining the coefficients of a system of differential equations whose response is known. Such a requirement frequently arises in the field of aerodynamics and particularly in the analysis of flight-test data for aircraft and for guided missiles. The general form of the aerodynamic equations is known in these applications; however, the magnitudes of the aerodynamic coefficients are only approximately determined from the design configuration of the vehicle. Flight-test data from experimental models provide exact response characteristics from which modifications of the aircraft or missile may be specified or auxiliary equipment such as autopilots may be precisely designed for optimum performance. In order to make the desired system studies on an analog computer, it is necessary first to obtain the correct aerodynamic coefficients of the problem.

Analytic methods of determining the coefficients of a system of differential equations for which a graphical solution is known are available for linear systems with constant coefficients. The labor involved for higher-order systems becomes very great, however, and if non-linearities are introduced, the methods become useless. Analog computers have been found very valuable as an aid in the solution of this type of problem.[11]

In determining the coefficients of a system of differential equations, the general form of the problem is set up on the computer using the best available estimate of the aerodynamic coefficients. The best operating procedure seems to be to investigate first the effect of each coefficient of the problem on the system response. After becoming familiar with the effectiveness of each parameter, it is then possible for the computer operator to vary the coefficients systematically, to produce a reasonably good fit of the curves obtained from the experimental data. A large plotting board is a helpful device in accomplishing the curve-fitting job, as the desired response may be plotted on a graph sheet and covered with a transparent overlay or tissue that may be discarded upon becoming cluttered with trial solutions.

Another technique of curve matching that has been found useful makes use of an automatic function generator. The curve that is to be matched is generated on the function generator. An error signal is then obtained by subtracting the voltage representing the desired function from the computer results. This form of representation allows the application of curve-fitting criteria such as the method of least squares. A curve-fitting criterion similar to the method of least squares but better adapted to use on an analog computer is the integral of the absolute value of the error. In applying this error criterion, the difference between the desired and trial curves is rectified by using diodes and the resulting voltage is integrated. Adjustment of the fit is then made until the output of the integrator is a minimum. The method minimizes the area between the two curves and provides a very good means of determining a best fit.

The ability to fit experimental data on an analog computer has opened a large field of application for analog computers. An autopilot or other automatic control system can be evaluated and adjusted by coupling it to a computer almost as exactly as can be accomplished by actual flight test. The computer can be used in all phases of the system development. In early stages the entire system usually is simulated mathematically, while in the later stages of development actual hardware is sometimes introduced into the setup to determine more exactly the system response. Tremendous saving of time and money has been realized in recent years by the application of these techniques.

9-7. The Roots of Polynomial Equations. A class of problems that can be solved on an analog computer is the determination of the roots of polynomial equations. These problems are important in many fields of application and in particular in the evaluation of servomechanism systems by classical methods.

In the past, little use has been made of the analog computer for the determination of the roots of polynomials. Probably the greatest reason for this lack of use is that the roots of polynomial equations can be very readily determined on digital computers. Also, the use of the analog computer for determining the roots of polynomial equations is impractical if there is only one or just a few polynomials to be solved, because of the computer setup and check-out time required.

In order to understand the method of determining the roots of polynomials on an analog computer, it is necessary to discuss the nature of polynomial equations and also to introduce Nyquist's criterion to the reader.

Consider the polynomial

$$W(z) = a_0 + a_1 z + a_2 z^2 + \cdots + a_n z^n \qquad (9\text{-}13)$$

where z may be a complex quantity of the form

$$z = re^{j\theta} = r(\cos\theta + j\sin\theta) \qquad (9\text{-}14)$$

and where the a's similarly may be complex quantities of the form

$$a_i = ce^{j\theta_i} \qquad (9\text{-}15)$$

From Eq. (9-14) it follows directly that the powers of z in the polynomial W can be expressed as

$$z^2 = r^2 e^{j2\theta} = r^2(\cos 2\theta + j\sin 2\theta)$$
$$z^n = r^n e^{jn\theta} = r^n(\cos n\theta + j\sin n\theta) \qquad (9\text{-}16)$$

Substituting Eqs. (9-14) and (9-16) into Eq. (9-13) gives a new expression for the polynomial W:

$$W(z) = a_0 + a_1 r(\cos\theta + j\sin\theta) + a_2 r^2(\cos 2\theta + j\sin 2\theta)$$
$$+ \cdots + a_n r^n(\cos n\theta + j\sin n\theta) \quad (9\text{-}17)$$

Collecting the real and imaginary terms of Eq. (9-17) gives the expression

$$W(z) = a_0 + a_1 r \cos\theta + a_2 r^2 \cos 2\theta + \cdots + a_n r^n \cos n\theta$$
$$+ j(a_1 r \sin\theta + a_2 r^2 \sin 2\theta + \cdots + a_n r^n \sin n\theta) \quad (9\text{-}18)$$

or
$$W(z) = \text{Re } W + \text{Im } W \qquad (9\text{-}19)$$

where Re W signifies the real part of the polynomial W and Im W signifies the imaginary part of W.

In order to determine the roots of a polynomial it is necessary to determine the value of z that causes both the real and imaginary parts of the polynomial to vanish simultaneously. It is readily apparent that, if Eq. (9-18) is set up on the analog computer and Re W is plotted against Im W on a plotting board, it will be obvious when a zero of the polynomial has been found.

In order to understand the method of systematically determining the zeros of the polynomial, it is necessary that the reader be familiar with Nyquist's criterion, which states, in part, that the number of net encirclements of the origin in the W plane equals the number of zeros encircled by a closed path in the z plane minus the number of poles encircled in the z plane. Since there can be no poles in a polynomial equation, the statement of Nyquist criterion reduces to a simple statement concerning the number of roots in a given region and the number of encirclements of the origin in the plane of the polynomial.

In order to prove the portion of Nyquist's criterion with which this section is concerned, consider the polynomial in z:

$$W(z) = a_n z^n + a_{n-1} z^{n-1} + \cdots + a_0 \qquad (9\text{-}20)$$

If $z_1, z_2, \ldots, z_n$ are the roots of Eq. (9-20), then the equation can be rewritten as

$$W(z) = a_n(z - z_1)(z - z_2)(z - z_3) \cdots (z - z_n) \qquad (9\text{-}21)$$

Figure 9-3 gives a geometrical interpretation of the Nyquist criterion for the polynomial in z expressed in Eq. (9-21).

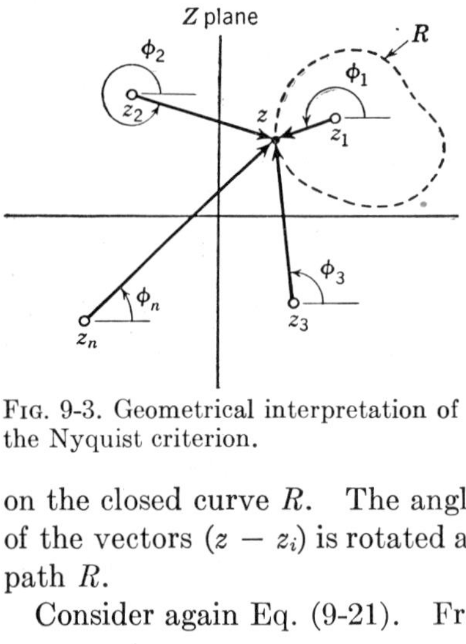

FIG. 9-3. Geometrical interpretation of the Nyquist criterion.

If a closed curve R is drawn in the z plane, it will enclose any number of roots from zero to n. Nyquist's criterion states that the number of encirclements of the origin in the W plane is equal to the number of roots inclosed in the z plane. This can be seen by considering Fig. 9-3. In Fig. 9-3 a vector $(z - z_i)$ is drawn from each of the roots z_i to a point z on the closed curve R. The angle ϕ_i is the angle through which each of the vectors $(z - z_i)$ is rotated as z progresses once around the closed path R.

Consider again Eq. (9-21). From Fig. 9-3 it can be seen that

$$\begin{aligned} (z - z_1) &= L_1 \angle \phi_1 & (z - z_2) &= L_2 \angle \phi_2 \\ (z - z_3) &= L_2 \angle \phi_3 & (z - z_n) &= L_n \angle \phi_n \end{aligned} \qquad (9\text{-}22)$$

Stated in words, each vector drawn from a root of the polynomial to a point z can be expressed as a length L_i and an angle ϕ_i. Substituting

Eqs. (9-22) into Eq. (9-21) gives the expression

$$W(z) = a_n L_1 L_2 L_3 \cdots L_n \angle \phi_1 + \phi_2 + \phi_3 + \cdots + \phi_n \quad (9\text{-}23)$$

From Eq. (9-23) it is readily apparent that the plot of the polynomial in the W plane, as z forms a closed path R, is formed as a vector of magnitude

$$W(z) = a_n L_1 L_2 L_3 \cdots L_n \quad (9\text{-}24)$$

having a phase angle

$$\phi(W) = \phi_1 + \phi_2 + \phi_3 + \cdots + \phi_n \quad (9\text{-}25)$$

Referring again to Fig. 9-3, it is apparent that the net contribution to the total phase shift in the W plane $\phi(W)$ is 2π for those roots enclosed by the curve R and is zero for those roots outside the region formed by R. Thus the number of encirclements of the origin in the W plane is equal to the number of roots encircled by a closed path in the z plane. This statement of Nyquist's criterion gives a very rapid means of determining the region in which the roots of a polynomial lie.

Figure 9-4 shows the computer setup of a fourth-degree polynomial. In the figure the scale factor has been chosen such that 100 volts is equal to 100 $|r|$. The absolute value of r is then restricted to lie in the region $0 \leq |r| \leq 1$. A satisfactory method of procedure in determining the roots is to first set $|r| = 1$ and allow θ to vary through 2π radians. From the plot of W formed as θ varies from zero to 2π, the number of roots in the region $0 \leq |r| \leq 1$ can be determined by the number of encirclements of the origin.

The entire region $|r| < 1$ can thus be rapidly searched for the number of roots known to exist in the region. The real part of the root is $|r|$ and the phase angle of the root is the angle $\omega t = \theta$ that causes both the real and imaginary parts of the polynomial to vanish simultaneously.

After all the roots of the polynomial that lie in the region $0 \leq |r| \leq 1$ have been determined, a simple transformation $u = 1/z$ can be made in the polynomial in z, giving a polynomial in u, $P(u)$. The roots of $W(z)$ lying in the region $r > 1$ can be found by determining the roots of $P(u)$ in the region $0 < |r| < 1$ and inverting these roots. The labor involved in making the substitution $u = 1/z$ to determine $P(u)$ from $W(z)$ is practically negligible, as the new polynomial $P(u)$ has the same coefficients as $W(z)$ except that the coefficients are in reverse order; i.e., the coefficient of the zero-power term in $W(z)$ becomes the coefficient of the highest power of u in the new polynomial $P(u)$, as

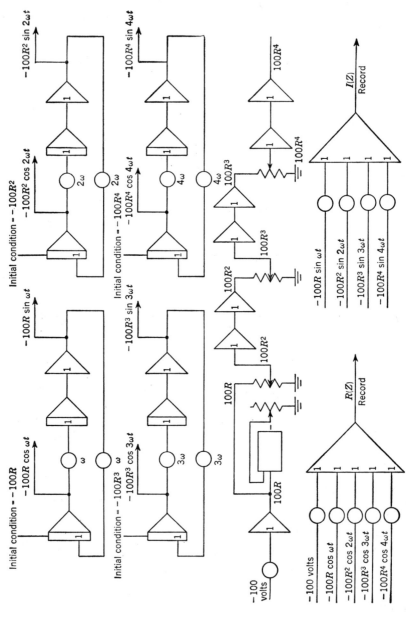

Fig. 9-4. Circuit diagram for determining the roots of a fourth-degree polynomial.

180

illustrated below. Making a substitution $u = 1/z$ in Eq. (9-13) gives

$$W\left(\frac{1}{u}\right) = a_0 + a_1 \frac{1}{u} + a_2 \frac{1}{u^2} + \cdots + a_n \frac{1}{u^n} \qquad (9\text{-}26)$$

Multiplying the equation through by u^n gives

$$P(u) = u^n W\left(\frac{1}{u}\right) = a_0 u^n + a_1 u^{n-1} + \cdots + a_n \qquad (9\text{-}27)$$

If some roots have too small an absolute value of z (or u) to permit accurate evaluation by the methods described above, a substitution of the form $z = ay$ or $u = ax$ can be made to allow those roots to be properly determined.

9-8. Conclusions. In this chapter the solutions of a few problems that do not fit in the category of ordinary differential equations have been discussed. The treatment here has been for the purpose of making the reader aware of some of the efforts that have been made to extend the usefulness of the electronic analog computer. It should be emphasized that the most important applications of such a computer are in the solution of ordinary differential equations and will probably remain there because of the inherent capabilities and limitations of the electronic analog computer.

Many investigators have examined the possibility of utilizing the analog computer in the solution of partial differential equations. Among the most significant research efforts in this field are those conducted at the University of Michigan. The results of a portion of the investigations carried out at the University of Michigan are included in the References,[4,8] together with other articles of significance reporting the results of research in the solution of partial differential equations.[15,16]

Curve-fitting techniques have probably been utilized by every computer installation that concerns itself with the solution of problems involving aerodynamic studies. The techniques of curve fitting described in this chapter were described in a paper by Teague and Gilpin.[11] A curve-fitting technique that is useful in the fitting of an analog-computer solution to data in the form of discrete points is described by Murphy.[12] This technique is highly specialized and will not be discussed further in this book.

The use of the analog computer in the determination of the roots of polynomial equations was first discussed in a paper by Bauer and Fifer[13] of Reeves Instrument Corporation. The origin of the basic method goes back considerably further, however. In 1950 a contract was let by the U.S. Air Force with Reeves Instrument Corporation for the development of a special-purpose analog polynomial evaluator. Prior to this time a prototype of the polynomial evaluator had been constructed by Warshawsky and described in a thesis.[14]   It remained for Bauer and Fifer to recognize the possibility of implementing the scheme on the general-purpose analog computer.

PROBLEMS

9-1. The equation of unidirectional heat flow through a continuous homogeneous medium is

$$\frac{\partial u}{\partial t} = k \frac{\partial^2 u}{\partial x^2}$$

where u = temperature = $u(x,t)$
$\quad t$ = time
$\quad x$ = distance
$\quad k$ = thermal conductivity/(density $\times$ specific heat)
Write the difference-differential equations of heat flow for the temperature distribution in a medium between two infinite slabs.   The slabs are held at temperatures T_1 and T_2, respectively.   Use five points $x_0, x_1, \ldots, x_4$ in representing the partial differential equation as a difference-differential equation.   Assume that at $t = 0$ the temperature throughout the medium is uniform at temperature $u(x,0) = T_3$.

9-2. The function

$$f(x) = 1 \qquad 0 \leq x \leq \pi$$
$$f(x) = -1 \qquad \pi < x \leq 2\pi$$

has a Fourier-series expansion

$$f(x) = \frac{4}{\pi}\left(\sin x + \sin \frac{3x}{3} + \cdots \right)$$

Show a computer setup to plot $f(x)$ using the first three terms of the expansion.

9-3. In determining the roots of the fourth-degree polynomial in z

$$W(z) = z^4 + 1.5z^3 - 0.5z^2 + 0.75z - 0.05$$

by means of the computer setup shown in Fig. 9-4, it is found that a plot of Re z vs. Im z for $|z| = 1$ encircles the origin three times as ωt varies from 0 to 2π.   (a) How many of the roots of the polynomial have magnitudes $[\sqrt{(\text{Re } z)^2 + (\text{Im } z)^2}]$ less than unity?   (b) How many roots have magnitudes greater than unity?   (c) What is the auxiliary polynomial $P(u)$ that must be set up on the computer to determine the magnitude and angle of the roots of $P(z)$ that are outside the unit circle?   (d) If it is determined that a root of the auxiliary polynomial $P(u)$ is $u_1 = -0.5$, what is the value of the corresponding root z_1?

REFERENCES

1. Korn, G. A., and T. M. Korn: "Electronic Analog Computers," p. 111, McGraw-Hill Book Company, Inc., New York, 1952.

2. Frazer, R. A., W. J. Duncan, and A. B. Collar: "Elementary Matrices," p. 96, The Macmillan Company, New York, 1946.

3. Gephart, L.: Linear Algebraic Systems and the REAC, "Mathematical Tables and Other Aids to Computation," p. 203, The National Research Council, Washington, D.C., July, 1952.

4. Corcos, G. M., R. M. Howe, L. L. Rauch, and J. R. Sellars: Application of the Electronic Differential Analyzer to Eigenvalue Problems, "Project Cyclone Symposium II on Simulation and Computing Techniques, Part 2," Reeves Instrument Corporation (under sponsorship of the U.S. Navy Special Devices Center and the U.S. Navy Bureau of Aeronautics), New York, Apr. 28–May 2, 1952.

5. Pipes, L. A.: "Applied Mathematics for Engineers and Physicists," McGraw-Hill Book Company, Inc., 1946.

6. Wylie, C. R., Jr.: "Advanced Engineering Mathematics," p. 216, McGraw-Hill Book Company, Inc., 1951.

7. Sokolnikoff, I. S., and E. S. Sokolnikoff: "Higher Mathematics for Engineers and Physicists," p. 370, McGraw-Hill Book Company, Inc., 1941.

8. Howe, R. M., and V. S. Haneman: The Solution of Partial Differential Equations by Difference Methods Using the Electronic Differential Analyzer, "Proceedings of Western Computer Conference (Joint IRE-AIEE-ACM Conference), Feb. 4–6, 1953, Los Angeles," pp. 208–226, June, 1953.

9. Scarborough, J. B.: "Numerical Mathematical Analysis," Johns Hopkins Press, Baltimore, 1930.

10. Southwell, R. V.: "Relaxation Methods in Engineering Science," Oxford University Press, New York, 1946.

11. Teague, D. S., and R. D. Gilpin, Jr.: Preliminary Investigation of Suitability of REAC for Experimental Curve Fitting, "Project Cyclone Symposium I on REAC Techniques," pp. 69–74, Reeves Instrument Corporation (under contract with the U.S. Navy Special Devices Center), New York, Mar. 15–16, 1951.

12. Murphy, C. H.: Use of the REAC as a Curve Fitting Device, "Project Cyclone Symposium II on Simulation and Computing Techniques, Part 2," Reeves Instrument Corporation (under sponsorship of the U.S. Navy Special Devices Center and the U.S. Navy Bureau of Aeronautics), New York, Apr. 28–May 2, 1952.

13. Bauer, D. L., and S. Fifer: The Solution of Polynomial Equations on the REAC, "Project Cyclone Symposium I on REAC Techniques," pp. 31–36, Reeves Instrument Corporation (under contract with the U.S. Navy Special Devices Center), New York, Mar. 15–16, 1951.

14. Warshawsky, Leon M.: An Electrical Analogue Polynomial Evaluator, thesis, The Ohio State University, Columbus, Ohio, 1949.

15. Evans, G. W., II: Some Partial Differential Equations Solvable by the REAC, "Project Cyclone Symposium I on REAC Techniques," pp. 19–26, Reeves Instrument Corporation (under contract with the U.S. Navy Special Devices Center), New York, Mar. 15–16, 1951.

16. Hartree, Douglas R.: "Calculating Instruments and Machines," University of Illinois Press, Urbana, Ill., 1949.

CHAPTER 10

ANALOG COMPUTER COMPONENTS AND COMPUTER CONTROL

10-1. Introduction. In this chapter a few of the component parts of the analog computer will be discussed. No attempt will be made to treat the components in great detail, but only those characteristics which directly affect the machine operator will be considered. Topics to be considered are the stabilized d-c amplifier, potentiometer-setting schemes, operate-reset systems, and overload warning systems. The discussion will be concluded with the application of previously discussed techniques to simple problems involving the automatic control of analog computers.

10-2. Stabilized D-C Amplifiers. In the early days of the analog computer, the d-c amplifiers in use were based upon design techniques which had been known for some time. In the computer application, however, the drift associated with d-c amplifiers was found to be particularly troublesome. The constant effort to improve the accuracy of analog computers was focused upon two points: to improve the d-c amplifier, and to obtain more precise components to use as feedback and input impedances. The improvement of passive components was of little value, however, until the errors associated with the amplifier were reduced.

The drift in d-c amplifiers arises from several sources. Among the main factors contributing to drift are variations in heater voltage, particularly in the early amplifier stages; fluctuations in the power-supply voltages; variations in tube characteristics; and amplifier grid current. The improvement in amplifier characteristics was carried out in two ways. First, circuitry was refined to increase the amplifier gain and particular care was taken to reduce drift due to the causes mentioned above. The resulting amplifiers were good but still did not allow the computer operator freedom from occasionally balancing the amplifiers in order to obtain highly precise results. The second and most significant improvement came about when Goldberg[1] introduced a method of stabilizing the d-c amplifier by an external means.

The automatic-balance system of Goldberg is incorporated in the REAC amplifiers. Balance systems that operate in a similar manner are present in all the precision computers being manufactured at present. A simplified schematic of a REAC amplifier as used in the C-101 model D computer is shown in Fig. 10-1. In this circuit the effects of drift voltages are compensated for by the use of an auxiliary balancing amplifier. The voltage at the grid of the first stage of the amplifier (a triode) is filtered, and the resulting voltage is modulated by means of a synchronous vibrator. The modulated d-c signal is amplified in a drift-free a-c amplifier and demodulated by the synchronous vibrator. The error signal obtained from the a-c amplifier and filter is then introduced to the grid of a second triode, cathode coupled to the input tube. The effect of the filtered signal obtained from the a-c amplifier is to vary the grid voltage of the second half of the input triode in such a manner that the average potential of the grid of the first triode will remain approximately at zero.

A better concept of the manner in which the drift voltage of an amplifier is reduced by the stabilizing circuit can be gained by considering the action of the circuit with an assumed positive potential at the grid of the input tube V101 (Fig. 10-1). The voltage at the grid of V101 is modulated by the synchronous vibrator, and the resulting signal is amplified by the a-c amplifier which consists of tubes V104 and V105. The signal at the output of the a-c amplifier is demodulated by the action of the second half of the synchronous vibrator as it alternately grounds and opens the circuit connected to the junction of C110 and R128. The demodulated signal is then filtered by the action of C111 and R128. It is important to note here for later reference that the time constant of the filter is very long (25.5 sec).

The filtered demodulated signal is introduced to the second grid of V101 and is of opposite polarity (negative) to the drift voltage that was assumed to exist at the first grid of V101. The stabilizing signal causes the cathode potential of V101 to decrease and thus causes the input triode to conduct more heavily, producing a larger signal at the output of the amplifier. The negative feedback through the external 1-megohm resistor then drives the input grid of the amplifier back toward zero, reducing the initial error voltage at the grid of the amplifier.

An important feature of the auxiliary stabilizing circuit is that the over-all gain of the d-c amplifier is effectively increased for low frequencies by the gain of the a-c amplifier. In summary, it can be stated that the low-frequency portion of the signal is amplified both

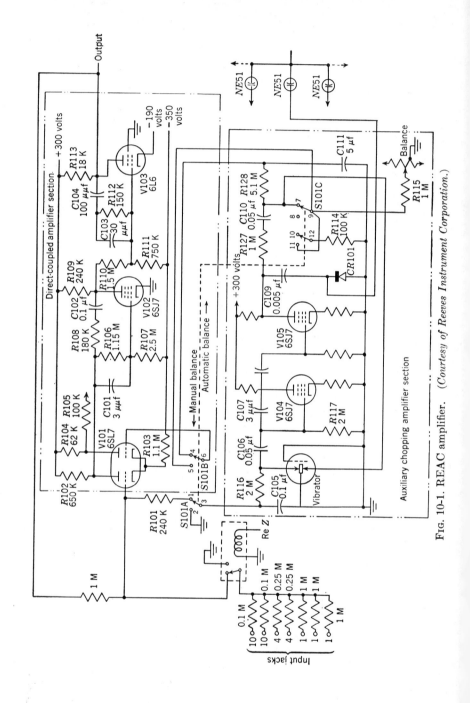

FIG. 10-1. REAC amplifier. *(Courtesy of Reeves Instrument Corporation.)*

186

by the a-c and d-c amplifiers, whereas the higher frequencies are amplified mainly by the d-c amplifier.

The d-c amplifier circuits in use today vary considerably in their configuration. However, the introduction of automatic stabilization has made feasible low-frequency gains in the order of 10^6 to 6×10^8 rather than the 20,000 to 200,000 normally achieved in unstabilized computer amplifiers. Reference to the derivation of the transfer function of the high-gain amplifier in Chap. 2 will show that, with gains over a million, the ability of the amplifier to perform accurately the operations of summation and integration rests almost entirely on the quality of the resistors and condensers available as input and feedback impedances.*

Consistent improvement in the quality of the passive components has been made. Plastic condensers, such as polystyrene, are the most commonly used in forming an integrator and have leakage resistances as high as 10^{12} to 10^{14} ohms. These may be matched to a standard to considerably better than 0.1 per cent of the nominal value. The resistors commonly used are either noninductively wound, wire-wound resistors, or stabilized deposited-carbon types with a low temperature coefficient. The deposited-carbon types may be matched to closer than 0.1 per cent, but superiority still lies with the wire-wound resistors, as their temperature coefficients are lower than the best deposited-carbon resistors available. It is common practice with some computer manufacturers to pad each resistor to obtain an extremely close tolerance in resistance value and to group all resistors on a common panel to reduce temperature effects. Herein lies one of the greatest arguments for wiring all components internally in the computer rather than patching them externally.

In the introduction to this chapter, it was indicated that only those features of machine design having a direct bearing upon the computer operation would be discussed. An understanding of the principle of operation of the stabilized d-c amplifier is necessary to make its limitations clear. If a d-c amplifier is operated over a range of voltages which does not overload the amplifier, the grid input is at all times very close to zero potential because of the very high gain of the amplifier. If the amplifier is caused to overload, the voltage at the grid of the amplifier no longer remains close to zero, as the voltages applied to the grid through the feedback and input impedances are no longer equal and opposite in sign. It may be recalled, by once again referring to the diagram of Fig. 10-1, that the a-c amplified balancing signal is

---

* Significant errors are still present because of phase shift and finite adder bandwidth. These errors are discussed in the next section.

filtered before being applied to the second triode of the d-c amplifier. The time constants commonly used in this filter are of the order of 10 to 25 sec. The result is that, if an overload occurs, a large signal is sent to the filter and considerable time must be allowed for the a-c amplifier to recover. The time it takes for an amplifier to recover from an overload is to some extent a function of the time the amplifier

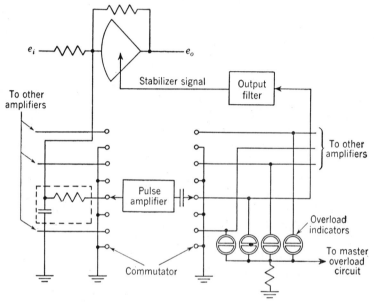

Fig. 10-2. Block diagram of the Ingerson stabilization system.

remained overloaded. In the operation of problems on a computer it is important to keep in mind that a temporary overload will have much more detrimental effects upon the problem results when using stabilized amplifiers than when unstabilized amplifiers are used. This is due to the long time constant of the filter circuit in the stabilized amplifier.

In a few applications, the nonlinear characteristics of amplifiers, when allowed to overload, are desirable in the design of circuitry to perform specific functions. Typical of these operations is the use of a high-gain amplifier to cause a diode to conduct or be cut off in a very sharp manner. In applications where overloading is desirable, the automatic-balance feature of the amplifier must be made inoperative. A switch is sometimes provided on the amplifier chassis to allow the convenient choice of manual or automatic-balance operation. If the automatic-balance system is disengaged, the operator must then monitor the amplifier occasionally and make any balance adjustments necessary.

In 1951, Ingerson[2] modified the system of Goldberg to a considerable extent. He eliminated the chopper and a-c amplifier from each individual amplifier and replaced these with a motor-driven commutator and single pulse amplifier capable of stabilizing several amplifiers. For a large number of amplifiers the system offers considerable economy of construction.

A block diagram of the stabilizer circuit developed by Ingerson and used on the L-3 Goodyear computer is given in Fig. 10-2. The voltage at the grid input of each d-c amplifier is filtered and is then sampled three times per second by a motor-driven commutator. The pulses obtained from the commutator are amplified by a pulse amplifier, and the resulting signal is reintroduced to the proper d-c amplifier by means of the commutator. The output signal from the commutator is filtered before being introduced to the d-c amplifier in order to provide a d-c signal to the amplifier.

10-3. Inherent Errors of D-C Amplifiers. In Chap. 2 the transfer functions of integrating and summing amplifiers were derived; however, little was said at that time about the imperfections of the amplifiers. It will be the purpose of this section to discuss these limitations and show the effect they can have upon problem solutions.

The transfer function of a high-gain d-c amplifier with feedback was shown in Sec. 2-2 to be

$$\frac{e_o}{e_i} = - \frac{z_f}{z_i} \frac{1}{1 + 1/A(z_f/z_i + 1)} \tag{10-1}$$

where z_f = feedback impedance
z_i = input impedance
$-A$ = amplifier gain
For an integrator Eq. (10-1) becomes

$$\frac{e_o}{e_i} = - \frac{1}{j\omega k} \frac{1}{1 + 1/A + 1/j\omega Ak} \tag{10-2}$$

where $k = RC$ is the reciprocal of the gain of the integrator. For $A \gg 1$ the term $1/A$ can be neglected, and if $k = 1$, Eq. (10-2) reduces to

$$\frac{e_o}{e_i} = - \frac{\tau_0}{j\omega\tau_0 + 1} \tag{10-3}$$

where τ_0, the integrator time constant, is equal to A.

In Sec. 2-2 the assumption was made that if τ_0 (the amplifier gain) was sufficiently large the integrator could be assumed to be perfect, giving

$$\frac{e_o}{e_i} = -\frac{1}{j\omega} \qquad\qquad (10\text{-}4)$$

A logarithmic plot of Eqs. (10-3) and (10-4) reveals the extent of the assumption made. Figure 10-3 is a plot of magnitude in decibels

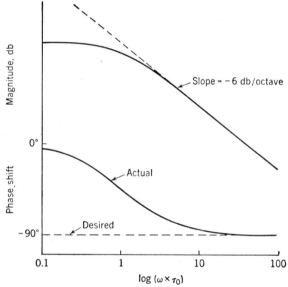

Fig. 10-3. Logarithmic plot of integrator-gain and phase-shift characteristics. The dashed line indicates the desired characteristic; the solid line, the physically realizable characteristic. The magnitude plot crosses the 0-db line at $\omega = 1/k$, where k is the reciprocal of the integrator gain.

vs. log ω for the ideal and for a physically realizable integrator. The dashed line represents an ideal integrator, and the solid line represents the physically realizable characteristic as expressed by Eq. (10-3).

It is apparent that the ideal characteristic of an integrator should have a slope of -6 db per octave over the entire frequency spectrum. At extremely low frequencies the actual integrator characteristic must deviate from the ideal characteristic because of finite amplifier gain. Furthermore, at some high frequency practical integrators again deviate from the ideal slope of -6 db per octave. This is not shown in Fig. 10-3 but can be represented as an additional small time constant

τ_1 in the integrator transfer function.   Including this effect gives the more realistic integrator transfer function

$$\frac{e_o}{e_i} = \frac{\tau_0}{j\omega\tau_0 + 1} \frac{1}{j\omega\tau_1 + 1} \tag{10-5}$$

For best computer operation, examination of Fig. 10-3 reveals that the break in the logarithmic plot of the integrator characteristic must occur at a frequency lower than any frequency normally encountered in problem solutions.   Similarly, the slope of the integrator characteristic curve should be controlled to well beyond the highest frequency to be encountered in problem solutions.

The summing amplifiers used in analog computers are not without inherent errors.   The ideal transfer function of a summing amplifier is

$$e_o = - \sum_{i=1}^{n} k_i e_i \tag{10-6}$$

where k_i is the gain associated with each individual input e_i.

This simple transfer function is not physically realizable because of stray capacitance in the adder circuit.   The simplest expression giving a realistic representation of the actual adder transfer function is of the form

$$e_o = \frac{\sum_{i=1}^{n} k_i e_i}{1 + j\omega\tau_2} \tag{10-7}$$

where τ_2 is the time constant of the adder.   The magnitude and phase plot of the desired and realizable response curves are shown as Fig. 10-4.

Macnee[3] has shown that, for imperfections in integrating and summing amplifiers of the form given by Eqs. (10-5) and (10-7), the solution of the general ordinary differential equation

$$\sum_{n=0}^{m} A_n \frac{d^n y}{dt^n} = f(t) \tag{10-8}$$

on an electronic analog computer is not the true solution of Eq. (10-8). For problem frequencies that are remote from both the upper and lower cutoff points of the computer components, Macnee shows that the difference between the characteristic roots of the computer results γ_n' and the true characteristic roots γ_n of the equation is expressable as

$$\gamma_n' = \gamma_n + \epsilon_n \tag{10-9}$$

In addition there are $m + 1$ additional roots introduced into the solution by the amplifier imperfections. These $m + 1$ additional roots have large negative real parts; thus they are heavily damped and can be neglected in further analysis of the computer components.

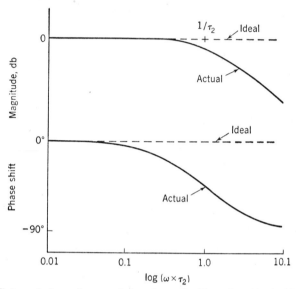

Fig. 10-4. Gain and phase characteristics of a realizable and an ideal adder for $k = 1$. The break point of the magnitude plot occurs at $\omega = 1/\tau_2$ radians/sec.

The error term in Eq. (10-9) is shown by Macnee to be

$$\epsilon_n = -\frac{1}{\tau_0} - \tau_1 \gamma_n{}^2 - \frac{\tau_2 \gamma_n{}^{m+1}}{C'(\gamma_n)} \qquad n = 1, 2, \ldots, m \qquad (10\text{-}10)$$

where $C'(\gamma_n)$ indicates the derivative of the characteristic equation of Eq. (10-8) evaluated at the point $\gamma = \gamma_n$. Thus

$$C(\gamma) = \sum_{n=0}^{m} A_n \gamma^n = 0 \qquad (10\text{-}11)$$

and $\quad C'(\gamma) = m A_m \gamma_n{}^{m-1} + (m-1) A_{m-1} \gamma_n{}^{m-2} + \cdots + A_1$

If the roots of the characteristic equation of an ordinary differential equation of the form given in Eq. (10-8) are known and if in addition the time constants τ_0, τ_1, and τ_2 of the computer components are known, it is possible to use Eq. (10-10) to determine the error in each root of the computer solution. By evaluating the error ϵ_n for simple differential equations, it is thereby possible to determine the effect of amplifier imperfections on the computer results.

Before proceeding with an actual calculation demonstrating the error present in simple problems, let us consider first the effect of each of the computer time constants. The low-frequency cutoff of the integrator, determined by the time constant τ_0, is seen to enter into Eq. (10-10) in the first term only. Thus all roots of the characteristic equation (10-11) are reduced by the factor $1/\tau_0$. This is the equivalent of introducing a damping factor of the form e^{-t/τ_0} into the problem solution.

The high-frequency integrator error associated with the time constant τ_1 is a function of τ_1 and the square of the root. Considering this imperfection alone, the actual term of the problem solution will be of the form $C_n e^{\gamma_n(1-\tau_1\gamma_n{}^2)t}$.

The error due to adder bandwidth is

$$-\frac{\tau_2\gamma_n{}^{m+1}}{C'(\gamma_n)} = -\frac{\tau_2\gamma_n{}^{m+1}}{mA_m\gamma_n{}^{m-1} + (m-1)A_{m-1}\gamma_n{}^{m-2} + \cdots + A_1}$$

Macnee proceeded further in his analysis of computer errors to show the effects of amplifier imperfections in the equation of simple harmonic motion. The equation for simple harmonic motion is

$$\frac{d^2y}{dt^2} + \omega_0{}^2 y = 0 \tag{10-12}$$

The roots of the equation are

$$\gamma = \pm j\omega_0$$

The errors due to amplifier imperfections are, therefore, obtained by substituting these roots into Eq. (10-10), giving

$$\epsilon_1 = \epsilon_2 = -\frac{1}{\tau_0} - \tau_1(j\omega_0)^2 - \frac{\tau_2(j\omega_0)^3}{2j\omega_0} = -\frac{1}{\tau_0} + \omega_0{}^2\left(\tau_1 + \frac{\tau_2}{2}\right)$$

The computer solution of Eq. (10-12) is therefore

$$y = e^{[\omega_0{}^2(\tau_1+\tau_2/2)-1/\tau_0]t}\cos\omega_0 t \tag{10-13}$$

Several important conclusions can be drawn from Eq. (10-13). First, the high-frequency error of integrators is as important as the error due to limited adder bandwidth. Second, the error in the solution of Eq. (10-12) is a maximum at the end of the computer solution where t is maximum. Further, it can be shown that the maximum permissible solution time for a given percentage error ϵ in the problem solution is

$$t \ (\text{max}) \ = \ \frac{|\epsilon|}{50\omega_0} \sqrt{\frac{\tau_0}{2\tau_1 + \tau_2}}$$

From Eq. (10-12) it can be easily shown that the effect of finite adder bandwidth is great. Neglecting integrator imperfections by setting $\tau_0 = \infty$ and $\tau_1 = 0$, it is easily determined that a 1 per cent divergence occurs in the solution of Eq. (10-12) in $4/\pi$ sec for a ratio of adder bandwidth $(1/2\pi\tau_2)$ and problem frequency ω_n of 2,000:1. The proof of this statement will be left for the reader as an exercise.

The example chosen here is an extreme case, as the roots of the characteristic equation lie on the imaginary axis. Any perturbation from this position causes a marked change in the form of the problem solution.

10-4. Overload Warning Systems. To achieve satisfactory results on a computer, it is necessary to know if an amplifier overload occurs at any time during the running of a problem. The early overload warning systems used on computers consisted of a light or other device which signified that the output of an amplifier had exceeded some fixed voltage level. This overload scheme is notoriously poor, as it does not indicate an actual overload. In the case of the early model REAC computer, an overload was signaled if the voltage at the amplifier output exceeded ± 100 volts. Examination of the circuit diagram of the REAC amplifier (Fig. 10-1) reveals that the amplifier is capable of outputs up to almost $+300$ volts if no current is drawn from the amplifier and approximately -190 volts regardless of the loading. If, however, a load of 5,000 ohms to ground is placed on the amplifier, it will overload at approximately $+65$ volts. The early overload warning system was, therefore, practically worthless. The introduction of the chopper-stabilized amplifier soon led to the adoption of an overload warning system that actually did signify an overload.

In normal operation the input grid of the d-c amplifier is at zero potential. Only if an overload actually occurs does the grid differ appreciably from zero. Based on this principle, a satisfactory warning system was devised for stabilized amplifiers that operates at any time the output of the a-c amplifier reached a predetermined value. The system used in the REAC rectifies the output of the a-c amplifier with a crystal diode and applies the resulting voltage to a neon indicator lamp and to an overload amplifier which operates an audible warning device such as a chime.

The d-c amplifiers using the commutator-pulse amplifier-stabilizing circuit of Ingerson are also provided with an overload warning system. The operation of the overload warning system is similar to that described for the REAC amplifiers in the preceding paragraph.

10-5. Boost.   Another feature commonly provided on analog computers is a *boost*.   The boost is a provision that allows the circuitry of the amplifiers to be modified conveniently in order to provide greater output currents from the amplifiers.   The boost is used whenever the load on an amplifier is sufficient to cause the amplifier to overload in its normal operating voltage range.   The boosts on a REAC computer consist of a group of 18,000-ohm resistors connected permanently at one end to the +300-volt supply.   The free ends of the resistors are brought to the patch board of the computer, where they may be connected by patch cords to the output of the various computer amplifiers.   The effect of connecting a boost to the output of a computer amplifier is to reduce the plate resistance of the output stage of the amplifier.   The reduced plate resistance allows the amplifier to supply more power to the output.   The penalty paid for achieving the increased amplifier power output is a reduction in the gain of the amplifier.   The reduction in gain is not serious in most chopper-stabilized amplifiers, as the amplifier gain is usually greater than 10^6 before applying the boost.

10-6. Operate-Reset Systems.   Some control system to permit the starting and stopping of a problem is necessary in any computer.   The control system may seem to be a relatively unimportant portion of the computer design, but a well-thought-out system contributes much to the versatility of a computer and the convenience of using it.

The basic function of starting and stopping a problem need involve only the integrators.   To start a problem, it is necessary to connect the inputs to the integrators.   To stop or *hold* the solution involves only removing the inputs of the integrators.   To reset the integrators to zero requires that the feedback condensers be discharged.   To be able to apply initial conditions to an integrator is a refinement that is very convenient but is not absolutely necessary.   An initial condition can be applied by starting the integrator always from zero and adding the initial value to the output of the integrator by means of a summing amplifier.   Needless to say, this is wasteful of equipment but is actually done in some equipments such as the Philbrick repetitive computer (see Chap. 12).

Most computers utilize an elaborate means of applying initial conditions to the integrators.   A block diagram showing one scheme of applying initial conditions is given in Fig. 10-5.   The figure is over-simplified but demonstrates the principle adequately.   Relays 1, 2, and 3 are connected to the OPERATE-RESET switch of the computer in such a manner that relay 1 is open and relay 2 is closed downward (connecting the normal inputs to the amplifier) and relay 3 is closed downward when the switch is in OPERATE.   In RESET position, relay 1 closes, relay 2 switches to the up position, and relay 3 connects the

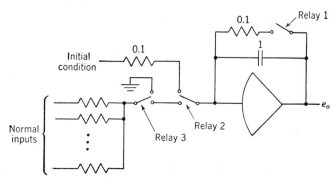

FIG. 10-5. Simplified diagram showing method of applying initial conditions. Impedance values are in megohms and microfarads.

normal inputs to ground.   The transfer function for the amplifier, when connected in this manner, becomes

$$\frac{e_o}{e_i} = -\frac{1}{0.1p + 1} \qquad (10\text{-}14)$$

where e_i is the voltage applied as an initial condition.

If the input to the initial-condition terminal is zero, the output voltage e_o will decay toward zero in an exponential manner with a time constant of 0.1 sec.   Correspondingly, if a voltage e_i is placed on the initial-condition terminal, in the steady state $e_o = -e_i$ and the initial condition has been applied.

It is occasionally desirable to *hold* the computer solution at any point in a problem.   This may be accomplished by grounding relay 3 and thereby disconnecting the normal inputs of the integrators.   In the hold position, relays 1 and 2 remain in their normal or OPERATE positions.

A circuit diagram of the control system used on the REAC computer is shown in Fig. 10-6.   The X and Y relays, identified on the diagram, are arranged so that the relays will be in the OPERATE position (switched to the left) when deenergized.   This is done in order to reduce the noise level in the computer while operating.   In RESET, both the X and Y relays are energized.   In hold position only the Y relay is energized.   The lower portion of the diagram shows the initial condition switches that are provided on six of the integrators. The switches, together with the accompanying 30,000-ohm potentiometers, provide for the convenient application of either positive or negative initial conditions to the integrators.

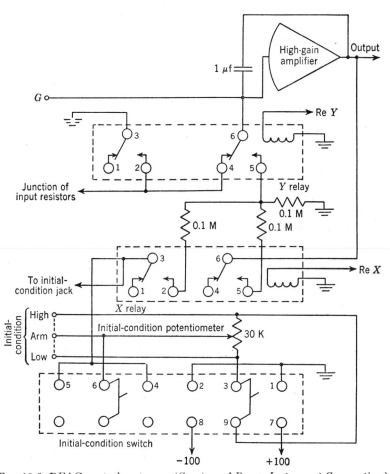

Fig. 10-6. REAC control system.   (*Courtesy of Reeves Instrument Corporation.*)

A fourth position (balance check) is provided on the REAC control switch.   In this position the X and Y relays are energized but in addition a Z relay, found only on the summing and inverting amplifiers, is energized.   The purpose of the Z relays is to remove the input resistors from the amplifiers and ground the summing junction in a manner similar to the functioning of the Y relay on an integrator.   The balance-check position provides an easy way of checking the zero of the summing amplifiers without first removing the problem from the machine. A second purpose served by the balance-check position is to allow the use of the REAC potentiometer setting scheme (see Sec. 10-7).

The coils of the X, Y, and Z relays are normally energized by throwing a control switch. Connections from these relays are also brought to the front of the patch board, however, so that they may be energized by some external means. The X, Y, and Z terminals on the patch board serve another purpose, as they provide a convenient means of ganging several computers together so that they can all be controlled by the same OPERATE switch. If the X, Y, and Z relays of two computers are interconnected and the OPERATE-RESET switch of one is left in OPERATE, the OPERATE-RESET switch of the other is then in complete control of both machines.

Considerable convenience in operation can be achieved by providing a self-holding relay system to replace the OPERATE-RESET switch. This allows the control of the computer to be accomplished from positions remote to the computer itself.

10-7. Potentiometer-setting Systems. It is necessary to correct for the loading effects on potentiometers in order to set accurately problem coefficients and initial conditions of problems. There are two basic methods of correcting for potentiometer loading: (1) a correction chart may be prepared for each value of load to be placed on the potentiometers, and the loading correction can be added to the theoretical potentiometer setting to obtain the actual setting; or (2) the output of the potentiometer can be measured with the load applied. The disadvantages of the first scheme are fairly obvious. By necessity, the different loads that may be placed on the potentiometers are limited, and each potentiometer must have a linearity compatible with the results desired. The system is relatively slow and cumbersome to use and is an additional source of human error. The preferred scheme of compensating for loading errors is to set the potentiometer to the desired setting with the load applied.

The system commonly in use on REAC computers consists of an individual switch for each potentiometer and a potentiometer selector switch to select the individual potentiometer to be adjusted. The individual switch associated with each potentiometer removes the normal input to the potentiometer and replaces it with $+100$ volts from the reference supply. The potentiometer selector switch connects the arm of the particular potentiometer to a terminal on the patch board. From there an external connection may be made to the input of a servomultiplier or other high-precision voltmeter.   When using this scheme the potentiometer setting may be read directly on the servo dial as a percentage of 100 volts.   Since the servo follow-up potentiometers most commonly used on REAC computers are linear to within 0.05 of full scale, the setting may be made accurate to 1 part in 1,000 or better.

On the REAC the initial-condition potentiometers are set by reading directly the output of the integrator on which the initial condition is being set.   A multiple-position switch is provided to facilitate the easy selection of any amplifier output to make this reading possible.

The system in use in the Goodyear computer is similar to the REAC scheme in that it allows adjustment of the potentiometers with the load applied.   In this system, however, the potentiometer output is compared against a high-precision potentiometer by means of a bridge circuit.   The comparison potentiometer is linear to within 0.05 per cent, so that again precise settings can be made.

The assembly of very large computer installations has introduced a requirement for improved means of setting potentiometers.   In some problems on large-scale computers, in excess of 1,000 potentiometers must be set.   Manual setting of this number of potentiometers involves several hours' labor and allows considerable opportunity for human error.   To overcome this difficulty, Electronic Associates, Inc., and others have developed devices for the automatic setting of potentiometers.

The system used by Electronics Associates consists of a keyboard, a control chassis, and the selection matrix, servo, and clutching system necessary to select and automatically set one of 1,000 or more potentiometers.   In operation, the operator types on the keyboard the number of the potentiometer to be set and the potentiometer setting to an accuracy of 1 part in 100,000, if desired.   The correct potentiometer is selected and servoed to an accuracy of 0.01 per cent of the correct value by comparison against a precision resistance standard.   At the completion of the operation a light is lit signifying that the desired setting has been made.   The system is also adaptable to the precise storage of values at the output of the computer amplifiers for later permanent recording.

10-8. Automatic Programming.   Analog computers can be made to operate automatically for some types of problems.   This can be carried out to a sufficient extent that a computer can be left unattended for periods of an hour or more.   The extent to which it is practical to provide automatic controlling features is dependent upon the type of problem to be encountered in a laboratory.   In other words, the most elaborate automatic programming system may be completely ineffective unless it is designed for the particular job that it must do.

The type of problem which lends itself best to automatic programming is one in which the parameters of the problem remain constant and the initial conditions must be varied in incremental steps from run to run. If a large number of problems fitting this category are to be solved by a computer laboratory, an automatic programmer should seriously be considered.

Follin[4] of the Applied Physics Laboratory at Johns Hopkins University has constructed what is perhaps the most elaborate automatic programmer in use today. The work of the laboratory is of such a nature as to warrant it, however. The laboratory is concerned largely with the simulation of guided-missile systems. The launch phase of guided missiles entails the study of the missile behavior for a large number of initial launch angles, a situation ideally suited to automatic programming. The use of an automatic programmer has many advantages where it is applicable. The programmer eliminates many human errors in setting initial conditions, it appreciably increases the work output of a computer, and it reduces operator fatigue.

It is possible to perform many simple automatic operations on a computer without an elaborate programming device. A few of these applications will be discussed in the remainder of this section. All the operations may be performed by the use of diodes or differential relays and RC components that are easily obtainable.

A simple application of automatic computer operation can be made in plotting bomb trajectories on a plotting board. In a problem such as this, for uniformity of plotted results, it is desirable that all trajectories terminate at a certain value of h, namely, h_1. This can be accomplished by automatically lifting the plotting-board pen at the predetermined value of h. Circuits capable of energizing a pen-lift relay are shown in Fig. 10-7. Figure 10-7a utilizes diode circuitry, and Fig. 10-7b makes use of differential relays.

In Fig. 10-7a assume that h is greater than h_1. The output of the high-gain amplifier will, therefore, be negative and the diode will conduct, clamping the amplifier output to zero. As soon as h becomes less than h_1 the amplifier output becomes a large positive value and causes relay 1 to close, applying +26 volts to the pen-lift relay. Simultaneously, 26 volts is applied to relay 1, keeping it energized regardless of the magnitude of h. To lower the pen, it is necessary to press the push button breaking the self-holding circuit. Figure 10-7b demonstrates a means of performing the same job with differential relays. Again, DR 2 is provided only to make the circuit self-holding.   A standard 26-volt relay could have been used in a manner similar to the circuit of Fig. 10-7a if the second differential relay were not available.

To perform only the operation of lifting the pen with the circuits described above is somewhat wasteful, as the same circuit may also be made to reset the computer.   This is accomplished by connecting

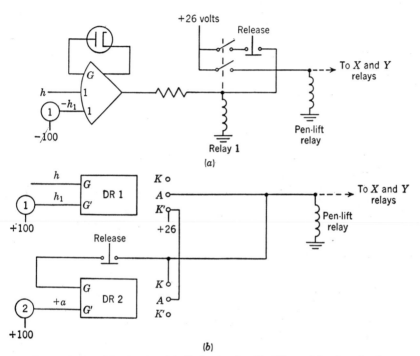

FIG. 10-7. Pen-lift circuits: (a) diode circuit; (b) differential-relay circuit.

the lead to the pen-lift relay to the X and Y relays of the computer, as indicated in Fig. 10-7.   Then, as soon as h falls below the predetermined value h_1, the pen will lift and the computer will reset.   To lower the pen and place the computer in operation on the next run, it is necessary to press the release button.

Problems arise in which it is desirable to reset the computer and again place it in operation without changing any parameters of the problem.   This is a useful mode of operation in problems where the statistical effects of random noise are to be evaluated, or it is particularly effective when adapted to the problem of automatically optimizing control-system components.   Figure 10-8 provides a circuit capable of operating for a fixed time, resetting, and again operating after a brief interval in RESET position. The two inputs $-t$ and t_1 cause the output of the first high-gain amplifier to be zero or a positive overload, depending on whether t_1 or t is the greater. When t exceeds t_1, a large positive voltage is suddenly applied to the input of the integrator, causing it to increase negatively until the relay switches the machine to RESET. The voltage at the output of the integrator will then decay until the relay releases, allowing the machine to operate once more. The point at which the computer resets is determined by the nature of the signal t and the magnitude of the constant t_1. The period of time it remains reset is a function of the voltage $-a$ applied to the integrator. A high-gain amplifier is used to form an

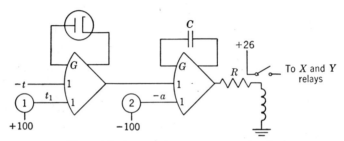

FIG. 10-8. Automatic operate-reset circuit.

integrator in this application, as a prewired integrator would be affected by the resetting of the computer. In this application the first high-gain amplifier in the circuit should be used in its manual-balance position, as it will be overloaded each time the computer resets.

Other circuits can easily be devised to perform this same operation. Differential relays lend themselves readily to this application, as do other circuits involving high-gain amplifiers and relays. This is to be expected, however, as a differential relay is nothing more than a high-gain amplifier and relay combined into a single unit.

In certain problems it is desirable to construct memory circuits and cumulative adders, or devices capable of summing discrete voltages at predetermined points in the solution of a problem. Most frequently these requirements arise in problems where repetitive operation is required. A cumulative adder may be prepared as in Fig. 10-9.

The differential relay is caused to position the relay so as to charge the condenser C_1 at a predetermined time in the problem solution, depending on the inputs of the differential relay. After charging the condenser, the relay is switched to connect the condenser C_1 to the integrator input. Each time the condenser is charged and its output is subsequently connected to the integrator, the integrator output

increases proportional to the charge placed on C_1.   The circuit becomes
a memory circuit if only one cycle of relay operation is accomplished
between intervals when the integrator is reset.   The integrator shown
in Fig. 10-9 can be reset completely independent of the operate-reset
cycle of the other integrators by shorting its output to its grid by
means of a second differential relay, thus giving still another mode of
operation of the circuit.

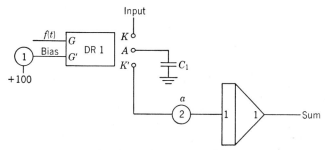

FIG. 10-9. Cumulative adder.

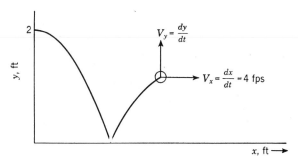

FIG. 10-10. A bouncing-ball trajectory.

A trivial problem that demonstrates an interesting mode of computer operation is the simulation of a bouncing ball.   Assume that a
ball is projected horizontally from a height of 2 ft with an initial velocity V_x of 4 ft/sec, as in Fig. 10-10.   Further, assume that the friction
drag of the ball in air is negligible but that 40 per cent of the vertical
component of the ball's kinetic energy is dissipated each time it strikes
a frictionless surface.

The solution of this problem that will be demonstrated uses two
similar circuits to generate alternately those portions of the trajectory
that lie between the points at which the ball contacts the surface.   In
other words, one circuit is used to calculate the trajectory until the
point is reached at which the ball first contacts the frictionless surface.
During that portion of the trajectory the appropriate initial conditions

of the second circuit are automatically charged to the proper value. At the time of contact of the ball with the surface, the first computer is automatically reset and the second circuit begins operating so as to continue the calculation of the trajectory over the second portion of the solution. While the second computer is operating, the initial con-

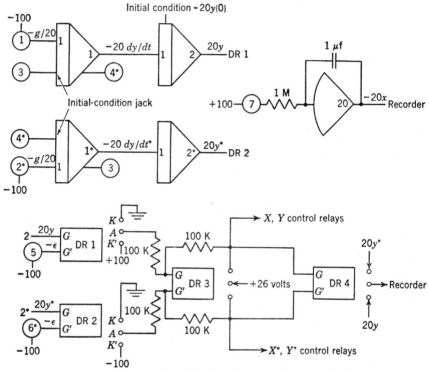

FIG. 10-11. A two-computer circuit for the solution of the bouncing-ball problem.

ditions of the first circuit are reset to the proper value so that the solution can be continued for the third portion of the solution.

In order to facilitate the setup of the circuit, two computers have been used. The components associated with the second computer are denoted by asterisks in the circuit diagram (Fig. 10-11).

The equations of motion of the ball are

$$y = \int V_y \, dt$$
$$\frac{d^2y}{dt^2} = -g$$
$$x = \int V_x \, dt$$

where $V_x = V_x(0) = 4$ ft/sec and $y(0) = 2$ ft.

The first step in preparing the setup is to determine the range of the problem variables during the problem solution.   The maximum values of the variables are

$$y \, (\text{max}) = 2 \, \text{ft}$$

$$\frac{dy}{dt} \, (\text{max}) = \sqrt{2gh} \cong 11 \, \text{ft/sec}$$

In the problem the velocity initial condition on one computer is to be continuously set to the value calculated by the other computer. The problem must, therefore, be slowed down until the time constant of charging the condenser in the feedback of an integrator can be neglected.   For a REAC this time constant is 0.1 sec.   For the purpose of this demonstration problem it is assumed that slowing the problem solution by a factor of 20 will produce satisfactory results.   Applying this time-scale change to the problem equations and adjusting the amplitude-scale factor gives

$$20 \frac{d^2y}{d\tau^2} = -\frac{g}{20}$$

$$x = \int \frac{V_x}{20} \, d\tau$$

$$\frac{dx}{d\tau} \, (0) = \frac{V_x(0)}{20} = 0.2 \, \text{ft/machine sec}$$

The setup of these equations is shown in Fig. 10-11.

Differential relays 1 and 2 are used to sense the time at which the ball strikes the surface.   At that time the differential relay associated with the operating computer switches, causing +100 volts to be applied to the corresponding grid of DR 3 and thus switching that relay.   This resets the operating computer, since DR 3 applies 26 volts to the coil of the operate-reset relays of the appropriate computer.   (The REAC operate relay windings have their terminals brought to the patch board, so that this can be conveniently done.)   At the same time the 26 volts is removed from the relays of the alternate computer, allowing it to start operating.   After DR 3 has switched, it is held in the appropriate position by the feedback applied to its grid from the corresponding relay contact.   It should be noted here that DR 1 and DR 2 must be biased to switch slightly after the ball has reached the surface, so that the armatures of both DR 1 and DR 2 are returned to the k position after the appropriate computer resets.   This allows DR 3 to switch the next time y becomes slightly less than zero.   Providing the relay circuits are sufficiently sensitive, this error can be kept negligibly small.

The purpose of DR 4 is to connect the plotting device at all times to the operating computer so that a continuous plot of the results can be made.   The plot of the problem solution is given in Fig. 10-12.

Other circuits can be devised to perform the automatic solution of this problem.   It is possible to devise a similar circuit using only one computer.   The same principle that was used here can be used in the preparation of a one-computer diagram if multiple contact relays are available.

The examples of circuits cited here have only touched upon the many possibilities of automatic computer operation.   It is hoped that

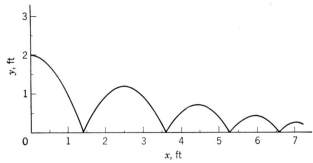

Fig. 10-12. Plot of the solution to the bouncing-ball problem.

the illustrative circuits given will aid the reader in designing circuits to meet the requirements of individual problems.   If a more elaborate programming scheme is necessary, the reader is referred to a paper by Follin, Emch, and Walters[4] describing the programmer they have found useful.

PROBLEMS

10-1. Show that in the computer solution of the equation

$$\frac{d^2y}{dt^2} + \omega_0^2 y = 0$$

the maximum permissible solution time for a given percentage error ϵ is

$$t \ (\text{max}) = \frac{|\epsilon|}{50\omega_0} \sqrt{\frac{\tau_0}{2\tau_1 + \tau_2}}$$

where τ_0 = low-frequency integrator time constant
       τ_1 = high-frequency integrator time constant
       τ_2 = adder time constant

HINT: Express the exponential function in Eq. (10-13) as a power series.   Since the error is small, the higher-order terms in the expansion may be neglected.

10-2. Show that in the equation

$$\frac{d^2y}{dt^2} + \omega_0{}^2 y = 0$$

the effect of finite adder bandwidth will cause a 1 per cent divergence of the solution in $4/\pi$ sec if $\omega_0 = 5(2\pi)$ radians/sec and the adder bandwidth is 10,000 cps. Assume perfect integrators ($\tau_0 = \infty$ and $\tau_1 = 0$).

10-3. Determine the expression for the error in a computer solution of

$$\frac{d^2y}{dt^2} - y = 0$$

For $\tau_0 = 30 \times 10^6$, $\tau_1 = 0$, and $\tau_2 = 1.59 \times 10^{-5}$, what is the error after 5 sec of computer operation?

10-4. For a REAC amplifier (Fig. 10-1), what is the positive output voltage at which the amplifier will overload for (a) a 30,000-ohm load to ground; (b) a 10,000-ohm load to ground; (c) a 5,000-ohm load to ground; (d) a 5,000-ohm load to ground and a boost connected to the amplifier output?

REFERENCES

1. Goldberg, E. A.: Stabilization of Wide-band Direct Current Amplifiers for Zero and Gain, *RCA Rev.*, vol. 11, no. 2, pp. 296–300, June, 1950.
2. Ingerson, W. E.: Drift Compensation in D-C Amplifiers for Analog Computers, paper presented at the convention of the IRE, New York, 1951.
3. Macnee, A. B.: Some Limitations on Accuracy of Electronic Differential Analyzers, *Proc. IRE*, vol. 40, no. 3, pp. 303–308, March, 1952.
4. Follin, J. W., Jr., G. F. Emch, and F. M. Walters: Modifications and Additions to the REAC, "Project Cyclone Symposium II on Simulation and Computing Techniques, Part 2," pp. 173–182, Reeves Instrument Corporation (under sponsorship of the U.S. Navy Special Devices Center and the U.S. Navy Bureau of Aeronautics), New York, Apr. 28–May 2, 1952.

CHAPTER 11

THE CHECKING OF COMPUTER RESULTS

11-1. Introduction. One of the greatest problems confronting the analog-computer operator is the checking of computer results. Until the computer results have been checked by some independent means, it is impossible to say with certainty, "These solutions of the problem are correct."

Methods of checking computer results can be classified into two categories:

1. Complete checking
   a. Analytic
   b. Numerical analysis
2. Partial checking

The most desirable check for analog-computer solutions is, of course, an analytic check or a numerical solution of the problem. The analytic solution of many of the problems solved on analog computers is impossible, leaving only the numerical mathematical methods for the engineer to employ.

To attempt to solve by numerical methods all the runs for a particular problem which has been run on an analog computer would, of course, be prohibitive in most cases. Why employ the analog computer at all if this must be done? The best approach seems to be one of compromise, and to be able to say, "These results are precise to — per cent, I believe. Any chance of major errors' entering into them is small."

The compromise that many computer installations have chosen is to perform a check by numerical mathematical methods on a few selected solutions of the problem. The analog-computer results for the corresponding problem solutions are then compared carefully against the check solutions. In this manner, it is possible to evaluate the precision of the runs obtained. All other computer solutions are then compared against the check solutions to see if the changes in the solution, due to variations of the problem parameters, are of a logical nature. If any questionable results occur, a check solution is rerun on the computer to ensure satisfactory operation of the computer. In this manner, reasonable assurance of correct results is obtained.

11-2. Checking Problem Preparation. Other than checks made independently on other types of equipment, there are many things the analog-computer operator can do to improve the probability of obtaining satisfactory problem solutions. Foremost among these is the checking of the equations or "mathematical model" of the system. Needless to say, if the equations of the system are incorrectly represented, no amount of checking of the computer setup and computer solution can give satisfactory results. This portion of problem checking may seem unworthy of mention, but a large percentage of unsatisfactory computer results arise from incorrect equations. People have a tendency to believe anything they see in print regardless of the reliability of the source. Adopting an attitude of looking upon any data with some suspicion will often pay dividends. Any equations taken directly from books or papers should be checked for possible errors.

A second precaution necessary in order to achieve satisfactory computer operation is to check carefully all steps in the preparation of a problem for computer solution. The check of all transformations made on the problem equations and the check of the problem setup can best be performed by a person other than the one who originally performed the work. For this reason, it is highly desirable that computer operators work in pairs. In preparing a circuit diagram, it is mandatory that the output of each amplifier and potentiometer be carefully labeled. It may seem, while preparing the circuit diagram, that it is unnecessary to do this, but it is very difficult to perform a check of a problem setup unless the diagram is properly labeled.

Let us now consider in greater detail the individual checks that aid in obtaining the correct solutions of problems on an analog computer. After the equations have been proved correct, any transformation made on a set of equations should be checked by performing the inverse transformation to again give the original equation. In checking any time-scale change, the problem initial conditions must be considered as well as the other equations of the system.

After ensuring that no errors have been introduced into the work by the mathematical manipulation of the equations, the circuit diagram should then be checked. A check of the circuit diagram is best performed by laying aside the original equations and rewriting the equations from the circuit diagram alone. Carrying out this process is simplified if all inputs and outputs on the problem circuit diagram are carefully labeled. Rewriting the problem equation from the circuit diagram is accomplished by equating the output of each amplifier to the negative of the inputs, taking into account any integration which may be performed in the amplifier. Following the check of the circuit diagram, it is desirable to recheck the equations of the potentiometer settings. The work should again be carried out independently to avoid duplicating original errors.

After all these checks have been completed, a brief check of the computer should be made before placing the problem on the machine. The minimum check that should be made is to scan each amplifier output with all inputs set to zero. This simple check will reveal several possible computer malfunctions. Typical of the possible malfunctions that can be detected by this check are:

1. Faulty tubes or circuitry in the operational amplifiers.
2. Inoperative automatic-balance system
3. Faulty relay system (if malfunctioning amplifier is used as an integrator)
4. Need for rebalancing the computer amplifiers (whether amplifiers are the stabilized or the unstabilized type)

A check of the computer power-supply voltages should also be made, since malfunctions in the reference power supply cannot be detected by the above amplifier check.

The minimum machine check-out outlined here should be supplemented frequently by a careful check of all components, including the input and feedback impedances employed in the summing and integrating amplifiers. A circuit that has been found useful in performing a dynamic check of a REAC computer is included in Sec. 11-7.

Another important check that should be made is to check the wiring of the computer in order to ensure that it agrees with the circuit diagram. A partial check can be made by counting the number of inputs and outputs of each amplifier. The best check, of course, is actually to check each wire used in the circuit. A convenient means of carrying out this check is to check the inputs and outputs of each amplifier in turn. All connections other than the inputs of potentiometers setting constants in the problem are checked in this manner. These may be checked separately.

11-3. Partial System Checking. Even after all these checks have been made, it is still possible that troubles will arise in the solution of a problem. These troubles may be due to malfunctioning auxiliary equipment such as relays, multipliers, or arbitrary-function-generating equipment, or they can be due to faulty contacts in removable patch boards. In order to aid in determining the source of computer malfunctions, a static check can be performed at the output of all com-

puter components. In order to make this check as complete as possible, all integrators that are used in the problem should be assigned an
initial value other than zero even though they may have an initial
value of zero in the problem. Using these initial values it is then
possible to determine the voltage that should be present at the output
of each component in the circuit. This check is extremely valuable in
trouble shooting a problem setup that does not operate properly. In
order to clarify the procedure, the bomb-trajectory problem of Sec. 5-6
will be considered here in detail. For convenience in referring to the
circuit diagram of the problem, it is reproduced here as Fig. 11-1.

TABLE 11-1. PROBLEM CHECK-OUT SHEET

Amplifier	Output	Voltage
1	$V/20$	25
2	$57.3\theta/2$	15
3	$-h/200$	-100
4	$x/200$	0
8	$-V/200$	-2.5
9	$-50(1 - 0.135 \times 10^{-4}h)$	-36.5
10	$10,513\rho$	13.32
11	$-5.265\rho V$	-3.33
12	$+0.002633\rho V^2$	0.83
20	$-(100g \cos \theta)/V$	-5.67

In the diagram of Fig. 11-1, if the initial values $V(0) = 500$ ft/sec,
$h(0) = 20,000$ ft, and $\theta = 30°$ are assigned to the problem variables,
a static check of the problem solution can be made. For the initial
values of the variables listed above, the voltage at the output of each
amplifier should be as listed in Table 11-1. Using Table 11-1, it is a
relatively easy task to determine whether the computer circuit is operating properly in the static condition. Unfortunately this check-out
scheme does not check the performance of the integrators, but it does
provide a systematic procedure of problem check-out that has proved
to be of great value in the past.

Any variation of amplifier output voltages from the calculated values
given in Table 11-1 indicates a computer error and provides a ready
means of locating the error. In general, the larger the problem the
more valuable a check-out sheet of the type shown in Table 11-1
becomes.

Often a slight modification of the equations of a problem changes
the problem from a form that is extremely difficult to check to one for

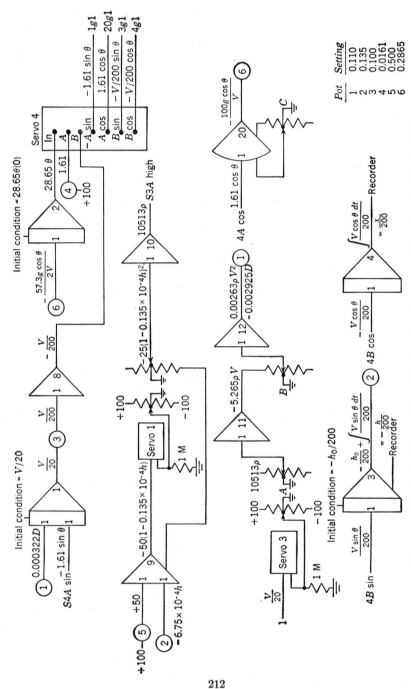

Fig. 11-1. Circuit for the solution of the bomb-trajectory problem described in Sec. 5-6.

Pot	Setting
1	0.110
2	0.135
3	0.100
4	0.0161
5	0.500
6	0.2865

212

which the solution is known.   This is true for many problems involving limiting and other nonlinearities.   Full advantage should be taken of this form of problem checking whenever possible.

The bomb-trajectory problem of Sec. 5-6 offers an excellent example of this type of checking.   If the drag is made equal to zero, the time of fall and the range are easily calculated.   A "vacuum" trajectory is, therefore, an important part of the problem check-out.   This, combined with a static check, as previously discussed, makes a check by numerical analysis practically unnecessary.

A check of problem operation performed by modifying the system equations is a form of partial checking.   Although partial checking is certainly not so adequate as complete checking, it plays an important role in computer operation.   In the application of computers to the study of servomechanisms, partial checking is extremely important. The complete system may frequently be broken down into smaller parts for which the solution is easily predicted.   Checks performed in this manner are most valuable as an aid in locating trouble in a computer circuit, but they do not prove conclusively that a problem, when operated as a whole, is operating correctly.

11-4. Checking Problem Stability.   At times, the intuitive guesses made by an engineer about the behavior of a system are completely erroneous.   It can happen that a system that is presumed to be stable is actually unstable.   To an analog-computer operator, the appearance of an unstable solution usually is interpreted to mean that a mistake has been committed in the circuit preparation.   The mistake may be in the form of an error in sign, or it may be an error in computing a potentiometer setting.   Occasionally, it may mean a malfunction of the computer.   The result is almost always, however, that the computer operator will frantically hunt for errors in the problem setup.

Upon encountering an unstable analog-computer solution and after making a reasonable effort to ensure satisfactory computer operation, it usually is wise to stop and check the system equations, to determine whether the system should really be stable.   For linear systems, Routh's criterion[1]* is the easiest stability check to apply.   This method does require that the characteristic equation of the system be obtained, but it is far simpler than other methods.   Only by performing a stability check can the engineer ever be sure that an error was not made in the setup of problems having an unstable computer solution.   Even though the physical system that a problem represents is known to be stable, a stability check of the problem equations is not out of order.   By performing a stability check, it can occasionally

* Routh's criterion is stated in Sec. A-4.

be determined that the system equations do not properly represent the system.

If a nonlinear system proves to be unstable, the best approach in determining the reason for the instability is to linearize the system and investigate the system in simplified form. If, upon placing the linearized version of the system upon the computer, the solution is still determined to be unstable, it will then be relatively easy to justify the instability. If the solution of the linearized system is found to be stable, the problem nonlinearities may then be reintroduced, one at a time. The reason for the instability can be readily isolated in this manner.

11-5. Specialized Checking Procedures. Occasionally, the roots of the characteristic equation of a system of differential equations that are to be solved on an analog computer are known. This is frequently true in the case of the analysis of servomechanism systems for which a stability analysis has previously been made. Knowledge of the roots of the characteristic equation allows checking to be performed by analysis of the computer results. From the computer results the frequencies and damping of the modes of oscillation of the problem can often be determined. The method is not too satisfactory, however, as in many applications it is impossible to identify all the roots of the characteristic equation from the problem solution. This is particularly true in the case of negative real roots that introduce small time constants into the problem. It is easy to visualize how roots of this type may be completely masked by a pair of conjugate complex roots.

Richmond and Loveman[2] have shown that the initial conditions of a problem can be adjusted to give zero as the value of the coefficient of each of the roots or complex pair of roots in a system, except the root under investigation. In this manner, each root of the problem may be properly identified. The method, unfortunately, requires that the system of differential equations be solved and thus, in many cases, is extremely difficult to apply. It is therefore of limited usefulness in the checking of analog-computer results.

The method of substituting the values of the variables of a problem (obtained from the computer solution) back into the system equations has proved of little value in checking analog-computer solutions in the past. The basic difficulty encountered in the method is that the integrations in the problem are not checked. Richmond and Loveman have proposed a scheme for checking computer results that is actually a substitution check repeated at sufficiently close intervals to allow a check of the problem integrations by numerical differentiation. The method further employs a statistical analysis of the errors obtained.

Without the statistical evaluation of errors, the method would have little value, as a large or small error does not necessarily identify correct or incorrect results. The method is based upon the assumptions that an error δ made in reading the recorded variable of a problem solution has a normal distribution, a mean of zero, and a standard deviation of σ and further that δ is independent of the magnitude of the variable.

In evaluating the error in the solution of an equation by this method, the values of the problem variables, as determined from the recorded problem solution, are substituted into the differential equations of the problem. This substitution is performed at frequent increments of the problem independent variable. The error found is then divided by the standard deviation of the distribution η, giving a new error expression

$$E = \frac{\epsilon}{\eta} \tag{11-1}$$

having a normal distribution, a mean of zero, and a variance of 1. In the analysis of a given equation, the value E is calculated for each point read from the graphs. If n values have been examined, this mean may be expressed as

$$M = \frac{\displaystyle\sum_{i=1}^{n} E_i}{n} \tag{11-2}$$

The disadvantages of the system seem to lie in the assumptions made as to the errors commonly encountered in recording devices. In particular, the assumption that the reading error δ is independent of the magnitude of the variable would imply that the recording device is linear. Standard galvanometer-type recorders are often nonlinear in action, so that an error must be introduced into the analysis. Recordings made on devices such as plotting boards, where linearity is good, would seem to be well adapted to this type of error analysis. In fact, Richmond and Loveman have indicated that errors as small as 5 per cent are detectable by the method even from recordings made on Brush recording equipment.

The chief advantage of this method of error analysis seems to lie in a reduction of the numerical calculation required over a straightforward step-by-step numerical solution of the problem. This is brought about by the fact that the points chosen for checking need not be as closely spaced as is required for the direct numerical solution of the problem. Another advantage lies in the adaptability of the method to simulation problems involving actual hardware in the computer setup.   Step-by-step numerical solution cannot be applied in this type of problem.

To take full advantage of the checking method proposed by Richmond and Loveman, digital read-out equipment should be employed.   The output of the various amplifiers should be recorded at specified time intervals on cards or punched paper tape to be used directly as an input for a digital computer used to perform the problem check.

As in any other method of complete checking employing numerical methods, a hand solution is quite lengthy and costly of time.   IBM punched-card equipment or other digital computing equipment is very helpful in the economic use of such checking methods.   The treatment of numerical methods, useful in the checking of analog computer results, is beyond the scope of this discussion.   The reader is referred to the excellent books available on the subject.[3,4]

11-6. The Role of the Digital Integrating Differential Analyzer in Problem Checking.   Another possibility for checking the results of the electronic analog computer lies in the use of digital integrating differential analyzer type of equipment.   The advantage of checking electronic-analog-computer results with this equipment lies in the ability of the equipment to carry out calculations to six-significant-figure accuracy and in the ease with which problems can be coded for solution on the computer.   The coding is analog in nature and resembles very closely the coding for mechanical differential analyzers of the type constructed by Vanevar Bush.[5]

The question may arise, then, "Why not replace the electronic analog computer with the digital integrating differential analyzer?"   The answer to this question lies in the speed of operation of the two devices.   The digital integrating differential analyzer is in the order of 10 times slower than the electronic analog computer when operated to approximately the same accuracy.   The addition of each significant figure of accuracy to the problem solution on a digital integrating differential analyzer (by coding) increases the problem-solution time by a factor of 10.   The computer operates at one one-thousandth the speed it can achieve using three-significant-figure accuracy, if it is coded for six-significant-figure accuracy.   The digital differential analyzer will be discussed in more detail in Chap. 13.

11-7. A Dynamic Check of Computer Operation.   For a considerable time, analog-computer operators have sought a rapid and convenient means of checking a computer to determine whether its operation is satisfactory.   In order to be most useful, a check should be dynamic in nature so as to check integrations as well as summations.   To be complete, the check should utilize all inputs and all outputs of the equipment undergoing test.

To devise a test problem fulfilling all the above requirements seems at first virtually impossible, and consequently little has been done along this line by most computer installations.

In reality, the preparation of a test problem capable of checking the operation of all integrating and summing amplifiers is not difficult. The approach that has been found useful on a REAC computer is to prepare a patch board to generate three sinusoids using excessive equipment in the circuit. By this means, all inputs and outputs of each amplifier, with the exception of one summer and one integrating amplifier, are used in the problem. The sum of two of the sinusoids at a time, operating 180° out of phase, are compared on a Brush recorder. Any error signal obtained by summing the sinusoids indicates a malfunction of some sort. Experience in using the circuit has shown it to be very sensitive to errors in the gains of the inputs of the various amplifiers. It is interesting to note that the very first application of the check problem on a relatively new computer located two cold-solder joints in the wiring of the patch bays. These cold-solder joints had remained undetected by the more conventional checks that had been made on the computer prior to that time. The check problem's usefulness is further increased by the ease with which any errors that are detected can be localized to a very few components on the computer. A comparison of frequencies of the sinusoids makes this possible.

The circuit diagram of the check problem devised by Warshawsky is included as Fig. 11-2. Brush recordings showing the response obtained from a properly operating computer are shown in Fig. 11-3a. A recording showing the effect of a 1 per cent error in a gain-1 input of an amplifier is shown in Fig. 11-3b. The error shown is typical of the errors present when amplifier gains are faulty.

11-8. Accuracy and Precision. No discussion of the methods of checking solutions obtained on an analog computer would be complete without at least a brief discussion of the terminology normally used in describing the degree of adequacy of analog-computer results. In the past, much confusion has been caused by the improper use of the terms error, percentage error, accuracy, and precision.

Error is defined as the difference between an observed or calculated value and the true value. *Precision* is the quality or state of being precise; exactness; accuracy; definiteness. *Accuracy* is defined as the state of being accurate; freedom from mistake or error; exact conformity to the truth. *Percentage error*, however, is a term that is completely meaningless unless the term is carefully defined by the user.

To ask: "What is the accuracy of an analog computer?" is meaningless. The capability of an analog computer to produce precise results

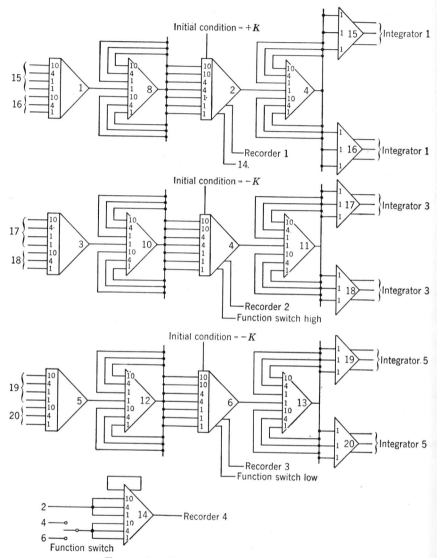

Fig. 11-2. A dynamic REAC check problem.

can be described most easily in terms of the precision of the individual components of the computer. As an example, the conventional means of describing the precision of a linear potentiometer is to state that it is linear to within 0.05 per cent of full scale.

A great deal of misunderstanding can arise from the indiscriminate

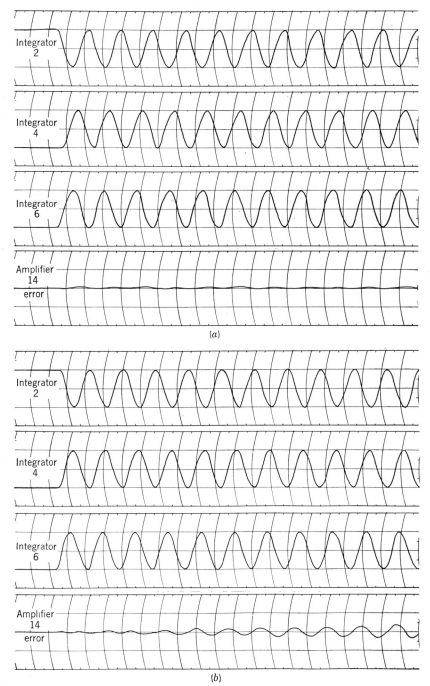

FIG. 11-3. Dynamic computer check. (a) Properly operating computer; (b) 1 per cent error in the value of the resistor used in the upper gain-1 input of amplifier 8.

219

use of the term *percentage error*. The improper usage of terms is illustrated by an actual incident with which the author is familiar. A particular problem was solved on an analog computer, and the graphical solutions of the problem were returned to the person who had submitted the problem. Shortly thereafter, a complaint was registered, stating that a numerical check of the problem solutions revealed that the problem results were in error by 150 per cent. The solutions of the problem were of such a nature that they approached zero asymptotically as t tended to infinity. In the region $t \gg 0$ the numerical solution and the analog-computer results differed slightly. It was this difference that had been reported as a 150 per cent error. If the error had been calculated as a percentage of the maximum value of the variable, the percentage error would have been found to be approximately 0.2 per cent. Proper definition of terms could have prevented the confusion that arose in this instance.

It is interesting to note that it was later determined that the analog-computer solution of the above problem was more precise than the numerical solution with which it was compared. In the numerical check of the problem solution the increments of tabulation were chosen to be too large, thereby introducing an appreciable error into the solution.

The precision of the results obtained on an analog computer is frequently influenced greatly by several factors. Most important among these is the very nature of the problem itself. A second factor that plays an important part in the precision of the computer results is the state of repair of the computer. High-accuracy multiplication, for example, is impossible on poorly aligned servomultipliers. A third factor that contributes greatly to the precision of a problem solution is the ability of the computer operator. The differences between a good computer setup and a relatively poor computer setup are often small. Similarly, the time required to modify a circuit diagram to improve it is usually a small percentage of the total time spent in problem preparation. If a computer operator takes the time to make needed refinements in a circuit diagram, he is almost always repaid for his efforts by a feeling of satisfaction for having completed a task that is well done.

PROBLEMS

11-1. From the circuit diagram of Fig. 11-1, write the equations of the bomb-trajectory problem. This check should include writing the identity satisfied by all summing amplifiers and multipliers. Compare your results with the original equations of the system (Sec. 5-6).

11-2. Check the circuit diagram given in Fig. 4-3 by writing the system equations from the circuit diagram.

11-3. Check the circuit diagram given in Fig. 5-10 by writing the system equations from the circuit diagram.

11-4. Prepare a problem check-out sheet, similar to that in Table 11-1, for the circuit diagram of Fig. 5-10.   Use $x(0) = y(0) = 1$ as initial values of x and y for the check-out.

REFERENCES

1. Gardner, Murray F., and John L. Barnes: "Transients in Linear Systems," p. 197, John Wiley & Sons, Inc., New York, 1942.
2. Richmond, W. F., Jr., and B. D. Loveman: Checking Analog Computer Solutions, "Project Cyclone Symposium II on Simulation and Computing Techniques, Part 2," pp. 147–154, Reeves Instrument Corporation (under sponsorship of U.S. Navy Special Devices Center and the U.S. Navy Bureau of Aeronautics), New York, Apr. 28–May 2, 1952.
3. Scarborough, James B.: "Numerical Mathematical Analysis," Johns Hopkins Press, Baltimore, 1930.
4. Milne, W. E.: "Numerical Calculus," Princeton University Press, Princeton, N. J., 1949.
5. Bush, Vannevar, and S. H. Caldwell: A New Type of Differential Analyzer, *J. Franklin Inst.*, vol. 240, no. 4, pp. 255–326, October, 1945.

CHAPTER 12

REPETITIVE ANALOG COMPUTERS

12-1. Introduction. In the preceding chapters little mention has been made of repetitive electronic analog computers. However, most of the techniques previously presented are, with a few exceptions, readily applicable to repetitive computers. In order to be able to apply those techniques, it is necessary only that the computer operator be familiar with the characteristics of the repetitive computer and particularly with the ways in which repetitive computers differ from real-time computers. It is the purpose of this chapter to familiarize the reader with repetitive computing equipment so that he may realize the limitations and capabilities of the equipment.

12-2. Advantages and Disadvantages of Repetitive Computers. The field of application in which the repetitive computer shows up to best advantage is in the simulation of servomechanism problems. In this field, some workers claim the repetitive computer to be superior to the real-time computer. This view is not shared by a great number of other workers in the computer field, and it is not the author's intention to become engaged in this discussion. Let it suffice to point out that the repetitive computer has gained widespread recognition and use and is capable of satisfactory results when used for the solution of many types of problems.

The basic characteristic of the repetitive computer that distinguishes it from the real-time computers previously discussed is that in the repetitive computer the solution of problems is carried out at an accelerated time scale. The problem solution is repeated sufficiently often to allow its presentation on an oscilloscope. The most common repetition rates of problem solution used on repetitive computers are 10 and 60 solutions per second. Of these solution repetition rates, the slower rate has certain definite advantages and is gaining more widespread acceptance among users of repetitive computing equipment. The advantages of the slower repetition rate of problem solution will be made clear in a later section.

222

In the past, little or no emphasis has been placed on the production of a high-precision repetitive computer. As far as is known to the author, no existing repetitive computer has been equipped with feedback and input impedances having a precision of better than 1 per cent of standard values. In fact, ordinary 5 per cent carbon resistors are commonly used in the computing circuits. The use of low-cost condensers in the integrators of repetitive computers is made possible by the short computing time required in the solution of problems. Integrator drift in a repetitive computer is relatively unimportant as compared to real-time computers, as problem-solution times are usually measured in milliseconds rather than in seconds. The short solution time of problems relaxes the requirements placed on the other computer components as well. The gain of amplifiers used in repetitive computers is frequently much lower than the gain of amplifiers found in most real-time computers. In the repetitive computer, the manner in which the equipment is used does not justify the use of more expensive high-gain amplifiers. The repetitive computers can, therefore, be in general classified as low-cost computers.

An operational advantage of the repetitive computer over the real-time computer is its ability to show almost instantaneously the effect of varying the parameters of a problem. This advantage is greatest, perhaps, in the synthesis of servomechanism systems. On the repetitive computer, a problem parameter can be changed and the results of the change can be viewed as a continuously varying system response. On the real-time computer, the computer must be reset and again placed in operation for every change of problem parameters. The operator is, therefore, able to scan the entire interesting range of problem parameters much more rapidly on the repetitive computer than on the real-time computer.

A major disadvantage of the repetitive computer is its relatively low accuracy. It is difficult to obtain results precise to more than 5 or 10 per cent of full scale using this type of equipment. This is fortunately not a serious handicap in the solution of many problems. The analysis of a servomechanism system, for example, requires that the form of the solution be known rather than the quantitive values of the problem variables at all times. Other problems require as high-precision results as can be obtained. For these problems the repetitive computer is not satisfactory.

12-3. Philbrick Computer. The most widely used repetitive computer is the GAP/R Philbrick computer.* The earlier and still more commonly used Philbrick equipment consists of a relatively large num-

* George A. Philbrick Researches, Inc., Boston, Mass.

ber of highly specialized components. The most important of the Philbrick components are integrators, summers, and constant multipliers. The other components that are available are adapted to the generation of highly specialized functions commonly encountered in the simulation of physical systems.

Because of the number of different components available, the symbolic representation of the Philbrick components differs from the symbolism used in the preparation of circuit diagrams for real-time computers. Each individual Philbrick computer component has been assigned a letter designation. Table 12-1 gives the Philbrick letter designation, the function performed, and the symbolic representation of the component. In Table 12-1, it should be noted by the reader that the output of each component is indicated as $\pm$. In the Philbrick components a one-tube inverting amplifier is provided to supply the positive output. To obtain the best possible results when using Philbrick computing equipment, the negative output of each amplifier should be used whenever possible. Using the negative output will reduce somewhat the error inherent in the inverting stage of the components.

It should be noted that no provision is made on the K3-J or K3-C components to sum several quantities at their inputs. Similarly, no gains other than unity are provided on the K3-J and K3-A. This inflexibility of components is one very serious disadvantage of the specialized-component design philosophy adopted by Philbrick.

At this point in the discussion of Philbrick computing equipment, it may be well to consider in greater detail the time scale of the equipment. The ratio of feedback to input impedances used in all the components performing the operations of calculus, i.e., the K3-J, K3-D, K3-K, K3-E, and the K3-L, is fixed so as to produce a time-scale change in the computer. The change made speeds up the solution so that 1 sec of real time is represented on the computer by 0.4 msec. Thus, if a problem having a sinusoidal solution with a period of 1 sec is solved on the computer, the period of the computer results will be 0.4 msec. In the case of the integrator, the time-scale change is accomplished by using a 0.004-μf condenser and a 0.1-megohm resistor as the feedback and input impedances, respectively.

The input stimulus used as a forcing function on the Philbrick repetitive computer is normally of the form of a step-voltage input. Frequently, a more complex voltage waveform than a simple step voltage is used. In the older Philbrick central control unit a complex rectangular voltage is generated for use as a computer stimulus. This waveform is commonly referred to by Philbrick users as a *delta*

Component	Letter designation	Equation	Symbol
Integrator.....	K3-J	$z_o = \dfrac{1}{\tau_0}\displaystyle\int x_1\,dt$ $\tau_0 = 0.4$ msec	J x_1 $+$ $+x_o$ / $-$ $-x_o$
Adding component	K3-A	$z_o = x_1 + \cdots + x_4$	A $x_1 \cdots x_4$ $+$ $+x_o$ / $-$ $-x_o$
Coefficient component	K3-C	$z_o = K x_1$ $0 \le K \le 100$	C x_1 $+$ $+x_o$ / $-$ $-x_o$
Differentiating component	K3-D	$z_o = \tau_0\,\dfrac{dx_1}{dt}$ $\tau_0 = 0.4$ msec	D x_1 $+$ $+x_o$ / $-$ $-x_o$
Augmenting integrator	K3-K	$z_o = x_1 + \dfrac{1}{\tau}\displaystyle\int x_1\,dt$ $0 \le \dfrac{1}{\tau} \le 2.5 \times 10^3$ 1/sec	K x_1 $+$ $+x_o$ / $-$ $-x_o$
Augmenting differentiator	K3-E	$z_o = x_1 + k\tau_0\,\dfrac{dx_1}{dt}$ $0 \le k\tau_0 \le 0.4$ msec	E x_1 $+$ $+x_o$ / $-$ $-x_o$
Unit-lag component	K3-L	$z_o = x_1 - \tau\,\dfrac{dz_o}{dt}$ $0 \le \tau \le 0.4$ msec	L x_1 $+$ $+x_o$ / $-$ $-x_o$
Bounding component	K3-B	$z_o = x_1 \quad -B \le x_1 \le B$ $z_o = B \quad x_1 > B$ $z_o = -B \quad x_1 < -B$	B x_1 $+$ $+x_o$ / $-$ $-x_o$

Component	Letter designation	Equation	Symbol
Backlash component	K3-H	$x_1 - \dfrac{H}{2} \le z_o \le x_1 + \dfrac{H}{2}$	H x_1 $+$ $+x_o$ / $-$ $-x_o$
Inert-zone component	K3-Z	$z_o = 0 \qquad -\dfrac{D}{2} \le x_1 \le \dfrac{D}{2}$ $z_o = x_1 - \dfrac{D}{2} \quad x_1 > \dfrac{D}{2}$ $z_o = x_1 + \dfrac{D}{2} \quad x_1 < \dfrac{D}{2}$	Z x_1 $+$ $+x_o$ / $-$ $-x_o$
Squaring component	K3-S	$z_o = A x_1^2$	S x_1 $+$ $+x_o$ / $-$ $-x_o{}'$
Square-root component	K3-T	$z_o = K\sqrt{x_1}$	T x_1 $+$ $+x_o$ / $-$ $-x_o$
Absolute-value component	K3-V	$z_o = A|x_1|$ or $z_o = 2A|x_1| - 50A$	V x_1 $+$ $+x_o$ / $-$ $-x_o$
Dynamic component	K4-DY	$A\tau_0^2\,\dfrac{d^2y}{dt^2} + A_1\tau_0\,\dfrac{dy}{dt} + A_0 y = x_1(t)$ $\tau_0 = 0.4$ msec $0 \le A_1, A_2, A_3 \le 100$	DY x_1 $+$ $\dfrac{d^2y}{dt^2}$ $-$; $+$ $\dfrac{dy}{dt}$ $-$; $+y$ / $-y$
Function multiplier	K4-MU	$z_o = \dfrac{x_1 x_2}{10}$	MU x_1, x_2 $+$ $+x_o$ / $-$ $-x_o$
Function generator	K4-FF	Diode-type arbitrary-function generator	FF x_1 $f(x_1)$

225

wave and will be so designated in the remainder of this chapter. The form of the delta wave is shown in Fig. 12-1.

The delta wave is formed by clipping the peaks from a 60-cycle sinusoidal signal and then reamplifying and amplitude-clipping the

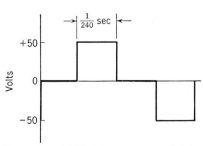

peak signals. A block diagram of the delta-wave generator is shown in Fig. 12-2 to make clear the technique utilized in generating the delta wave.

Since the delta wave is formed from a 60-cycle sinusoidal signal, the duration of one complete cycle of the delta wave is $\frac{1}{60}$ sec $\cong$ 16 msec. Each segment of the delta wave is, therefore, approximately 4 msec in duration

FIG. 12-1. Philbrick computer "delta wave" used as a forcing function in problems.

when the delta-wave generator is properly adjusted.

It will be recalled now that the time scale of the Philbrick components is such that 1 sec of real time is represented by 0.4 msec on the computer. Since each segment of the delta wave is approximately 4.0 msec in duration, each segment of the delta wave represents 10 sec of real time. In order to interpret the time scale of the

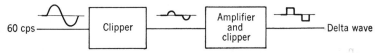

FIG. 12-2. Delta-wave generator.

computer when the computed results of a problem are presented on an oscilloscope, it is necessary to adjust the horizontal gain of the oscilloscope to cause the delta wave to occupy 10 convenient units on the oscilloscope screen. Each unit on the screen then represents 1 sec of problem time on the computer.

When the horizontal gain of the oscilloscope is attenuated until a complete cycle of the delta wave can be seen on the oscilloscope, the solution of a problem appears to take place four times on the computer. The computer transient is excited by each step change in voltage of the delta wave. In use, the horizontal gain of the oscilloscope is adjusted as previously described in order that the transient response due to only one segment of the delta wave can be seen on the oscilloscope. Normally, the positive step of the delta wave is the portion displayed.

The very nature of the delta wave imposes a limitation on the variety of problems that can be solved on the computer when using it as a computing stimulus. Effectively, only 10 sec of real time can be observed in the solution of a problem. Of course, a time-scale change can be made in a problem such that the problem solution is slowed or speeded up as desired. Similar to the real-time computers, the repetitive computer is troubled by phase shift. There is, therefore, an upper limit to the problem frequencies usable in the solution of problems and a very finite problem time interval that can be displayed on the oscilloscope when using the delta wave as the stimulus.

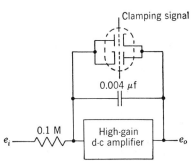

Fig. 12-3. System for clamping an integrator output to zero at predetermined times.

It is this restriction in problem-computing time that has led to the more widespread use of a simple rectangular voltage form as the computing stimulus for repetitive computers. For the same reason, a computing stimulus having a repetition rate of 10 cps has become more widely used. Utilizing a rectangular wave as the computing stimulus and a repetition rate of 10 cps, each computing interval can be used to represent over 200 sec of real time.

12-4. Initial Conditions. On the repetitive computer the techniques used in resetting the computer integrators to zero and applying the proper initial conditions to them must, by necessity, differ from the methods used on real-time computers. Providing the problem being solved on the repetitive computer is sufficiently stable to allow the transient response to die out during the computing interval and providing that no initial conditions are present in the system, no provision need be made for resetting the computer integrators to zero, since one complete cycle of a rectangular computing stimulus automatically returns the output of the computing amplifiers to zero. If, however, the problem transient does not die out in a computing cycle, provision must be made to reset the integrators to zero. Figure 12-3 shows one way of clamping the output of an integrator to zero at a predetermined time. The double triode shown in the figure is normally biased beyond cutoff. At a predetermined time a positive bias is placed on the grids of the double triodes and one or the other of the triodes conducts, forming a low-impedance shunt around the integrating condenser.   Most of the Philbrick computer integrators have provision for introducing a clamping signal.

The manner in which the clamping signal is generated is of interest, since it makes use of the delta wave and a K3-V component.   As indicated in Table 12-1, the K3-V is an absolute-value component.   Also, in Table 12-1, it is indicated that the K3-V has two alternate outputs. The selection of the desired output is made by throwing a switch located on the front of the component.   With the switch in the up position, the transfer function of the component is

$$\pm x_o = A|x_1| \qquad (12\text{-}1)$$

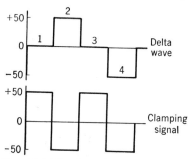

Fig. 12-4. The clamping signal derived from the delta wave using the K3-V component.

where $0 \leq A \leq 100$ is a constant that can be set by a dial on the component.   With the switch in the down position, the transfer function is

$$x_o = A(2|x_1| - 50) \qquad (12\text{-}2)$$

It is the negative output of the K3-V component that is used as the clamping signal for the integrators when the delta wave is used as the input and the switch is set so that Eq. (12-2) is satisfied by the component.

Figure 12-4 shows the delta wave and the clamping signal derived from the delta wave by using a K3-V component.   It is apparent that the voltage waveform shown in Fig. 12-4 satisfies the requirements of a clamping signal.   During the portion of the delta wave indicated by 1 and 3 in the diagram, the clamping signal is a large positive voltage so that the triodes shown in Fig. 12-3 conduct, shorting the output of the integrator to zero.   During the portions of the delta wave indicated by 2 and 4 in Fig. 12-3, the clamping signal is a large negative voltage that cuts off both triodes in the integrator feedback path.   The integrator is, therefore, allowed to function in a normal manner.

The clamping provision on the integrator satisfies the requirement that the integrator output be made equal to zero at the start of a compute cycle.   It does not in any way provide for the insertion of initial conditions other than zero in a problem.   If initial conditions on the output of integrators are needed in the solution of a particular problem, they must be provided by adding an appropriate voltage to the output of the integrators.   An adder component must, therefore, be provided at the appropriate place in the computing circuit to provide for the insertion of initial conditions when they have values other than zero.

12-5. Problem Setup. A few illustrative examples of problem set-ups for a Philbrick computer will help clarify the use of the equipment in the solution of problems.

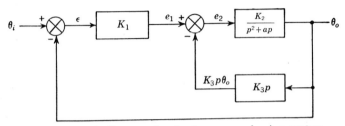

FIG. 12-5. Block diagram of a simple servomechanism system.

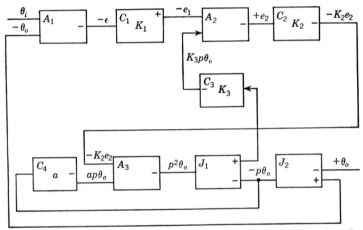

FIG. 12-6. Philbrick computer setup for the servomechanism system described by Fig. 12-5.

Example 12-1. Set up the simple servomechanism system described in Sec. 4-3. For convenience, the block diagram of the system is repeated here as Fig. 12-5. A Philbrick computer diagram of the simple servomechanism system described in Fig. 12-5 can be set up very easily from the block diagram. The circuit diagram using only K3-A, K3-C, and K3-J components is shown in Fig. 12-6.

Examination of the circuit of Fig. 12-6 reveals that it is very wasteful of equipment. Since each computer component in a circuit adds to the error in the problem solution, the results obtained from this circuit would probably not be as satisfactory as can be obtained by reducing the amount of equipment used.

In Fig. 12-7 the circuit diagram of Fig. 12-6 has been redrawn and considerable equipment has been eliminated from the circuit. In this system the major disadvantage arises from the fact that the settings of coefficient amplifiers C_1 and C_2

are functions of more than one parameter of the problem. In some cases it is desirable to retain some of the coefficient components that were eliminated from the circuit of Fig. 12-6, in order that the parameters of the problem K_1, K_2, K_3, and a can be adjusted separately. The most important saving of equipment in this

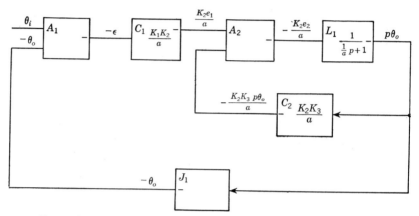

FIG. 12-7. Improved circuit diagram for the system of Fig. 12-5.

circuit is that made by replacing A_3, J_1, and C_4 by the unit lag component L_1. This is made possible by noting that the transfer function

$$\theta_o = \frac{k_2 e_2}{p^2 + ap} \tag{12-3}$$

can be expressed as

$$\theta_o = \frac{k_2 e_2}{p(p + a)} \tag{12-4}$$

An integrator and a K3-L component can be used to represent Eq. (12-4). The constant K_2 must, of course, be adjusted at some other point in the circuit diagram as indicated in Fig. 12-7.

The highly specialized nature of the Philbrick components almost always leads to very wasteful circuit diagrams unless care is taken to use the special components provided such as the augmenting integrator, the augmenting differentiator, the unit lag component, and the dynamic component when they are applicable in a circuit diagram.

Example 12-2. Set up the circuit for solution of the system

$$\frac{dy}{dt} + ay = 0 \tag{12-5}$$

with the initial condition

$$y(0) = 1 \tag{12-6}$$

In this system an initial condition on the problem variable is specified, and since there is no provision on the equipment for the inclusion of initial values, provision must be made in the preparation of the circuit diagram to introduce the initial values into the system. Figure 12-8 shows a circuit capable of generating the function described by Eqs. (12-5) and (12-6).

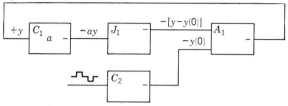

FIG. 12-8. Circuit for the solution of $dy/dt + ay = 0$ for $y(0) = 1$.

The adjustment of scale factor on a repetitive computer is just as important as the adjustment of scale factor on a real-time computer. In fact, amplitude-scale factor is perhaps even more critical than on the real-time computer, since the operating voltage range for most repetitive computers is ± 50 volts rather than ± 100 volts as is used on most real-time computers. Furthermore, it is difficult to adjust voltage levels in a problem so that the operating voltage range of the components throughout a Philbrick computer setup is uniform. This difficulty is due to the absence of gain adjustments on any but the K3-C components. It is necessary, therefore, that voltage levels in a problem be controlled almost entirely by the adjustment of the problem time scale.

In the use of Philbrick equipment, very often the problems solved are linear differential equations with constant coefficients. In the solution of this class of problems, the scale factor of the computer setup can be changed by changing the magnitude of the problem forcing function. In calibrating the oscilloscope, the forcing function of the problem can be displayed on the oscilloscope as a ready means of calibrating the scope to the desired scale. When used in this manner, the actual voltage level in the problem is unimportant. The voltage level should, however, be made as large as possible in order that noise effects in the problem solution may be minimized.

12-6. Trends in the Design of Repetitive Computers. The design of analog computer components as highly specialized special-purpose units, which can be interconnected in cookbook fashion to give the solution of dynamic problems, has served a useful purpose in the past. This design technique has permitted people with little or no previous knowledge of analog-computer techniques to set up successfully systems of equations on the analog computer.

Sooner or later, as the experience of the user becomes greater, the specialized components become a handicap instead of an advantage. More components are required in the solution of problems than are required using general-purpose equipment, and furthermore there are always unused components sitting on the shelf, since the particular problem being solved may not require their use. At the same time, there may be a shortage of other components needed in the problem.

Recently, the trend in the manufacture of repetitive computers has been to make them more similar to real-time computers. For example, the newer Philbrick K-2 components consist only of the high-gain d-c amplifiers, and the desired input and feedback impedances are patched on the computer as needed in the solution of a particular problem. The techniques of using the Philbrick K-2 components are, therefore, very similar to the techniques of using a real-time computer.

The main source of information dealing specifically with the Philbrick computer components is the manufacturer of the equipment. An excellent source of information regarding problems that have been solved on repetitive computers and also regarding modifications that have been made on repetitive equipment to make it more useful is the *Proceedings* of the Philbrick Computer Symposiums. These conferences were organized by Philbrick computer users of the Middle West to acquaint each other with problems they had encountered and the solutions they had obtained for these problems. To date, four symposiums have been conducted.

A repetitive computer that should receive mention at this point is that built at the Massachusetts Institute of Technology under the direction of Macnee.[1] Unlike the Philbrick repetitive computer, the Macnee computer employs a-c rather than d-c amplifiers. The use of a-c amplifiers in the computer eliminates the need for regulated power supplies such as are necessary for d-c amplifiers. The accuracy of the computer is of the same order of magnitude as that of the other existing repetitive computers.

REFERENCE

1. Macnee, A. B.: An Electronic Differential Analyzer, *Proc. IRE*, November, 1949.

CHAPTER 13

THE DIGITAL INTEGRATING
DIFFERENTIAL ANALYZER

13-1. Historical Development. A more recent innovation in the computing field than even the electronic analog computer is the *digital integrating differential analyzer*. The forerunner of the present-day digital integrating differential analyzers was built at Northrup Aircraft Corporation[1] under an Air Force contract. Although the prototype computer was designed for possible air-borne applications, it did not take long for the designers to realize the commercial possibilities of the computer. A production model computer, the MADDIDA, was built and placed on the market in 1950.[1]

A series of unfortunate circumstances delayed the widespread acceptance and use of the MADDIDA. Like its prototype, the MADDIDA design was based upon the binary number system, a system very awkward to use without adequate conversion equipment. To make matters worse, the early binary-to-decimal conversion equipment and the early recording equipment gave considerable difficulty in actual use. Other disadvantages of the early computers were that (1) troubles were frequently encountered in the computer that were attributed to insufficient design tolerances in the computer components, and (2) the input of data into the computer required the operator to perform the tedious process of *filling* each integrator serially, using a binary keyboard.

The warm reception that the MADDIDA first met soon faded, and eventually the computer was withdrawn from the market. Recently, more mature versions of the digital integrating differential analyzer type of computers have been introduced to the market, and it is believed that they will make a real place for themselves in the computing field.

13-2. Design Features of the Newer Digital Integrating Differential Analyzers. There are presently two digital integrating differential analyzers in commercial production; one is produced by Bendix Aviation Corporation[2] and the other by the Computer Research Corporation.[3] No attempt will be made here to compare the features of the two machines, as the basic principles of operation are similar. A general description of these computers will be made, however, to indicate in a general way the capabilities of this class of computing equipment.

The more recently designed digital integrating differential analyzers operate in the decimal number system, so that no external conversion equipment needs to be provided for converting numbers from the base 2 to the base 10 number system, as was necessary with the MADDIDA. This one design feature provides considerable operating convenience over the earlier MADDIDA computer.

The present-day digital integrating differential analyzers have 60 integrators. Each integrator has a capacity of six digits plus sign in its storage registers and has the capability of multiplying its output by a six-digit constant multiplier that is restricted to lie in the range ± 1. Other features have been incorporated into the design of the computers that provide considerable flexibility of operation. For example, special coding is provided in the computers to multiply a variable arbitrarily by the sign of any other variable in the problem. This feature allows choice functions to be performed. Similarly, any integrator can be coded to limit its output arbitrarily. This allows the representation of nonlinear phenomena to be accomplished on the computer.

Other features that make the newer digital integrating differential analyzers more convenient to operate than their predecessors are their input-output systems. The filling of coding instructions into the present-day computers is accomplished by typing the required information on a 10-key decimal keyboard. The computers can be coded to stop at predetermined points in the calculation and print out desired data on an electric typewriter.

To one familiar with electronic analog computers, a 60-integrator computer sounds like quite a large-capacity machine. It should be pointed out, however, that these integrators are used for all the mathematical operations performed by the computer. The processes of addition, subtraction, and integration require one integrator each, while multiplication requires two or three integrators, depending upon how the output is to be used. A 60-integrator differential analyzer has, therefore, somewhat less capacity than a 60-amplifier electronic analog computer. Just as in the electronic analog computers, several digital integrating differential analyzers may be ganged together to solve problems requiring capacities greater than that provided by a single machine.

13-3. Operation of the Digital Integrating Differential Analyzer.
The digital integrating differential analyzer operates in a manner very
similar to the mechanical differential analyzer of the Bush type.[4]   The
coding for the mechanical differential analyzer and the digital integrating differential analyzer is very similar; in fact, identical coding
sheets may be used for the coding of the two devices.   The main difference lies in the manner of performing integrations and in the manner
of transmitting information between the components of the computers.
To provide an analogy and to thus
simplify the explanation of the digital integrator, the mechanical integrator will first be described.

The mechanical integrator (see
Fig. 13-1) consists of a flat disk,
a wheel resting upon the disk, and
a lead-screw mechanism to control
the radial postioning of the wheel
on the disk.   Any incremental rotation of the disk dx causes a rotation of the wheel dz proportional
to y and to dx and inversely pro-
portional to the size of the wheel k.   The angular incremental rotation of the wheel may, therefore, be defined as

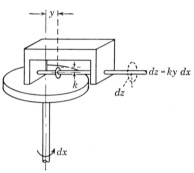

FIG. 13-1. Mechanical integrator.

$$dz = \frac{1}{k} y \, dx \qquad (13\text{-}1)$$

If, at the same time that x is rotated, a differential input dy is applied
to the lead screw, the shaft position z is proportional to the integral
of y with respect to x, or

$$z = \frac{1}{k} \int y \, dx \qquad (13\text{-}2)$$

The graphical interpretation of integration as the summation of the
area under a curve is useful in understanding the digital integrator.
The original concept of the definite integral is based upon just such a
summation.   In Fig. 13-2, $y(x)$ is a function of x and is continuous
in the interval a to b.   If the interval (a,b) is divided into m sub-
intervals by inserting points of subdivision

$$a = x_0 < x_1 < x_2 < \cdots < x_m = b$$

and $\Delta x_i = x_{i+1} - x_i$, the limit of the sum as $m \to \infty$ in such a manner that $\Delta x_i \to 0$ simultaneously is

$$\lim_{\substack{m \to \infty \\ \Delta x_i \to 0}} \sum_{i=1}^{m} y_i \, \Delta x_i = \int_a^b y \, dx \qquad (13\text{-}3)$$

If the method of subdivision is specialized such that all intervals Δx_i are equal, then

$$\int_a^b y \, dx = \lim_{m \to \infty} \Delta x \sum_{i=1}^{m} y_i \qquad (13\text{-}4)$$

For any preassigned error ϵ, a $\Delta x > 0$ can be found such that

$$\int_a^b y \, dx - \Delta x \sum_{i=1}^{m} y_i < \epsilon \qquad (13\text{-}5)$$

Equation (13-5) simply states that an integral may be approximated

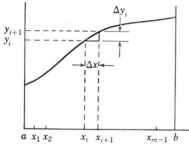

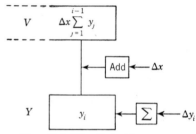

FIG. 13-2. Geometrical interpretation of the definite integral.

FIG. 13-3. The digital integrator.

arbitrarily close by summing the dependent variable y_i at discrete steps of the independent variable x_i and multiplying the sum by Δx. It is this process that is mechanized in the digital integrator.

Considering again the diagram of Fig. 13-2, it is evident that y_{i+1} may be formed by adding Δy_i to y_i. This immediately leads to the configuration of an integrator given in Fig. 13-3.[5] It consists of two summing registers V and Y, where incremental inputs Δy_i are added into the Y register and the contents of the Y register is added to the V register at each incremental step Δx of the independent variable. The lower register contains the value of y_i at the time the calculation has reached the point x_i; the upper register contains the partial sum

$$V = \Delta x \sum_{j=1}^{i-1} y_j \qquad (13\text{-}6)$$

which is a satisfactory approximation to $\int y \, dx$.

Consider the upper register V to be split into two parts, a Z and an R section. The R section contains the same number of digit spaces as the Y register and overflows from its highest-order digit into the Z section. It is the overflow from the R section which corresponds to the change Δz of the mechanical integrator as the disk is rotated an increment Δx. The rate at which the overflow occurs is a function of the magnitude of the quantity stored in Y and the number of digits carried in the Y and R registers. A schematic diagram showing the overflow from the R section of the integrator is shown in Fig. 13-4.

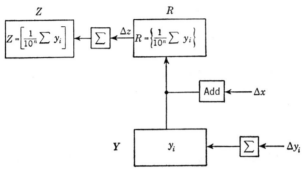

FIG. 13-4. The digital integrator showing the overflow from the R section of the integrator into a *hypothetical* Z section not actually incorporated in the digital integrator.

In the figure the square brackets [ ] are used to signify *the greatest integers in* and the braces { } are used to signify *the fractional part of.*

The operation of the digital integrator may be summarized by saying that Δx corresponds to $1/10^n$ where n is the number of digits in the registers, Δz is the incremental change in the output of the integrator. The sum of Δz stored in the Z register represents the total integral. It is the incremental change Δz that is of greatest interest, as this quantity may be used as the inputs to other integrators. The actual computer *does not* contain a register corresponding to the Z register shown in Fig. 13-4. If it is desired to sum the incremental changes Δz, it is necessary to do so in the Y section of another integrator. The Z register shown in the figure was included only as an aid to the reader in understanding the integration process.

13-4. The Number System. The requirements placed on a general-purpose integrator are such that it must handle *signed* information at its inputs and outputs. The mechanization of such a requirement, by considering the sign of both y and dx and attaching the correct symbol, offers considerable difficulty. One method of overcoming this apparent difficulty is by the use of a simple but ingenious number system. In order to mechanize this number system, it is necessary to add one binary digit space to the left end of the Y and R registers. The decimal point is then assigned to lie just to the right of this digit.

The number system used[5] extends from zero to 2. Corresponding to zero and 2 in the machine-number system are -1 and $+1$ in the real-number system. Problems to be solved on the computer must, therefore, be scaled, or normalized, so that the largest expected magnitude of any variable lies in the range ± 1.0.

A maximum negative input rate to an integrator is defined as an absence of pulses in every pulse position, and a maximum positive rate corresponds to a sequence of pulses in every pulse position. A zero rate similarly corresponds to an alternating series of 0, 1, 0, 1, 0, 1, . . . , where 1 is used to signify the presence of a pulse and 0 represents the absence of a pulse in a pulse position. A few numerical examples will illustrate the characteristics of this number system.

Assume that zero is the value placed in the Y register and that this value is to be integrated. A zero in the machine-number system corresponds to a 1 in the binary digit space to the left of the decimal point with all other digits equal to zero. Further, assume that the calculation is proceeding in successive steps of dx. With each step in dx the contents of the Y register is added to the contents of the R register. The quantity in the Y and R registers and the R overflow dz appears as in Eqs. (13-7). Note that an overflow dz occurs each time the sum of the quantities in the Y and R registers exceeds 1.999 $\cdot$ $\cdot$ $\cdot$.

$$
\begin{array}{rl}
& 0.000 \; R \\
& 1.000 \; Y \\
dz = 0 \leftarrow & \overline{1.000 \; R} \\
& 1.000 \; Y \\
dz = 1 \leftarrow & \overline{0.000 \; R} \\
& 1.000 \; Y \\
dz = 0 \leftarrow & \overline{1.000 \; R} \\
& 1.000 \; Y \\
dz = 1 \leftarrow & \overline{0.000 \; R}
\end{array}
\tag{13-7}
$$

The dz overflow is 0, 1, 0, 1, 0, 1, . . . , which in the machine-number system represents zero, the correct output for $y = 0$. As a further illustration, consider the representation of the real number 0.5. In the machine-number system this is represented as 1.500 $\cdot$ $\cdot$ $\cdot$. Again, assuming this number to be present in the Y register and the computation to be proceeding for successive steps in dx, the contents of the registers and overflows are as represented in Eqs. (13-8).

$$
\begin{array}{r}
0.000 \; R \\
1.500 \; Y \\
dz = 0 \leftarrow \overline{1.500 \; R} \\
1.500 \; Y \\
dz = 1 \leftarrow \overline{1.000 \; R} \\
1.500 \; Y \\
dz = 1 \leftarrow \overline{0.500 \; R} \\
1.500 \; Y \\
dz = 1 \leftarrow \overline{0.000 \; R} \\
1.500 \; Y \\
dz = 0 \leftarrow \overline{1.500 \; R} \\
\cdot \quad \cdot \\
\cdot \quad \cdot \\
\cdot \quad \cdot
\end{array}
\qquad (13\text{-}8)
$$

Similarly, the real number -0.5 is represented as $0.5000 \cdot \cdot \cdot$ in the machine system. If this is placed in the Y register and summed in the R register, there results

$$
\begin{array}{r}
0.000 \; R \\
0.500 \; Y \\
dz = 0 \leftarrow \overline{0.500 \; R} \\
0.500 \; Y \\
dz = 0 \leftarrow \overline{1.000 \; R} \\
0.500 \; Y \\
dz = 0 \leftarrow \overline{1.500 \; R} \\
0.500 \; Y \\
dz = 1 \leftarrow \overline{0.000 \; R} \\
\cdot \quad \cdot \\
\cdot \quad \cdot \\
\cdot \quad \cdot
\end{array}
\qquad (13\text{-}9)
$$

Tabulating the results of Eqs. (13-7) to (13-9) for the first eight steps in dx and assigning a weight of $+1$ to each pulse and -1 for each absence of a pulse makes it readily apparent that the results are completely compatible with the real numbers represented. These results are tabulated in Table 13-1.

Another important aspect of the number system used in the digital integrating differential analyzers is that it is effectively circular. By this it is meant that, upon reaching the maximum positive number that may be stored in the Y register, 1.999 $\cdots$, corresponding to a maximum positive rate dz, the addition of one more pulse into the Y register changes its value to 0.000 $\cdots$, corresponding to the maximum negative rate. This peculiarity of the number system has proved very valuable in the setup of certain functions, as it permits a servoing action to be achieved.

TABLE 13-1

Maximum negative rate:	$Y = 0.0$	0	0	0	0	0	0	0	0
	Weight	-1	-1	-1	-1	-1	-1	-1	$-1 = -8$
Half maximum negative rate:	$Y = 0.5$	0	0	0	1	0	0	0	1
	Weight	-1	-1	-1	$+1$	-1	-1	-1	$+1 = -4$
Zero rate:	$Y = 1.0$	0	1	0	1	0	1	0	1
	Weight	-1	$+1$	-1	$+1$	-1	$+1$	-1	$+1 = 0$
Half maximum positive rate:	$Y = 1.5$	0	1	1	1	0	1	1	1
	Weight	-1	$+1$	$+1$	$+1$	-1	$+1$	$+1$	$+1 = +4$
Maximum positive rate:	$Y = 1.99 \cdots$	1	1	1	1	1	1	1	1
	Weight	$+1$	$+1$	$+1$	$+1$	$+1$	$+1$	$+1$	$+1 = +8$

In the setup of problems on the computer, quite frequently the dx input of one integrator is supplied by the dz output of another integrator. The dx input of an integrator must, therefore, be in the same number system that is used as the dz output of the integrators. An actual step in dx is accomplished only when two pulses occur in succession. What this means is that each time a pulse input dx occurs, the contents of Y must be added to R, and in the absence of a pulse input to dx, Y must be subtracted from R.

Constructing a subtractor as well as an adder would be very wasteful of equipment. The necessity of providing a subtractor is eliminated by accomplishing subtraction by the addition of the machine complement on 2 rather than actually performing the operation of subtraction. As will subsequently be shown, obtaining the 2's complement of a number is a very simple process.

In order to obtain the 2's complement of a number in the number system being discussed, all that is necessary is to replace all zeros by 1's and all 1's by zeros in the number. To clarify this statement, consider the machine number 1.75. The complement on 2.0 of 1.75 is 0.25. The machine number 1.75 is represented as the repeating sequence

Machine 1.75 = 0, 1, 1, 1, 1, 1, 1, 1, 1, . . .

Changing all zeros to 1's and 1's to zeros gives the sequence

1, 0, 0, 0, 0, 0, 0, 0, . . .

Again assigning a weighting of $+1$ to each pulse (1) and -1 to each absence of a pulse (0), gives an average over the eight pulses of one-quarter the maximum negative number. But one-quarter the maximum negative number is the machine number 0.25, the desired complement.

A numerical example amply demonstrates the validity of adding to the R register the content of the Y register, or the complement of the content of that register, depending upon whether the Δx input is a 1 or zero respectively. Assume $Y = 1.75$; this is the machine number for 0.75. The machine complement is 0.25. If dx is a zero rate,

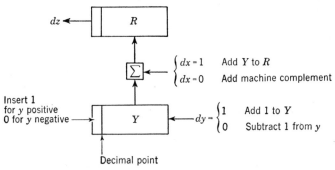

Fig. 13-5. The complete digital-integrator configuration.

the quantity in the Y and R registers and the dz overflow will be as in Eqs. (13-10):

$$
\begin{array}{ll}
0.000\ R & \\
1.75\ Y\ dx = 1 & \text{add} \\
dz = 0 \leftarrow \overline{1.75\ R} & \\
0.25\ Y\ dx = 0 & \text{add machine complement} \\
dz = 1 \leftarrow \overline{0.00\ R} & \\
1.75\ Y\ dx = 1 & \text{add} \\
dz = 0 \leftarrow \overline{1.75\ R} & \\
0.25\ Y\ dx = 0 & \text{add machine complement} \\
dz = 1 \leftarrow \overline{0.00\ R} &
\end{array}
\qquad (13\text{-}10)
$$

It is readily apparent that the sequence of overflows

$$dz = 0, 1, 0, 1, 0, 1, \ldots$$

is correct for a zero input dx.

The actual form of the digital integrator is shown in Fig. 13-5. It is apparent that to represent the sign of a quantity in a Y register, it is necessary to insert a zero or 1 in the left-hand binary column of the register, depending upon whether the number to be represented is negative or positive.

13-5. Communication between Integrators. In the electronic analog computers, interconnections between machine components are made by physically interconnecting the components with patch cords. In the digital integrating differential analyzer a memory in the form of a magnetic drum serves as the Y and R registers of the integrators and as a means of communication between integrators. Similarly, a single track on the magnetic drum is provided for the storage of the single digit that is the dz output of each integrator. All arithmetic operations are performed serially for one integrator at a time in a single arithmetic unit empowered with the ability to add and complement numbers. The magnetic drum also has channels serving as the coding storage for each integrator to control the proper selection of information from the Y, R, and dz memory channels as determined by the coding.

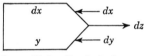

Fig. 13-6. Symbol for a digital integrator.

The operation of the computer can be broken down into steps. First, for a particular integrator, under control of the coding, the dz storage locations of all the integrators are scanned to obtain the correct dx and dy inputs for the integrator. The dx input is either a 0 or a 1. If more than one dy input is indicated in the coding, these quantities will be summed in the arithmetic unit and the sum will form the actual dy input. The dy input is *not* added to Y at this time. In the next operating step, the quantity in the Y storage register is added to the quantity in the R register and any overflow is placed in the appropriate dz storage space on the magnetic drum. Finally, the dy input is added to Y and the process is completed for the single integrator. A similar process of selection and addition is carried out in turn for each of the integrators in the computer in completing one cycle of operation.

13-6. The Coding Diagram. The symbol most commonly used to represent a digital integrator is shown in Fig. 13-6. The initial portion of the coding for the computer proceeds in a manner very analogous to that for a mechanical differential analyzer or for an electronic analog computer. A few simple problem setups will illustrate the similarity

Example 13-1

$$\frac{dy}{dx} = y \qquad (13\text{-}11)$$

As always, the setup can be started by assuming the existence of the highest-order derivative and then proceeding to form the quantities necessary to realize it. For Example 13-1, the circuit diagram is shown in Fig. 13-7. The dx input, the problem independent variable, is provided from a timing channel on the magnetic drum. Equation (13-11) states that $y = dy/dx$; therefore, summing dy (by intro-

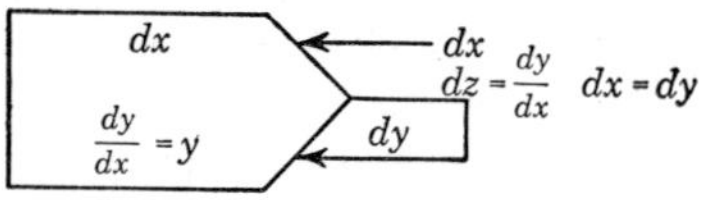

FIG. 13-7. Schematic diagram for the solution of Example 1.

ducing it in the dy input) produces dy/dx, the quantity originally assumed to be available.

Example 13-2

$$\frac{d^2\theta}{dt^2} + \frac{d\theta}{dt} + 2\theta = 0 \tag{13-12}$$

Again the setup may proceed as for the electronic analog computer and the circuit diagram can be drawn as in Fig. 13-8.

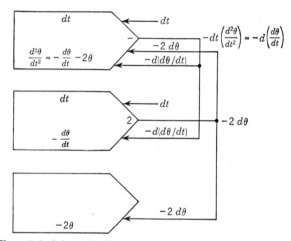

FIG. 13-8. Schematic diagram for the solution of Example 2.

A process that is very fundamental to analog computers is multiplication. As in the case of the mechanical differential analyzer, the digital integrating differential analyzer multiplies by the process of integration by parts. The following example will make the process clear.

Example 13-3. Form the product uv where u and v are dependent variables of the problem. The fundamental differential property

$$d(uv) = u\, dv + v\, du \tag{12-13}$$

provides the means of performing multiplication. This equation is mechanized in Fig. 13-9.

If the $u\,dv$ and $v\,du$ outputs shown in Fig. 13-9 are to be used as the dy inputs of a third integrator, they may be summed at the dy input of the third integrator. If they must be used as a dx input, they must first be summed in the Y section of a separate integrator, as no provision is made for multiple dx inputs. The number of integrators required in performing a multiplication is, therefore, either two or three, depending upon how the product is to be used in subsequent calculations.

The preparation of the symbolic diagram is only the first step of the problem preparation. The other major steps in preparing the problem for solution are:

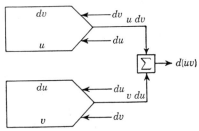

FIG. 13-9. A circuit for performing the operation of multiplication using digital integrators.

1. Coding to effect the proper selection of dx and dy inputs on the machine.

2. Determining the range of the variables so that proper scaling of the problem may be accomplished.

3. Scaling the variables or adjusting their magnitude to fit the numerical range of the computer.

4. Determining the proper initial condition for each integrand in the computer. This step is, of course, dependent upon the scales established in step 3.

5. Establishing the coding to provide the proper connection of input and output devices.

6. Placing the problem on the computer. This consists of typing the numerical information regarding each integrator into the computer on a keyboard. The information includes the location of the dx and dy inputs and the initial value of the integrand for each integrator.

13-7. Conclusions. The digital integrating differential analyzer is a very ingenious device that should establish a firm place for itself in the computing field. The equipment is more readily adapted to the solution of some problems than is the electronic analog computer. Notable among these problems is the solution of simultaneous algebraic equations. The greatest utility of the equipment arises, however, in the solution of systems of differential equations where the precision of the electronic analog computer is not sufficiently great to satisfy the problem requirements.

At present the digital integrating differential analyzer offers little threat of replacing the electronic analog computer. Its disadvantage is its operating speed. When it is coded to produce an accuracy approximately equivalent to that achieved by most electronic analog computers, its speed is approximately ten times slower. As each decimal digit of additional accuracy is required from the computer, its speed is slowed by a factor of 10. Thus, if it can operate at one-tenth the speed of an electronic analog computer while achieving three-significant-figure accuracy, its work output is reduced to one ten-thousandth of the work output of an electronic analog computer when it is coded for six-figure accuracy in its integrators.

The pulse rate at which the present-day digital integrating differential analyzers operate is approximately 100 kc. Although this compares fairly well with many large-scale digital computers (some achieve near-megacycle pulse rates) the serial nature of the computer results in considerably slower operation than a parallel digital computer operating at comparable pulse rates. In the solution of differential equations, however, the machine has the great advantage of retaining an analog coding scheme. The problem preparation time is, therefore, much less than for any general-purpose digital computer, as integrations must be programmed as step-by-step processes on the digital computers.

Perhaps in the future, as the rapid advance of digital computer technology continues, the large-scale digital computer will squeeze the lower-cost digital integrating differential analyzers from the market. When that day comes, the need for electronic analog computers will similarly be reduced. Before that day, however, several significant advancements must be made. The digital computer must be miniaturized, its cost must be greatly reduced, and, above all else, its coding must be simplified. Great strides have already been made in these directions in recent years, but there is still some distance to travel.

The most complete and authoritative descriptions of the mode of operation and the methods of setup of problems on the digital differential analyzers are contained in the manufacturers' operation manuals for the commercially available digital differential analyzers. The manuals contain a considerable number of illustrative examples giving the methods of setting up problems for the computers and in addition treat the problem of the proper scaling of problems for solution on the computers in considerable detail. The interested reader is referred to the manufacturers' manuals for more detailed information concerning the computers than is contained in this chapter.

Several papers have been written concerning the digital integrating differential analyzers. Some of these are listed below.[5-8]

PROBLEMS

13-1. What is the sequence of pulses representing the dz output of a digital integrator if the contents of the Y register is the real number 0.25 (machine number 1.25)? Show that the average dz output for eight pulse times corresponds to one-fourth the maximum positive output rate of the integrator.

13-2. What is the sequence of pulses representing the dz output of a digital integrator if the contents of the Y register is the real number -0.75? Show that the average dz output for eight pulse times corresponds to three-fourths the maximum negative rate of the integrator.

13-3. Show the interconnection diagram for the digital differential analyzer solution of the equation

$$5 \frac{d^2y}{dt^2} + 3 \frac{dy}{dt} + 10y = 10$$

13-4. Prepare an interconnection diagram for the internal generation of the function

$$y = e^{-\alpha t}$$

where time is the problem independent variable.

13-5. Prepare an interconnection diagram for the solution of the equation

$$\frac{d^2y}{dt^2} + 2y \frac{dy}{dt} + 4y = 10$$

REFERENCES

1. "MADDIDA Digital Differential Analyzer," Brochure 38, Northrop Aircraft, Inc., Hawthorne, Calif., December, 1950.
2. "Operation Manual, Digital Differential Analyzer Model D-12," Bendix Computer Division of Bendix Aviation Corporation, Los Angeles, Calif., April, 1954.
3. "CRC 105 Specifications: Decimal Digital Differential Analyzer," Computer Research Corporation, Hawthorne, Calif.
4. Bush, V., and A. H. Caldwell: A New Type of Differential Analyzer, *J. Franklin Inst.*, vol. 240, no. 4, pp. 255–326, October, 1945.
5. Mendelson, M. J.: The Decimal Digital Differential Analyzer, *Aeronaut. Eng. Rev.*, vol. 13, no. 2, February, 1954.
6. Weiss, E.: Applications of CRC 105 Digital Differential Analyzer, *Trans. IRE (Professional Group on Electronic Computers)*, December, 1952, pp. 19–24.
7. Sprague, R. E.: Fundamental Concepts of the Digital Differential Analyzer Method of Computation, *Math. Tables*, vol. 6, no. 37, pp. 41–49, January, 1952.
8. Palevsky, M.: The Design of the Bendix Digital Differential Analyzer, *Proc. IRE*, vol. 41, pp. 1352–1356, October, 1953.

APPENDIX

A-1. The Terminology of Differential Equations. A differential equation can be defined as a statement of the relationship between variables and their derivatives. A differential equation is *ordinary* if it contains only total derivatives and has only one independent variable (frequently time or distance). A differential equation is a *partial* differential equation when it involves a function of more than one variable and some of its partial derivatives. The solution of partial differential equations usually is more difficult than the solution of ordinary differential equations. Unfortunately this is true when using the electronic differential analyzer as well as when other methods are employed.

A *derivative* is the expression of the relative changes of two variables. More simply, a derivative can always be interpreted as a rate. The reader will find that if he interprets derivatives as rates he will be better able to use an analog computer as a tool to help him think in terms of the physical problem being solved.

Integration on an analog computer can be interpreted in the original sense of the Riemann integral, i.e., as the summation of the area under a curve. An alternate interpretation of an integral that is useful is that integration is the process of averaging or smoothing. These physical concepts aid the computer operator in understanding the analog computer operation.

The *order* of a differential equation is the order of the highest derivative that appears in the equation. Similarly the order of a system of differential equations is the order of the highest-order derivative that appears in the equation obtained by reducing the system to a single equation.

The *degree* of a differential equation is the degree that its highest-order derivative would have if the equation were rationalized and cleared of fractions with regard to all derivatives involved in it. As an example of the meaning of order and degree of a differential equation, consider the following equations:

$$\frac{dy}{dx} = x + 3 \tag{A-1}$$

$$x^2 \frac{d^2y}{dx^2} + 2x \frac{dy}{dx} + y = 2 \tag{A-2}$$

$$\left(\frac{d^2y}{dx^2}\right)^2 = \left(\frac{dy}{dx}\right)^3 + 3 \tag{A-3}$$

$$\frac{\partial^2 u}{\partial x^2} + \frac{\partial^2 u}{\partial y^2} + \frac{\partial^2 u}{\partial z^2} = 0 \tag{A-4}$$

Equations (A-1) to (A-3) are ordinary differential equations, whereas Eq. (A-4) is a partial differential equation involving three independent variables x, y, and z.

247

Equation (A-1) is of first order and first degree. Equation (A-2) is of second order and first degree. Equation (A-3) is of second order and second degree. Equation (A-4) is a second-order partial differential equation of first degree.

A differential equation is said to be *linear* when it is of the first degree in the dependent variable and the derivatives. By this definition Eqs. (A-1) and (A-2) are linear, and Eq. (A-3) is nonlinear. A further distinction can be made in the classification of linear differential equations. Equation (A-2) is linear but has nonconstant coefficients, whereas Eq. (A-1) is a linear differential equation with constant coefficients.

A *solution* of a differential equation is a relation between the variables of a differential equation which, when substituted into the equation, reduces it to an identity. To solve a differential equation is therefore to make known the relationship of these variables. The solution of a differential equation by classical methods results in the expression of the solution in terms of familiar functions such as exponentials, trigonometric functions, etc. The term *known* is used in a much broader sense here, however. If the relationship of the variables of a differential equation is known to any prescribed degree of accuracy, the result is a solution of the equation. A graphical plot of the variables as a function of the independent variable can, therefore, be a valid solution of the differential equations. Similarly the point-by-point solution of a differential equation by numerical methods is a valid solution of the equation if any prescribed accuracy is satisfied.

A standard method of solving linear differential equations satisfying one or more supplementary conditions is first to find all the solutions of the differential equation. This is normally called the *general solution* of the equation. It is then necessary to find the particular solution of the equations by applying the supplementary conditions expressed in the problem statement to the general solution already obtained. The supplementary conditions are usually stated in the form of initial conditions or boundary conditions.

In the solution of differential equations on an analog computer the reverse procedure is normally followed. The supplementary conditions are included in the computer setup, so that the results obtained from the computer are the unique solutions in which the operator is interested. In general it is easy to modify the supplementary conditions of the problem so that the solution of the differential equation under the influence of a large number of different initial conditions or forcing functions may be easily and rapidly obtained. Similarly, changing the parameters of the differential equation itself usually can be accomplished easily and rapidly in the analog computer setup.

A linear ordinary differential equation with constant coefficients is of the form

$$\frac{d^n y}{dx^n} + a_{n-1} \frac{d^{n-1} y}{dx^{n-1}} + \cdots + a_0 y = f(x) \qquad (A\text{-}5)$$

The solution of Eq. (A-5) is the sum of the general solution of the homogeneous equation

$$\frac{d^n y}{dx^n} + a_{n-1} \frac{d^{n-1} y}{dx^{n-1}} + \cdots + a_0 y = 0 \qquad (A\text{-}5a)$$

and any particular solutions of the complete equation.

The general solution of the homogeneous equation is of the form

$$y = \sum_{i=1}^{n} a_i y_i$$

where the a_i are arbitrary constants and the y_i are independent solutions of the equation. These n independent solutions of the homogeneous equation can be found by assuming that they are each of the form $y = e^{\gamma x}$. Substituting this value of y into the homogeneous equation, Eq. (A-5a), gives

$$(\gamma^n + a_{n-1}\gamma^{n-1} + \cdots + a_0)y = 0 \tag{A-6}$$

Since $y = 0$ is a trivial solution of Eq. (A-5a), the interesting solutions must be those obtained by setting the polynomial in $\gamma = 0$:

$$\gamma^n + a_{n-1}\gamma^{n-1} + \cdots + a_1\gamma + a_0 = 0 \tag{A-7}$$

This polynomial has n roots: γ_n, γ_{n-1}, . . . , γ_1. Providing the n roots are distinct, these n values of γ can each be substituted into the assumed form of the solution to give

$$y = \sum_{i=1}^{n} a_i y_i = \sum_{i=1}^{n} a_i e^{\gamma_i x} \tag{A-8}$$

as the general solution of the homogeneous equation. If repeated roots, say γ_r, occur then the general solution of the homogeneous equation is

$$y = \sum_{i=1}^{n-m} a_i e^{\gamma_i x} + (a_{n+1-m} + \cdots + a_m t^{m-1})e^{\gamma_r x} \tag{A-8a}$$

where m is the number of times the root γ_r occurs in the polynomial (A-7).

The general solution of the homogeneous differential equation is independent of any forcing function and is thus sometimes called the *transient* solution and designated by a subscript t. The use of the term *transient solution* arises since, for a differential equation representing a stable physical system, the solution of the homogeneous equation always vanishes as x tends to infinity. The term *steady-state solution* is used to designate the particular solutions that arise as a result of the forcing function of the nonhomogeneous equation. Again the term was originated from physical considerations, as it is the portion of the solution remaining after the transient solution has vanished.

Example A-1. A constant force F is applied to a mass M free to move in the direction of the applied force under the constraint of viscous friction K. The equation of motion of the system is

$$M \frac{dv}{dt} + Kv = F \tag{A-9}$$

Setting the left side of Eq. (A-9) equal to zero gives the homogeneous equation from which the characteristic roots of the equation can be obtained:

$$M \frac{dv}{dt} + Kv = 0 \tag{A-10}$$

Proceeding as suggested above, let

$$v_t = ae^{\gamma t}$$

where v_t is the transient solution; then

$$\frac{dv}{dt} = \gamma a e^{\gamma t}$$

Substituting these values for v_t and dv/dt into Eq. (A-9) gives

$$(M\gamma + K)ae^{\gamma t} = (M\gamma + K)y = 0 \tag{A-11}$$

Since Eq. (A-9) is a first-order differential equation, there is only one characteristic root. The value of this root is, of course,

$$\gamma = -\frac{K}{M}$$

The transient solution is therefore

$$v_t = ae^{-(K/M)t}$$

The steady-state solution of the equation can be obtained in this simple case by noting that in the steady-state condition the acceleration dv/dt is zero, since the forcing function is a constant. Setting dv/dt equal to zero in Eq. (A-9) gives

$$v_p = \frac{F}{K} \tag{A-12}$$

where v_p represents the particular or steady-state solution. Combining the transient solution v_t and the steady-state solution v_p gives the solution of the equation for the velocity v

$$v = v_t + v_p = ae^{-(K/M)t} + \frac{F}{K} \tag{A-13}$$

It is important to note here that the differential equation and forcing function do not completely determine the solution of the equation. This is apparent since the coefficient a in Eq. (A-13) is still undetermined. It is necessary to determine this constant in such a manner that the initial conditions of the problem are satisfied. Assume in this example that at time $t = 0$ the velocity is zero. Then from Eq. (A-13) it can be seen that

$$a = -\frac{F}{K} \tag{A-14}$$

Substituting this value of a into Eq. (A-13) gives

$$v = \frac{F}{K}(1 - e^{-(K/M)t}) \tag{A-15}$$

The linear differential equation solved here is one of the simplest differential equations having an interesting solution, but the method used in its solution is valid for all ordinary linear differential equations with constant coefficients. The task of solving even linear differential equations of higher order may become quite laborious, however, as it is always necessary to determine the roots of the polynomial in γ (the characteristic equation).

For linear differential equations with nonconstant coefficients and for nonlinear differential equations, more powerful techniques than that demonstrated above must be used. In fact it is not always true that an explicit solution of a differential equation can be found.

Since the solution of differential equations can be a very laborious task and since their solution is of such vital importance to engineers, methods of solving them by other than the classical methods have been sought with considerable success. Several methods of solving them by mechanical means have been devised. The direct-analog or network-analyzer class of equipment is one of the oldest methods used. The mechanical differential analyzer is another powerful tool for use in solving differential equations. The electronic differential analyzer is an even newer device developed as a tool for aiding in the solution of differential equations.

A-2. Time Constants and Natural Frequencies. The differential equations representing a great number of complex physical systems can be written in the form of simultaneous first- and second-order linear differential equations having constant coefficients. For this reason the analog-computer operator finds a knowledge of first- and second-order equations very helpful in making a computer setup of a system.

The first-order linear differential equation

$$\frac{dy}{dx} + ay = 0 \tag{A-16}$$

has a solution of the form

$$y = Ae^{-at} \tag{A-17}$$

The solution of the equation is stable if a is positive, since y then approaches zero as t becomes infinite. If a is negative, however, the solution is divergent or unstable, since y increases without bound.

The *time constant* of an exponential function is that value of time that causes the exponent to become equal to -1. Equation (A-17) is, therefore, expressable as

$$y = Ae^{-t/\tau} \tag{A-18}$$

where τ, the time constant, is equal to $1/a$. The time constant is thus the time required for an exponential function to decay to $1/e$ times its initial value. Similarly in a period of four time constants the exponential function approaches to within approximately 2 per cent of its final value. A useful assumption when estimating the solution time of a problem on an analog computer is that exponential transients die out in four time constants.

[margin note: 0.632 of max]

The second-order differential equation represented in general form as

$$M\frac{d^2x}{dt^2} + C\frac{dx}{dt} + Kx = 0 \tag{A-19}$$

can be written in the special form

$$\frac{d^2x}{dt^2} + 2\zeta\omega_n\frac{dx}{dt} + \omega_n^2 x = 0 \tag{A-20}$$

[margin note: $2\zeta\omega_n = \frac{C}{M}$ $\omega_n^2 = \frac{K}{M}$]

where ω_n is the *undamped natural frequency* and ζ is the *damping ratio*. The undamped natural frequency has the units of radians per second and is 2π times the frequency of oscillation of the system with zero damping. The damping ratio is nondimensional and is the ratio of the actual damping of the system to the damping required to produce a critically damped solution.

It is relatively simple to justify the definition of the parameters ω_n and ζ given above. Setting the damping term of Eq. (A-19) equal to zero gives

$$\frac{d^2x}{dt^2} + \frac{K}{M}x = 0 \tag{A-21}$$

[margin note: $p^2x + \frac{K}{M}x = 0$]

The roots of this equation are

$$r_1, r_2 = \pm j \sqrt{\frac{K}{M}}$$

A solution of the differential equation is therefore

$$x = A \cos\left(\frac{K}{M} t + \phi\right) \tag{A-22}$$

Comparison of Eqs. (A-19) and (A-20) reveals that $\omega_n = \sqrt{K/M}$, the same result that was indicated by the solution of Eq. (A-21).

The roots of Eq. (A-19) are

$$r_1, r_2 = \frac{-C \pm \sqrt{C^2 - 4MK}}{2M} \tag{A-23}$$

For stable systems the roots r_1 and r_2 can take on three forms: (1) conjugate complex roots with negative real parts (oscillatory), (2) equal negative real roots (critically damped), (3) unequal negative real roots (nonoscillatory). The conditions giving critical damping are those sets of parameters that cause the quantity under the radical sign in Eq. (A-23) to be equal to zero. The critical damped condition is therefore

$$C_c = 2 \sqrt{MK}$$

The actual damping term in Eq. (A-19) is C, so that

$$\zeta = \frac{C}{C_c} = \frac{C}{2 \sqrt{MK}} = \frac{C}{2M\omega_n} \tag{A-24}$$

This result is the same as that obtained by normalizing Eq. (A-19) and then comparing the terms of Eqs. (A-19) and (A-20).

An effort should be made by the reader to memorize the form of the second-order differential equation as given in Eq. (A-20). This form of the equation reveals immediately the undamped natural frequency of the system and the relative stability of the system in terms of the damping ratio.

The actual frequency of oscillation of the damped system, Eq. (A-19), is given by the expression

$$\omega = \omega_n \sqrt{1 - \zeta^2} \tag{A-25}$$

The proof of the validity of Eq. (A-25) will be left to the reader as an exercise.

A-3. Operator Notation. The use of operator notation has been widely adopted in some phases of engineering work. This is particularly true in the field of automatic control and in some aerodynamic studies. The satisfactory analog-computer solution of differential equations expressed in operator notation frequently requires the application of special techniques. These special techniques are discussed extensively in Chap. 4.

A brief description of the operator notation and its properties is given in the remainder of this section. It is believed that the material presented here will be sufficient to enable the reader with little previous exposure to the operator notation to read intelligently the material in Chap. 4 and the other portions of this book where the operator notation is used.

The conventional differential operator is represented by p and indicates the operation d/dt. The second derivative operator is written as p^2 and stands for d^2/dt^2. In all cases the operator is assumed to operate on the term to its right when multiplication of that term by the operator is indicated. The following examples illustrate the use of the operator:

$$py = \frac{dy}{dt}$$

$$p^2y = \frac{d^2y}{dt^2}$$

$$(p^3 + k_1p^2 + k_2p)y = \frac{d^3y}{dt^3} + k_1\frac{d^2y}{dt^2} + k_2\frac{dy}{dt}$$

$$pyz = zpy + ypz = z\frac{dy}{dt} + y\frac{dz}{dt}$$

One of the important properties of the operator is that for linear differential equations the characteristic equation may be obtained by substituting γ for p in the polynomial expression for the operator and equating the expression to zero. This property makes the operator form particularly helpful in solving differential equations by classical methods.

Similar to the differential operator is the integral operator p^{-1}, where p^{-1} is defined by the equality

$$p^{-1} = \frac{1}{p} = \int dt$$

To show that p^{-1} is the integral operator and to bring out certain restrictions in its use, consider the equation

$$p^{-1}f(t) = \int_{t_0}^{t} f(t)\, dt \tag{A-26}$$

Multiplying both sides of Eq. (A-26) by p gives

$$pp^{-1}f(t) = p\int_{t_0}^{t} f(t)\, dt = \int_{t_0}^{t} \frac{df(t)}{dt}\, dt \tag{A-27}$$

or

$$pp^{-1}f(t) = f(t) - f(t_0) \tag{A-27a}$$

Examination of Eq. (A-27a) reveals that p^{-1} is the integral operator but that certain restrictions apply in its use. First, $df(t)/dt$ must exist, and secondly, $f(t_0)$ must equal zero.

If $Y(p)$ is defined as an operator of the form

$$Y(p) = a_0p^n + a_1p^{n-1} + \cdots + a_{n-1}p + a_n$$

in which the a's are constants, we can associate with each $Y(p)$ a $Y^{-1}(p)$. $Y^{-1}(p)$ is called the inverse or reciprocal of $Y(p)$, or

$$Y^{-1}(p) = \frac{1}{Y(p)}$$

Similar to the relation between p and p^{-1}, the formula $Y^{-1}(p)Y(p)y = y$ is correct only when y and its first $(n-1)$ derivatives vanish at $t = t_0$. In working with inverse operators it should be kept in mind that $y = Y^{-1}(p)f$ always implies $Y(p)y = f$ and that $Y^{-1}(p)y = f$ implies $y = Y(p)f$ only in special circumstances.

The use of the inverse operator provides a very convenient method of expressing the relationship of two variables. Consider, for example, the equation of motion of a linear oscillator such as is shown in Fig. A-1. The equation of motion of the system can be expressed in the two forms:

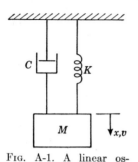

$$M \frac{dv}{dt} + Cv + K \int v \, dt = f \qquad (A\text{-}28)$$

$$M \frac{d^2x}{dt^2} + C \frac{dx}{dt} + Kx = f \qquad (A\text{-}29)$$

where v = velocity
x = displacement
C = coefficient of viscous friction
K = spring constant
M = mass
$f = f(t)$ = forcing function

Fig. A-1. A linear oscillator with viscous damping.

In operator notation Eqs. (A-28) and (A-29) can be written as

$$\left(Mp + C + \frac{K}{p}\right)v = f \qquad (A\text{-}30)$$

$$(Mp^2 + Cp + K)x = f \qquad (A\text{-}31)$$

Since $dx/dt = px = v$, both Eqs. (A-28) and (A-29) can be written as

$$(Mp^2 + Cp + K)v = pf \qquad (A\text{-}32)$$

This illustrates the fact that one variable may be replaced by an equivalent variable in the operator notation.

The *transfer function* is the expression that establishes the relationship of the input and output variables of a system as an operator equation. For example, the relationship between the voltage input and torque output of a d-c motor might be written as

$$T = \frac{a}{bp^2 + p} \, e_i$$

where a = constant
b = constant
T = torque
e_i = applied voltage

The expression $a/(bp^2 + p)$ is, therefore, the transfer function expressing this relationship.

An important property of the operator notation that makes it particularly useful in the block-diagram representation of physical systems is that linear transfer functions with constant coefficients can be multiplied as if they are algebraic expressions. Therefore the over-all transfer function of a physical system formed by the series connection of two components having transfer functions $Y_1(p)$ and $Y_2(p)$ is

$$Y(p) = Y_1(p)Y_2(p) \qquad (A\text{-}33)$$

The application of this property in writing equations for physical systems allows the engineer to represent a complex system as a group of smaller components properly interconnected. The differential equation or transfer function of each smaller component in the system can then be more easily represented mathematically. Application of Eq. (A-33) permits the engineer to combine the transfer functions of the component parts of the system into a single differential equation representing the composite system.

The representation of a system as a group of component parts is called a block diagram of the system. This form of representation is widely used in the study of servomechanisms and other phases of engineering wherein the transient behavior of a system is of interest. The block-diagram method of representing systems is discussed in Chap. 4.

A-4. Conditions for Stability. It is possible to find the characteristic roots of a system of differential equations and gain considerable knowledge about the nature of the solution of the system. For example, the system is stable and nonoscillatory in the steady state if all the roots of the equation have negative real parts. The presence of a single zero root does not affect this stable condition, but the presence of multiple zero roots or repeated pure imaginary roots causes the system to be unstable. The presence of conjugate complex roots indicates a damped oscillatory system response. If, however, any root of the system has a positive real part, the system is unstable. From the roots of the characteristic equation it is possible to determine the relative stability of the system. The study of servomechanisms includes a detailed treatment of the methods by which this can be done.

The task of determining the roots of a system of equations of third order or higher can be laborious. Fortunately a method does exist that permits one to determine system stability from the characteristic equation without solving for the roots. The method does not give information regarding the degree of stability of a system but nevertheless is very useful. This method is known as Routh's criterion.

The reader will find the method useful in checking analog-computer results and also as a basis for determining the approximate frequencies of higher-order equations as an aid in preparing problems for computer solution. The remainder of this section will be devoted to a statement, without proof, of as much of Routh's criterion as is useful in analog-computer work.

The characteristic equation of an nth-order differential equation from which any zero roots have been removed is

$$a_n p^n + a_{n-1} p^{n-1} + \cdots + a_1 p + a_0 = 0 \qquad \text{(A-34)}$$

where the a's are real, a_n is positive, and n is a positive real integer. To apply Routh's criterion it is necessary to form an array of the coefficients of the characteristic equation as

$$\begin{matrix} p^n \\ p^{n-1} \end{matrix} \quad \begin{vmatrix} a_n & a_{n-2} & a_{n-4} & \cdots \\ a_{n-1} & a_{n-3} & a_{n-5} & \cdots \end{vmatrix} \qquad \text{(A-35)}$$

The coefficients of the next row, as expressed in the form of determinants, are

$$p^{n-2} \quad \begin{vmatrix} -\dfrac{\begin{vmatrix} a_n & a_{n-2} \\ a_{n-1} & a_{n-3} \end{vmatrix}}{a_{n-1}}, & -\dfrac{\begin{vmatrix} a_n & a_{n-4} \\ a_{n-1} & a_{n-5} \end{vmatrix}}{a_{n-1}}, & \cdots \end{vmatrix}$$

Each succeeding row of the array is found by applying similar rules to the last two rows. The procedure is continued until no terms remain. If it simplifies the arithmetic of the procedure, each row of the array may be normalized before it is used in determining succeeding rows of the array. This is apparent from the theory of determinants.

Example A-2. Let the characteristic equation of a system be

$$4p^5 + 2p^4 - 5p^3 + 12p^2 + p + 6 = 0 \qquad \text{(A-36)}$$

The array is therefore

p^5	4	-5	1
p^4	2	12	6
p^3	-29	-11	
p^2	1	0.5338	(dividing by 11.24)
p^1	4.48		
p^0	0.5338		

The number of changes of sign in the left column of the array indicates the number of roots of the system that have positive real parts. In the above example there are two changes of sign in the first column of the array; the solution of the problem is, therefore, unstable, since it has two roots with positive real parts.

Two exceptions to the rules for developing the array can occur. The first exception occurs when the first term in any row is zero and the other terms in the row are not all zero. There are several methods of continuing the development of the array when this occurs, but the simplest is to replace the zero term by a small real constant ϵ. Terms in ϵ^2 can be neglected in completing the array providing they are small compared to the remaining terms.

The second exception arises when all the coefficients of a particular row are zero. When this occurs roots are present in the equation that are located radially opposite each other in the imaginary plane and spaced equidistant from the origin. These roots are contained in the polynomial formed from the last nonvanishing row of the array.

If the derived equation formed by the last nonvanishing row has conjugate imaginary roots, the system will exhibit a sustained oscillation as its solution. If the roots are not pure imaginaries, then of course one of them must have a positive real part and the system is unstable, as can be determined by completing the array.

The development of the stability array can be continued when a row of zeros occurs by replacing the row of zeros with the coefficients obtained by differentiating the polynomial formed from the last nonzero row of the array.

Example A-3. Consider the system

$$(p^5 + p^4 + 2p^3 + 2p^2 + 3p + 3)x = 0 \qquad \text{(A-37)}$$

The first two rows are

p^5	1	2	3
p^4	1	2	3

Performing the normal operations to obtain the third row of the array would produce a row of zeros, so that the alternative procedure must be followed. The polynomial derived from the second row is

$$p^4 + 2p^2 + 3 = 0 \qquad \text{(A-38)}$$

Differentiating gives

$$4p^3 + 4p = 0 \qquad \text{(A-39)}$$

The coefficients of this equation can now be used to form the third row of the array. After dividing by 4 to simplify the work, the remainder of the array is

$$
\begin{array}{c|cc}
p^3 & 1 & 1 \quad \text{(dividing by 4)} \\
p^2 & 1 & 3 \\
p & -2 \\
p^0 & 3
\end{array}
$$

The system is unstable, since there is a change of sign in the terms of the left-hand column of the array.

A-5. The Equivalence of $j\omega$ and the Differential Operator p. A common equality used in electrical engineering is

$$
j\omega = p = \frac{d}{dt}
$$

To show that $j\omega$ in the frequency domain can be replaced by d/dt, the derivative with respect to time, in the time domain, is a simple procedure. This can be accomplished by twice differentiating the cosine function, as follows:

$$
y = \cos \omega t \tag{A-40}
$$
$$
py = -\omega \sin \omega t
$$
$$
p^2 y = -\omega^2 \cos \omega t \tag{A-41}
$$

Substituting Eq. (A-40) into Eq. (A-41) gives

$$
p^2 y = -\omega^2 y
$$

or

$$
p = \sqrt{-\omega^2} = j\omega \tag{A-42}
$$

The reader may immediately inquire as to the validity of the result stated in Eq. (A-42) for anything but sinusoidally varying functions. This is not a serious restriction, however, as most functions of interest can be expressed as a sum of sine or cosine terms by means of Fourier series or Fourier integral expansions.

INDEX